GAS TURBINES
and
JET PROPULSION
for Aircraft

ASSOCIATED
ILIFFE
TECHNICAL BOOKS

A MODERN JET-PROPELLED FiGHTER—the Gloster Meteor IV single-seat interceptor with twin Rolls-Royce Derwent V radial-flow turbine-jet units. The Service version depicted climbs to 30,000 feet in five minutes and differs only in detail from the Meteors which in November 1945 established the world record speed of 606 m.p.h. and in September 1946 raised the record to 616 m.p.h. Together with the de Havilland Vampire the Meteor forms the equipment of a number of R.A.F. Squadrons.

GAS TURBINES
and
JET PROPULSION
for Aircraft

By

G. GEOFFREY SMITH, M.B.E.
Editorial Director of *Flight* and *Aircraft Production*

FOURTH EDITION

Published by

LONDON, BIRMINGHAM, COVENTRY, MANCHESTER & GLASGOW

> Dedicated to the Royal Aeronautical
> Society as a small tribute to their
> constant endeavour to advance aero-
> nautical science and engineering
> from 1866 to the present day

First Edition - - - - - -	December, 1942
Second Edition - - - - -	June, 1943
Second Impression - - - -	January, 1944
Third Edition - - - - -	April, 1944
Second Impression - - -	September, 1944
Third Impression - - - -	April, 1945
Fourth Edition - - - - -	August, 1946
Second Impression - - - -	October, 1946
Third Impression - - - - -	November, 1947

U.S.A. EDITION

By arrangement with *Flight* and the author,
a U.S.A. Edition is published in North
America by Aircraft Books, Inc., 370
Lexington Avenue, New York 17, N.Y.,
U.S.A.

Published by Flight Publishing Co., Ltd., Dorset House,
Stamford Street, London, S.E.1
Printed in Great Britain by The Cornwall Press, Ltd.,
Paris Garden, London, S.E.1, and bound by The Chapel
River Press, Andover, Hants.

CONTENTS

ILLUSTRATIONS

FOREWORD

By

SIR GEOFFREY DE HAVILLAND, C.B.E., F.R.Ae.S.

IT gives me much pleasure to write a few lines to introduce this book. My acquaintance with Geoffrey Smith goes back to the year 1906 when we were both interested in a different kind of engine from those described in the following pages. I met him again during World War I when he was a Captain in the Royal Flying Corps, and his duties were wholly concerned with aero-engines. I know that during all these years his constant interest has been in aero-engines, of the history and development of which he has a knowledge which few possess. These facts may not be known to all his readers. They will serve to lessen the surprise which many will feel at the publication of such a full and clear survey of the designs and experiments which have led up to successful gas turbine power units.

New inventions or methods generally have to undergo long and pains-taking processes before they can be applied, and it often happens that the man who has contributed most in the way of original thought has not the qualities which can carry forward the idea and its development to a practical stage. This is indeed a great and difficult gap to close, since it requires not only the most intimate knowledge of the subject, but the faith, courage and perseverance to interest other people—and their financial support—and hold them in spite of delays and disappointments. It will thus be found that in the history of important inventions there is usually an outstanding name, that of the man who has succeeded in bridging this gulf between the idea and its practical realisation. Bessemer in steel production, Parsons in steam turbines and Marconi in wireless telegraphy are examples. By its very comprehensiveness this book may convey the impression of a great variety of names and nationalities being concerned in the development. This is undoubtedly true, but even in the absence of historical perspective, the name of Air Commodore Whittle stands out as having brought this invention to fruition.

It is true to say that any fluid-borne vehicle obtains its forward thrust from the reaction of a quantity of the fluid projected backwards. As is well known, this process is the more efficient the greater the mass of the ejected fluid, and the lower its velocity relative to the surrounding fluid.

Jet propulsion has often been considered for both ships and aircraft, but has been rejected in the past because it could not compete with the screw which produces a comparatively large and massive slipstream. This problem is something like the gun and projectile—the gun being analogous to a mass of fluid going backwards and the projectile to the vehicle. If one imagines the loaded gun to be freely suspended in air when the charge is fired, the gun will go backwards and the projectile forwards. If the gun and projectile were of equal weight, they would have equal speeds and 50 per cent. of the energy would reside in each, but if the gun is heavy, it will recoil at a lower speed, leaving the projectile with most of the speed and energy. It is this consideration which has hindered the development of jet propulsion in the past. If the jet issues from the aeroplane at 1,000 m.p.h., while the aeroplane only does 100 m.p.h. through the air, it is clear that most of the energy is going into the slipstream (or the gun) rather than into the aeroplane (or projectile).

Nevertheless, jet propulsion of aircraft has arrived. The demand for more and more performance forces technical development to the utmost limits. Under these conditions—the highest speeds at the greatest altitudes—the propeller begins to decline seriously in efficiency, while the propulsive power of a concentrated jet is rapidly improving. When the speed and height demanded are great enough the two systems of propulsion change their relative positions. It required the foresight of Whittle, in designing his apparatus so that the thermal characteristics of materials did not impose a crippling limitation on propulsive efficiency, to produce a power unit of a simplicity and lightness never before approached.

Thermal efficiency can only be obtained by employing the correct air-fuel ratio and a high operating temperature at the turbine blades. As available metals cannot withstand excessively high temperatures, the turbine must be cooled. This is effected by substantial air-dilution of the mixture, which necessarily lowers the thermal efficiency. However, in a jet system propulsive efficiency demands a large mass flow. In Whittle's system the excess air which lowers thermal efficiency is turned to good account by increasing the mass flow and thus promoting the propulsive efficiency.

As the reader will appreciate from a perusal of this book, there are other ways of using the gas turbine than producing a jet. The great speeds and altitudes called for in the interests of efficiency with pure jet propulsion will not be always convenient or necessary, while at the same time improvements in propeller design will extend their use to higher speeds than at first seemed likely. It cannot be said that the one method of propulsion is " better " than the other for this can only be judged when the results are visible in the form of completed aircraft where the greatest possible advantage has been taken of the properties of each. It is perhaps natural that the first aerial applications of the gas turbine have been by way of pure jet propulsion owing to its inherent simplicity and light weight. Now that the high-speed, light weight gas turbine has been developed to practical operation and jet-propelled aircraft have been successfully flown, an abundance of energy, brains and ability will be devoted to advance the new technique.

The younger generation is watching these possibilities with eager interest. In this book, and in no other, all the steps leading to the present development are described clearly and with a background of knowledge of the fundamental requirements. It would be difficult to over-estimate the value of having such a complete exposition of the subject at this early stage. This book will enable engineers and students to acquaint themselves with world activities in this new and promising field of development.

AUTHOR'S NOTE

IN the comparatively short space of five years, the turbine power unit has established itself on military types, and its employment is now being extended to civil aircraft. Already the modern gas turbine is available in units of far greater power than are obtainable with orthodox reciprocating engines.

After the successful early stage of development of turbine-jet units, the industry is now engaged on a second phase comprising turbines driving airscrews, which give improved performance at take-off and at normal flying altitudes. A renewed concentration on pure jet units may occur in the course of a few years when pressurised cabins have been perfected to enable regular and economical high-altitude flight, and the more complex problems of compressibility associated with ultra-high speed aircraft are finally overcome.

The three previous editions issued during the war were mainly devoted to the fundamentals of jet propulsion, the importance of the metallurgical problems, early projects, patent reviews and notes as to the possible lines of development of the gas turbine then in its infancy. In the interim several of the possibilities discussed have been developed to a practical stage as a result of intensive research and development. Opinion grows that the gas turbine will eventually displace the reciprocating power unit on aircraft, and will extend its influence to other fields of engineering such as marine work, locomotives, and stationary power plants.

In this, the fourth edition, a great deal of additional matter and comment have been introduced embracing almost every phase of modern gas turbine design, operation and servicing technique. Quotations from papers delivered by aeronautical and turbine engineers in recent months have been freely cited to provide a broad survey of the trend of thought and progress.

Aircraft design progresses at a phenomenal rate. Speed, operating height, rate of climb, carrying capacity and range have all been improved beyond recognition in recent years. Always the demand of the aircraft designer is for a power unit of greater output with reduced frontal area and lighter weight. In the case of orthodox reciprocating engines, practical considerations limiting the size of individual engine cylinders and also the tip speed of airscrew blades can be circumvented by multiplying the number of cylinders and increasing the number of relatively small diameter airscrews, but such measures are liable to lead to undue cost and complication. Purely rotary power units would seem to be both necessary and desirable to obtain a substantial measure of progress, which explains the general trend toward the gas turbine.

Propulsion by thermal jet reaction has proved a fascinating subject for study for a number of years. In collaboration with a technical assistant, F. C. Sheffield, whose expert and willing help is gratefully acknowledged, I have devoted much time to a search for information concerning the work that has been accomplished in this country, in Europe and in America. It was early in 1941 that the author discussed with Lord Brabazon, then Minister

9

of Aircraft Production, the desirability of reviewing the progress with turbine-jet propulsion designs, having regard to the fact that aircraft engineers of several countries were already carrying out experiments with power units bordering upon the practical stage. There was no technical book on the subject, but a great deal of technical material in the form of items had been gathered from various Continental sources. Lord Brabazon readily agreed and expressed the view that it would be a useful service to the British engineering world if the designs of this new form of prime mover were discussed and interest centred in further research; but, of course, nothing at that time was to be revealed of British activities.

A series of articles on the subject was commenced by the writer in "Flight" of August 28th, 1941, and so much interest and discussion was aroused that a widespread demand was met by the issue of a first edition of this book in the following year. The work was the first to be published dealing with gas turbine power units for aircraft propulsion. Both in this country and America successive editions have been extensively used in Service, educational and technical training centres.

The official announcement on January 7th, 1944, that jet-propelled fighter aircraft had been adopted by the British Royal Air Force and the U.S. Army Air Corps, made it possible to give due credit to Britain and, in particular, to the pioneering work of a young officer, Frank Whittle, of the Royal Air Force. The world is indebted to him, now Air Commodore Frank Whittle, C.B.E., for the first practical solution of the problem of aircraft propulsion by thermal jet reaction utilising a gas turbine-compressor unit. His original patent was dated 1930. He spent eleven years developing and perfecting a scheme that had attracted but eluded engineers in many countries. The name Whittle will always be associated with the development of the lightweight gas turbine and with the jet propulsion of aircraft as the name Parsons is linked with the marine steam turbine. Some notes on Frank Whittle's career are included in the present edition.

Not only in the field of power units has the advent of the light, simple gas turbine proved epoch making. The design of aircraft to accommodate such power units will almost certainly be revolutionised in the course of a few years, and a much closer collaboration between aircraft designer and power plant specialist is therefore imperative to ensure the best aerodynamic structures. Two outstanding problems remain to be solved: (a) The pressurized cabin to permit regular high altitude flight and (b) compressibility effects, and the control of boundary layer air to enable greatly increased operating speeds. In technical progress it would be true to say that turbine manufacturers are at this juncture ahead of the producers of aircraft structures.

Future progress with turbines will be influenced by the success of metallurgists in evolving new heat-resisting materials, by chemists, physicists, aerodynamic and thermodynamic specialists and, particularly, by development engineers translating theory into practice. Axial compressors which appreciably reduce frontal area, improved heat exchangers and thrust augmentors offer great scope for advancement.

World wide developments to date have unmistakably confirmed the writer's original confidence in this new form of prime mover.

G. S.

CHAPTER I

JET PROPULSION : VARIETY OF SYSTEMS : HOW THE GAS TURBINE WORKS

OF the scores of new technological developments made known during the war, probably none captured the public imagination more readily than the jet-propelled aircraft which flies without the aid of an airscrew. The news of its successful development was well kept. In England, where most of the pioneer work was done, the secret was preserved for eight years. Under the mutual aid agreement, full information regarding these astounding aircraft and their power units was communicated to the U.S.A. authorities in July 1941. Not until January 1944, however, was the existence of jet-propelled aircraft in Britain and America disclosed to the general public. British fighters of the new type fitted with twin turbine units were first used against the German V-1 flying bombs in the summer of 1944, and were later employed in operations over Europe.

People who on first acquaintance with discussions of the possibilities of jet-propelled aircraft were apt to term the notion as " fantastic " or " futuristic " may well be excused. Only a few years ago, when the author commenced a series of articles in *Flight*, many engineers and technicians were frankly sceptical of the practicability of jet propulsion. Owing to their training and long familiarity with the reciprocating internal combustion engine which has been developed to a high stage of efficiency, they were somewhat slow and seemingly reluctant to appreciate the enormous potential advantages of the new system of propulsion. The remarkable and well-established achievements of the orthodox airscrew-reciprocating engine combination had tended to obscure two facts :—

(1) Self-propelled bodies in a fluid medium, aircraft in air and ships in water, progress by displacing a mass of the medium rearwardly. Basically, therefore, all aircraft are jet-propelled.

(2) Despite its intensive development, the reciprocating engine with intermittent power impulses is fundamentally a retrogression from rotary units with continuous production of power, such as the early wind and water wheels.

Furthermore, the recorded experience with thermal ducts for aircraft and also with the early combustion gas turbines for producing shaft horse power were unfavourable. The views persisted that metals could not be evolved to withstand continuously temperatures of 550 degrees C. to 850 degrees C., that the individual efficiencies of the turbine and the air compressor were low, and that in combination the high ratio of negative to positive work (compression to expansion) rendered it impracticable.

It needed the inspiration of a young officer in the R.A.F., Frank Whittle, to realise that when employed to produce a propulsive jet for aircraft the lightweight combustion gas turbine became a practical possibility. This, indeed, was one of the rare successful cases of " killing two birds with one stone."

Not a New Idea

In view of the remarkably rapid advance in aircraft performance in recent years the question may arise in the mind of the reader as to why, in different countries of the world, serious attention was suddenly devoted to

11

the subject of jet propulsion. The idea was not novel. The " equal and opposite " effect of force and reaction was in fact known to the ancients and embodied in a physical law by Sir Isaac Newton nearly three hundred years ago. It may be suggested that it was for the reason that most important technical advances are made, namely in an attempt to meet a need which could not adequately be fulfilled by existing techniques. Builders of aircraft striving for better performance at higher speeds and higher altitudes were handicapped in their efforts by the lack of lightweight high-powered propulsion engines of small bulk, and the ability to maintain power at altitude. When the latest and best reciprocating engines were offered, units developing more than 2,000 h.p. with a specific fuel consumption of 0.5 lb./b.h.p./hr. and weighing only approximately 1 lb./b.h.p., the constructors demanded still more powerful units of less weight and reduced frontal area. In short, it was the problem, familiar to power engineers, of not merely forcing a quart into a pint pot, but of extracting a gallon out of a pint pot.

How was this demand to be met ? The development of existing multi-cylinder reciprocating engines could be continued or a diversion could be made to seek an entirely different type of prime mover. The first method, however, had become excessively complicated and limited in its results. The alternative method, which seemed at first to present such hazards and difficulties, was found to be more easy and offer greater potential advantages. Turbine-jet units have proved far simpler to design and quicker to produce than the orthodox engine. From the drawing board to successful bench tests in about six months has already been achieved, whilst even under the impetus of war it required four to five years to bring a large reciprocating engine to the fully operational stage.

It would seem that mechanical improvements to high-powered reciprocating engines could offer gains of only a few per cent. and no major changes are visualised. Radical improvement in fuel may well yield improved output, but would call for higher working pressures which would probably lead to increased specific weight, as in the diesel engine. As a result of intensive development it is already apparent that the gas turbine is destined to challenge and eventually supersede the reciprocating engine for units of high power output.

Multiplying Cylinders and Power

The pre-war " big " engine of 1,000 h.p. has already become a " medium-power " engine, and units of approximately 3,000 h.p. are now not uncommon. These large engines have 24, 32 and even 42 cylinders. Reasonable estimates of requirements in the immediate future suggest that engines of 5,000 b.h.p. to 10,000 b.h.p. will be demanded by aircraft constructors for the very large aircraft now envisaged. Multi-bank radial, " X," flat and H-type units in this class are, in fact, being seriously investigated by engine-manufacturers in several countries. For an output of this order it has become a necessary practice to couple two or more standardised engines. Any substantial increase of the diameter of individual cylinders would involve structural and cooling difficulties. Similarly, an increase in the length of the piston stroke would raise inertia loads and, unless the rotational speed were reduced, would result in unfavourable piston speeds. Either would lead to an undesirable increase in the specific weight per h.p., thus rendering the engine less attractive for aircraft installation.

To increase power, therefore, the tendency is to employ a larger number of cylinders, which means that the total energy is applied to the driving shaft in a series of small impulses occurring in rapid succession. A six-cylinder engine has three power impulses per revolution or, in other terms, the firing interval is 120 degrees of crankshaft rotation. On a twenty-four cylinder unit of the same capacity the firing interval would be 30 degrees of crankshaft rotation, and there would thus be twelve smaller power impulses per revolution. When this feature is considered, it is obvious that the running gear (pistons, connecting rods and crankshaft) and also the general engine structure (cylinders, heads and crankcase) can be of relatively light construction. It will be seen that the greater the number of cylinders employed the nearer is the approach to a *continuous* application of energy. Of course, the number of cylinders cannot be increased indefinitely ; the cost, the complication and the number of component parts assume staggering proportions. Logically, however, continuous instead of intermittent power is the aim. When multiplying the number of cylinders ceases to offer practical advantage, another solution must be sought.

To improve engine performance it has become necessary to add or incorporate severally multi-speed, multi-stage or exhaust turbine - driven superchargers ; fuel injection and water injection systems ; induction coolers or inter-coolers ; ducted radiators or fan cooling ; variable pitch, variable speed or contra-rotating airscrews ; and even jet exhaust systems. It will be noted that rotary and not reciprocating units are employed on both the compression side and the expansion side of the working cycle as superchargers and turbines. With so many variables and with such an aggregation of auxiliary equipment the long period required for design, development and test can be readily comprehended. The basic components, the cylinders and pistons, must perform four different functions in succession (induction compression, expansion and exhaust), and in consequence each design is essentially a compromise and a successful unit cannot readily be scaled up or down. Some lessons may be learned and embodied in units of a different size, but, in general, each engine must be designed as a whole.

Rotary Power Units

A rotary power unit, of course, has its own peculiar problems, but does not suffer the limitations of the reciprocating unit. Its chief merit is a relative simplicity in design, development and production which arises particularly owing to each component being called upon to perform only one function continuously. It compresses air, burns the fuel in air, employs the air as a carrier of heat, converts heat into continuous rotary motion at the turbine in order to drive the compressor and utilises the heat escaping from the turbine to further expand the mass of propulsion air. Within a considerable range it can be directly scaled up or down in size and output.

In operation it has virtually no out-of-balance forces, and the consequent absence of vibration is calculated to extend the working life of the power unit and the aircraft and also reduce the strain on crew and passengers. It has no rubbing surfaces beyond a few bearings, usually of ball or roller type, which can be given adequate lubrication without the losses involved in lubricating the sliding pistons of the orthodox engine. Weight and space occupied will be from one-third to at most one-half of those equivalent to multi-cylinder reciprocating engines.

The writer has examined the projects of inventors in Great Britain, U.S.A., France, Sweden, Switzerland, Italy and Germany, and material in the extensive library of the Royal Aeronautical Society, as well as papers issued from time to time by the Directorates of Scientific Research and Technical Development at the Ministry of Aircraft Production. From the advanced state of these designs and the progress to date it is clear that we are on the eve of further important developments with an entirely new form of power unit.

British engineers, it is of interest to record, quite early began investigations into the possibilities of applying jet propulsion systems to aircraft. It will be an inspiration and encouragement to young engineers to know that Frank Whittle, to whom we owe the successful development of turbine jet propulsion for aircraft, was only 22 years of age when he lodged his first patent in 1930. Seven years later, by dint of painstaking experiments and after many disappointments, his first turbine-compressor unit ran successfully on the test bench.

Methods of Jet Propulsion

It is desirable that a clear differentiation be made of the various methods of aircraft propulsion. As already mentioned, all function by the process of displacing a mass of air, the supporting medium, to the rear. In the case of an orthodox power unit a reciprocating engine drives a twelve-foot to sixteen-foot diameter airscrew which displaces a mass of air rearwardly at relatively low velocity. A jet unit projects a column of air about one foot diameter to the rear at an extremely high velocity, actually faster than the speed of sound. In both cases the resulting effect is to propel the aircraft in the forward direction.

Jet propulsion units may conveniently be grouped into four main classes :—

1. The liquid fuel rocket (the German Me 163 rocket propelled fighter).
2. The continuous thermal duct or athodyd (the Leduc projects).
3. The intermittent impulse duct (the German V-1 flying bomb).
4. The continuous turbine-compressor unit (the Whittle system).

A number of subdivisions and variations can, of course, be made to these four main classes.

Although rightly included as a form of jet propulsion, the rocket differs essentially from the other thermal jet systems and consequently is outside the scope of this volume. Instead of carrying only fuel and drawing oxygen for combustion from the atmosphere, the rocket must carry both fuel and the necessary comburent. This is a disadvantage for travel in the atmosphere but, of course, makes it the only means at present conceivable for space travel beyond the atmospheric belt. It is, however, a true jet reaction unit and a brief examination of its functions serves to make clear the reaction principle on which all the thermal jet plants operate. If a hydrocarbon fuel and oxygen are held in a closed vessel and ignited, Fig. 1, the latent heat of the fuel is released, and there is a rapid expansion of the resulting gases. Owing to the fixed volume of the vessel, there will be a rise in pressure which will be uniformly distributed in every direction. As the forces are balanced there will be no tendency for the vessel to move.

Fig. I. Combustion in a [closed vessel results in uniformly distributed internal pressure but no tendency for the vessel to move.

Next consider a similar vessel which, instead of being sealed, has at one end an aperture or nozzle. On ignition and combustion of the fuel the expanding gases will rush out of the nozzle at a high velocity, Fig. 2. The internal pressure at the nozzle end of the vessel is thus relieved, leaving an unbalanced pressure at the other end which tends to propel the vessel in the opposite direction to the issuing jet. Obviously it is dependent solely upon internal conditions, and there is no suggestion whatever of the jet

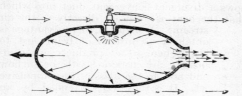

Fig. 2. Combustion in a rocket. The un-balanced internal pressure tends to propel the vessel in the opposite direction to the issuing jet.

" pushing against " surrounding external air. In fact it would function most efficiently in a complete vacuum. This is the basic principle upon which all jet plants operate.

Turning now to the thermal duct, suppose a plain cylinder with open ends is attached longitudinally to an aircraft flying at high speed, say 350 m.p.h. Air will enter at the forward end of the duct and will emerge as a jet at the rear. Nothing will be added to the force of the flow through the duct and, in fact, some energy will be lost owing to skin friction and disturbance of flow at the entrance and exit.

If some means of adding heat to the air as it passes through the duct is employed, the air will be expanded and the velocity of the jet from the tail will be increased. Fig. 3 shows diagrammatically a cylindrical duct heated externally by burning oil sprays.

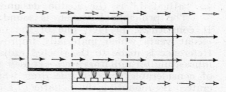

Fig. 3. Thermal duct with heat added externally to accelerate the air flow.

The amount of heat that can be added is largely dependent upon the pressure of the air being treated. A simple method of raising the pressure is to pass the air through a *divergent* entry nozzle as shown in Fig. 4. The effect of this shaping of the duct is to build up the pressure of the air whilst decreasing its velocity. More heat can be added to the air by burning more fuel with beneficial effects upon the velocity of the issuing jet.

A further advantage can be secured by forming the exit of the duct as a *convergent* nozzle. This

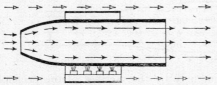

Fig. 4. A divergent entry nozzle raises the pressure of the air and allows more heat to be added.

has the opposite effect to the divergent entry nozzle and increases the velocity of the jet of air whilst lowering its unit pressure. Here in Fig. 5 is the most elementary type of propulsion unit. Air com-pression depends solely upon "ram" effect, only a limited amount of heat can be added, considerable heat will be lost by radiation, and the complete unit will be of too low an efficiency to be of practical use for the propulsion of aircraft.

The next obvious step is to improve the method of adding heat, and this can best be effected by

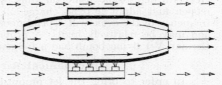

Fig. 5. A convergent discharge nozzle increases the velocity of the issuing jet.

internal combustion. Fig. 6 shows a divergent-convergent duct into which fuel is injected and burnt so that the heat is released directly to the air stream. A slight further advantage is obtained as, instead of being lost to atmosphere, the products of combustion are entrained with the air flow and add to the mass of the propulsive jet. It is, however, attended by an exorbitant fuel consumption and is incapable of providing initial power for take-off. Nevertheless some application may be found in specialised short-range intercepter fighters using rocket-assisted take-off or catapult launch. An example of such a simple " continuous thermal duct " unit, sometimes termed an " athodyd," is the Leduc design referred to on page 38.

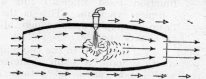

Fig. 6. Internal combustion provides better utilisation of the fuel and adds the products of combustion to the mass of air.

The principle, however, is sound, and has its practical applications. It constitutes, in fact, one of the outstanding aircraft developments of recent years which materially improved the speeds of military aircraft. Reference is made to the ducted radiator. Previously engine coolant and lubricating oil radiators were exposed to the slipstream and were the cause of considerable aerodynamic drag which lowered the performance of the craft. By mounting the radiator in a divergent-convergent duct the stream of cooling air is heated and accelerated to produce a jet which completely neutralises the internal drag of the radiator and even gives a slight propulsive effect.

Reverting to propulsion units, mention must now be made of the " intermittent impulse " or " explosion " duct, Fig. 7. This secures an

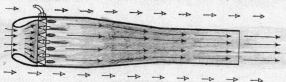

Fig. 7. The inter-mittent-impulse duct as employed on the German flying bomb.

improved compression of the air but only by the sacrifice of the principle of continuous power generation. It comprises a tube fitted at the forward end with a series of non-return admission valves and fuel injection nozzles. As it travels through the air, pressure on the nose opens the valves and air is rammed into the duct to mix with the fuel and form a combustible mixture. As the contents are heated by the combustion of the fuel, there is a rapid expansion and, by appropriate proportioning of the exit nozzle, a rise in pressure which serves to close the valves. The violent ejection of the gases creates a depression inside the duct which allows the flat spring valves to reopen and admit a fresh charge of air and the cycle is repeated. The frequency of the cycle will depend upon the designed proportions of the duct and may be relatively high. A propulsion unit of this type fitted to the German V-1 flying bomb had a frequency of about 2,800 cycles per minute.

Mechanical Air Compression

In order to bring the jet propulsion unit to a stage where it had any prospects of competing with the orthodox reciprocating type internal combustion engine it became necessary to mechanise the compression of the air. Reciprocating compressors have been suggested, but as the unit requires vast quantities of air and burns fuel continuously, the most appropriate mechanism to achieve the desired purpose is a rotary compressor. Both radial and axial flow types have been and are being employed for this purpose.

This brings more complication in its train as, of course, mechanical energy is required to drive the compressor. An obvious means was available

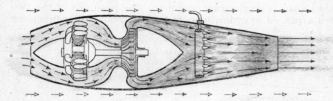

Fig. 8. Mechanical compression of the air by means of a conventional reciprocating engine, as in the Italian Campini system.

in the highly developed reciprocating type aircraft engine. Fig. 8 shows a plant having an air-cooled radial engine driving a centrifugal compressor and subsequently heating the air by a ring of fuel sprays. This is the principle of the Campini system, see page 48.

The next step is to eliminate the anomalous reciprocating engine and substitute a simple rotary power unit. A combustion gas turbine is mounted on a common shaft with the compressor and proportioned to extract merely sufficient energy from the issuing gas stream to furnish the necessary power

Fig. 9. Mechanical compression of the air by a gas turbine which is the basis of the Whittle system.

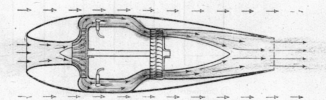

to drive the compressor and ensure continuous operation. Fig. 9 shows diagrammatically this turbine-compressor combination, the Whittle system, which is at present being employed in the air.

A Comparison with four-stroke Engines

The reader is probably acquainted with the orthodox, four-stroke, reciprocating engine fitted to motor cars, and with its cycle of operations—induction, compression, expansion and exhaust. However, for those who are not fully familiar with these operations, a brief description is included. All four of the above functions take place in regular sequence in each cylinder of the engine. The piston descends and the mixture of air and petrol enters the cylinder *via* the opened inlet valve ; the inlet valve closes and the piston ascends to compress the mixture ready for ignition by an electric spark. The expansion resulting from combustion forces the piston downwards, and this is the sole power stroke. Finally the piston once more ascends to expel the burnt gases *via* the exhaust valve. In an engine operating at a crankshaft speed of 3,000 r.p.m. each stroke is completed in 1/100 second and a complete cycle of operations in 1/25 second. Owing to the reciprocating motion the piston must be accelerated, decelerated and its direction of motion reversed 6,000 times per minute. As the power stroke occurs only once in every two revolutions of the crankshaft, the working energy is applied to the shaft intermittently. The frequency in a particular engine depends, of course, upon the number of cylinders.

In Fig. 10 is a series of sketches showing a complete cycle of four strokes and immediately above is a sectional diagram of a gas turbine with a multi-stage axial compressor and a single-stage turbine. The positions of the two diagrams have been arranged in order to show their corresponding functions

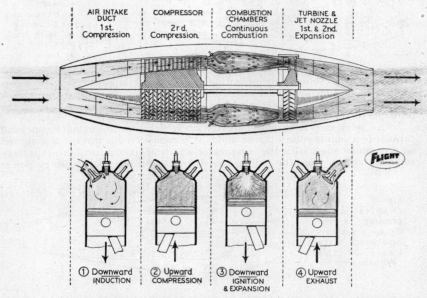

Fig. 10. A comparison of rotating and reciprocating power units. In the lower series of diagrams the four intermittent strokes of an orthodox reciprocating engine are approximately aligned with the four continuous functions of a turbine-jet unit.

in relation. In comparing the action of the two types of engines it is important to appreciate that the turbine produces power continuously, that is, there are no intermittent explosions as in a reciprocating engine.

How the Gas Turbine Works

A gas turbine unit consists of three essential components, (1) a rotary air compressor at the front, (2) a series of combustion chambers into which kerosene is sprayed and burnt continuously, and (3) a turbine revolving with the compressor on a common shaft. There are no pistons, valves or ignition apparatus save for two igniter plugs to attain a start. Initially an electric starter motor spins the main shaft at about one-eighth speed. Starting operations are automatically controlled by a time switch. The pilot opens a fuel cock, depresses a button, and in about half a minute the unit is running at idling speed. No " warming-up " period is necessary as bearings are few, there are no metal-to-metal sliding surfaces, and consequently only a simple lubrication system. After combustion of fuel is initiated in one of the two chambers fitted with igniter plugs, the flame is propagated to all the other chambers through interconnecting pipes.

On the ground air is induced at the front by the action of the rotating compressor, forced by the same compressor into the combustion chambers at a ratio of about 4 to 1 and into this compressed air, aviation kerosene is pumped at a pressure of about 750 lb. sq. in. and burnt continuously, somewhat in the manner of a plumber's blowlamp. In flight the work of compressing the air is greatly assisted by the forward motion of the aircraft. Air is " rammed " into the intake duct and at speeds over 300 m.p.h. the effect is of such magnitude that the thrust curve ceases to fall and commences to rise. Increasing altitude and consequent lower air temperature also improves the efficiency of the compression system.

Only a small quantity of air is used for combustion to provide the necessary air/fuel ratio of about 14 : 1. The major portion—the so-called " dilution " air in distinction to the " combustion " air—lowers the air/fuel ratio to about 60 : 1 and reduces the combustion temperature of, say, 1,800 deg. C. to about 850 deg. C. at the entry to the turbine. The tremendous heat released by the combustion of the fuel expands the air but as the chambers have an open end, in contrast to the closed cylinder of a piston engine, there is no rise in pressure. Actually there is a slight fall in pressure, say 2 or 3 lb./sq. in., from the entry to the outlet of the chambers.

By reason of the rapid expansion, the heated air and combustion products at increased velocity force their way through the only exit from the chambers, namely, between the guide vanes in the stator ring of the turbine. These vanes direct the flow to the appropriate angle of attack for the blades on the periphery of the turbine wheel. The rapid passage of the heated mixture through the airfoil-shaped blades (about 50 of them) causes the wheel to rotate rapidly—from 8,000 to 16,000 r.p.m., for example, at full speed. In this manner mechanical energy is created at the shaft, and the compressor fixed to the front end of the shaft is made to do its work in compressing more air into the combustion chambers and the process goes on so long as fuel is introduced. As in the orthodox engine, less fuel is required as altitude is increased and a barometric device is fitted to regulate automatically the supply injected into the combustion chambers. The usual fuel is kerosene but petrol or diesel oil can be employed. Calorific value is the prime fuel characteristic and the specific calorific value per gallon is of more importance than the value per lb. as weight can be more readily accommodated in high speed aircraft than bulk.

In a pure jet unit all the power delivered by the turbine is expended in driving the air compressor and the necessary auxiliary equipment. To drive the compressor approximately 100 h.p. is required for each lb. of air delivered per second. A pound of air per second gives about 50 lb. thrust, therefore the turbine of a unit developing 2,000 lb. thrust must deliver about 4,000 h.p. From the rear of the turbine the heated air, still expanding, emerges from the tail nozzle as a high-velocity jet, say, 1,800ft. per second, or 1,227 m.p.h. The temperature at the outlet is down to about 300 deg. C., compared with 690 deg. C. maximum as it enters the jet pipe. Specific pressure is relatively low, being only from one and a half to twice that of atmosphere.

A summarised list of the potential advantages of turbine propulsion units as compared with orthodox reciprocating engine installations is given on the following page.

ADVANTAGES OF TURBINE UNITS COMPARED TO PISTON ENGINES

(1) Development time is much reduced. A turbine unit can be designed, built and brought to the stage of practical operation in a quarter of the time usually necessary for a piston engine.

(2) Production is simpler and speedier. A turbine unit has only about one-third the number of parts required for a comparable piston engine.

(3) As turbine components each perform one specific function, a proved turbine unit can be readily scaled up or down to meet power requirements.

(4) Turbine units can be constructed to produce much higher power outputs. Practical considerations limit the increase in output of piston engines without adversely affecting the power/weight ratio.

(5) They are less critical regarding fuel. High calorific value not anti-knock rating is the criterion. Paraffin is the usual fuel but petrol, diesel oil or the so-called "safety" fuels may be employed.

(6) Power is produced continuously instead of intermittently. Consequently working pressures are low and the structure, casings and ducting are of light section and weight.

(7) By the exclusive use of rotating components, vibration is virtually eliminated. Weight can therefore be saved on the airframe.

(8) Absence of reciprocating parts enables higher operating speeds to be employed. Frontal area and space occupied are reduced and power/weight ratio is improved. A turbine-jet unit is about one-third the weight of a comparable piston engine.

(9) As there is no sliding friction (pistons in cylinders) and no heavily loaded bearings, lubrication is greatly simplified.

(10) A turbine unit is self-cooled by the air flow. It requires no radiators or projecting air scoops.

(11) They are easy to install and remove from the airframe and simple to service. Some units can be removed in less than half an hour.

(12) Auxiliary components, instruments and controls are all reduced in number. Less attention is required from the pilot.

(13) A turbine requires no preliminary warming-up. It will develop full power for take-off in two or three minutes.

(14) A turbine unit operates more efficiently at high altitude and consequent low temperature than at sea level. It needs no complicated supercharging system to maintain power at altitude.

(15) The higher the aircraft speed the more efficiently the turbine unit functions due to the influence of ram pressure.

(16) Size, shape and weight of a turbine unit facilitates complete enclosure in the fuselage or wing, conducing to better form of airframe and reduced drag. This feature will assist the development of all-wing and tailless types of aircraft.

(17) By suitable proportioning of the components the main compressor system could be arranged to supply air to charge a pressure cabin, to warm armament enclosures or to prevent icing of control surfaces.

(18) As such a large volume of air is continuously flowing through the turbine unit, it offers the possibility of effective boundary layer control over relatively large areas of the wings or control surfaces.

(19) The absence of an airscrew on turbine-jet units permits the use of a relatively light and low undercarriage. On flying boats increased clearance reduces one hazard.

(20) For military aircraft, turbine-jet units permit better location and an unrestricted field of vision for the pilot and do not obstruct forward armament.

(21) Vibrationless running, absence of mechanical noise and greatly reduced exhaust noise make turbine units particularly suitable for civil aircraft

CHAPTER II

THRUST AND PERFORMANCE

THRUST is an applied force tending to produce motion in a body or to alter the motion of a body. Horsepower is a measure of energy expended in a given period of time. The mechanical energy delivered by a piston engine or a gas turbine can be measured in terms of horsepower on the test bed by a water brake, an electric dynamometer or a torquemeter. This, however, is merely an expression of the energy available and is no criterion of their individual or comparative effect in propelling the aircraft. It is necessary to know the method by which the power will be applied and the efficiencies of the respective propulsion systems employed.

Whether using an airscrew or a jet the aircraft obtains its forward propulsion by reason of a mass of air being accelerated rearwards. Relatively, in the case of the airscrew a larger mass of air is projected rearwards at a lower speed, whilst with the jet a smaller mass is accelerated to a higher velocity, see Fig. 11. Thrust is the "equal and opposite" reaction to the

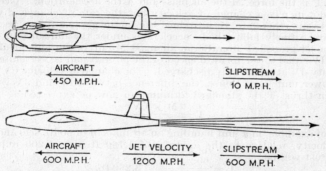

AIRCRAFT
450 M.P.H.

SLIPSTREAM
10 M.P.H.

AIRCRAFT
600 M.P.H.

JET VELOCITY
1200 M.P.H.

SLIPSTREAM
600 M.P.H.

Fig. 11. Both conventional and jet aircraft are propelled by reaction of a mass of air projected rearwards.

force producing this change of momentum which exerts a forward "push" on the aircraft. The term "push" is used deliberately for even a tractor airscrew pushes against a thrust collar in the engine nose in a similar manner to a horse which pushes against the collar of the harness when it is commonly described as "pulling" a cart.

The thrust horsepower THP of a piston engine-airscrew propulsion unit is the shaft horsepower SHP of the engine multiplied by the efficiency of the airscrew, say 80 per cent. at sea level and 400 m.p.h. On a turbine-airscrew unit energy is divided between the airscrew and the jet, so the available SHP of the turbine after driving the compressor must be multiplied by the airscrew efficiency and an addition must be made for the thrust of the jet. The whole of the power developed by the turbine of a pure jet propulsion unit is absorbed in driving the compressor and all thrust is obtained from the jet.

It is only possible to compare directly the propulsive effect of the different types of unit in terms of thrust. The efficiencies of different types under varying conditions of operation, however, do not follow similar curves. It follows that a direct comparison can only be made in terms of thrust under identical operating conditions. This involves such variables as aircraft speed, altitude, atmospheric conditions, temperature, airscrew efficiency, jet efficiency and aircraft drag. Certain of these factors are of such importance that they must not be regarded merely as modifying or auxiliary influences but as first order effects.

It would, for example, be unrealistic to ignore the effects of forward speed and altitude on the functions of a jet unit. Similarly, though for different reasons and to different effect, it would be unrealistic to disregard them in connection with a conventional piston engine-airscrew unit for aircraft propulsion. This, however, does not preclude or invalidate investigation of the piston engine under static, sea level, test-bed, laboratory or even hypothetical conditions.

A brief examination of some basic features of a jet propulsion unit, whilst unrepresentative of actual performance, will be of interest. First, it is desirable to ascertain what energy is available in a specific plant and resort is made to the standard formula to determine a force :—

$$F = M \times A$$

in which F is the force, M the air mass and A the acceleration. Acceleration denotes not merely a change of velocity but the rate of change of velocity. It is necessary, therefore, to introduce the factor $g=32.2$ ft./sec./sec., which is the rate a freely falling body accelerates under the influence of gravity.

On a jet-propelled aircraft the air mass M enters the unit at an intake velocity IV equal to the forward speed of the aircraft and is accelerated to the jet velocity JV at which it is discharged. The change of velocity CV effected in the power unit is, of course, the difference between IV and JV velocities. To obtain thrust T the standard formula can now be expressed :—

$$T = \frac{M \times CV}{g}$$

By way of example, in a unit handling an air-mass M of 60 lb./sec. and having a jet velocity, relative to the aircraft, of 1,760 ft./sec. (1,200 m.p.h.) the static thrust will be :—

$$T = \frac{60 \times 1760}{32.2} = 3,280 \text{ lb.}$$

Assuming a constant jet velocity, the thrust of the unit will vary according to the change of air velocity CV or in other words according to the forward speed of the aircraft. Obviously, thrust is highest when the aircraft is stationary and there is maximum acceleration of the air mass, whilst if it were possible for the aircraft speed, and consequently the intake velocity IV, to equal the jet velocity JV, there would be no thrust whatever. This would suggest that thrust falls directly with increase of aircraft speed, as indicated in the dotted curve, Fig. 12. In practice, however, thrust will fall until the aircraft speed reaches 300–350 m.p.h. Thereafter, increased speed operates to advantage due to ram pressure rise in the intake duct of

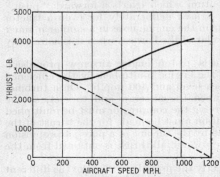

Fig. 12. Thrust tends to fall with increased aircraft speed but soon rises under influence of ram pressure.

the compressor. Thrust will rise to regain its static maximum at about 650–700 m.p.h., as shown in the full curve Fig. 12. Thrust will continue to rise until the aircraft reaches at least sonic velocity. Beyond that the rate of increase of thrust may be expected to lessen as a result of shock losses in the intake duct and compressor entry. The vital importance of ram pressure will thus be appreciated.

Thrust Horsepower

Thrust T, at any particular aircraft speed, may be converted to thrust horsepower THP by multiplying the thrust by the speed of the aircraft and dividing by the appropriate factor to obtain standard horsepower units of 33,000 ft.-lb./min. or 550 ft.-lb./sec. If thrust is expressed in lb. and aircraft speed in ft./sec. the product is ft.-lb./sec. and the formula is :—

$$THP = \frac{T \times IV}{550}$$

An alternative would be to obtain mile-lb./hr. by multiplying thrust in lb. by the aircraft speed in m.p.h. when the formula would be expressed :—

$$THP = \frac{T \times IV}{375}$$

When the aircraft is stationary no energy is expended on propulsion and should the aircraft travel at the same speed as the jet velocity JV again no propulsive work is done. If thrust horsepower THP is calculated from the dotted thrust curve of Fig. 12 it will be found to rise from zero when the aircraft is stationary, to a maximum when the aircraft speed is half the jet velocity, and then fall at a similar rate as the aircraft speed is increased to that of the jet velocity. This is plotted in Fig. 13 in dotted line together with a more realistic THP curve calculated from the full line thrust curve of Fig. 12. The specific rate of fuel consumption, lb. fuel per lb. thrust per hour (lb./lb./hr.) rises with increasing aircraft speed but if calculated on a basis of thrust horsepower (lb./ THP/hr.) it falls with increasing aircraft speed.

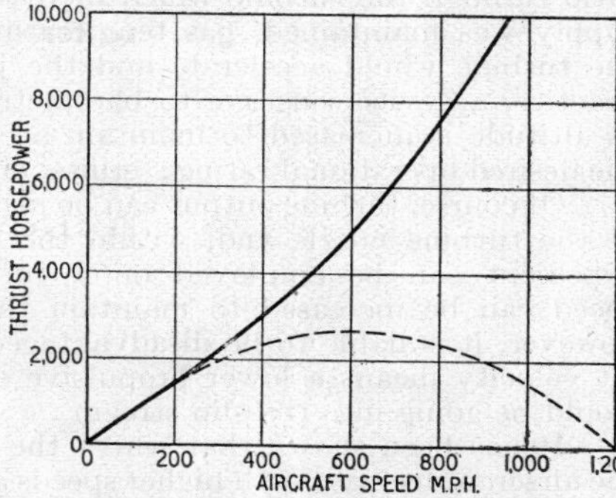

Fig. 13. Thrust horsepower rises as aircraft speed is increased.

Propulsive Efficiency

Again assuming a constant jet velocity, it will be found that the propulsive efficiency of the jet directly depends upon the ratio R of the jet velocity to the forward speed of the aircraft. Obviously, it is zero when the aircraft is stationary and 100 per cent. when the aircraft speed is the same as the jet velocity. Knowing the jet velocity, the efficiency at any aircraft speed can be determined by :—

$$\eta = \frac{2}{R + 1}$$

and the complete range is plotted in Fig. 14. This shows a remarkable contrast to the characteristic curve of airscrew efficiency which falls from about 80 per cent. at 400 m.p.h. to 70 per cent. at 500 m.p.h. and 50 per cent. at 600 m.p.h. Thus, at speeds above 500 m.p.h. the jet becomes the more efficient means of propulsion. High speed is doubly advantageous to the jet propulsion unit as it improves ram pressure and increases the propulsive efficiency.

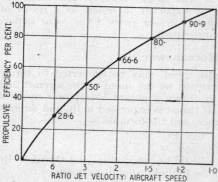

Fig. 14. Propulsive efficiency rises as the ratio of jet velocity to aircraft speed is reduced.

Effect of Altitude

Altitude has a number of conflicting influences on the component efficiencies of aircraft propulsion units. The reduction of air temperature with increasing altitude improves compressor efficiency, or in other words less mechanical energy is required to obtain a specific compressor output. Of course, the higher the speed the greater the temperature rise as the air in the duct leading to the compressor is accelerated to aircraft speed. At 500 m.p.h. this may produce a rise of 25 deg. C., but if the aircraft is flying at, say, 30,000 feet the atmospheric fall will be about 60 deg. C. yielding a net drop of 35 deg. C.

Output will fall due to the reduced density of the air and this tends to reduce the power delivered by the turbine. Conversely, owing to lowered temperature and pressure behind the turbine, there is a better expansion ratio through the turbine which increases its efficiency. If the rate of fuel supply was maintained, gas temperature at the turbine nozzle would rise, the turbine would accelerate and the jet velocity would be increased. In practice, a device sensitive to barometric pressure reduces the fuel delivery as altitude is increased to maintain a constant turbine speed of rotation at the desired operational rating; cruise, climb or combat.

Of course, turbine output can be increased by raising the gas temperature at the turbine nozzle and, within the capacity of the turbine metals, this expedient can be employed on a turbine-airscrew unit. Unless aircraft speed can be increased to maintain the jet velocity/aircraft speed ratio, however, it is liable to be disadvantageous on a turbine-jet unit as a higher jet velocity means a lower propulsive efficiency as too much of the energy would be going into the slip stream.

It has been shown that whilst the efficiencies of the piston engine and the airscrew decrease with higher speeds and altitudes the turbine-jet enhances its efficiency. There remains an aerodynamic factor adversely affecting airscrew propulsion. At high altitudes and consequent low temperatures, sonic velocity is reduced and thus problems of compressibility will arise at lower aircraft speeds. From about 750 m.p.h. at sea level, sonic velocity falls to about 650 m.p.h. at 36,000 ft. At speeds approaching the critical Mach number of the aircraft there will be a steep increase in drag with either airscrew or jet systems. On an airscrew, however, a further complication arises. As the linear air speed of the airscrew blade tips is a combination of rotational and forward speeds, compressibility burble at the blade tip, which will drastically reduce the airscrew efficiency, is likely to occur.

Comparison with Steam Turbines

A gas turbine resembles a reaction type, non-condensing steam turbine, in that a fluid medium under heat and pressure is expanded through stationary and rotating blades to produce mechanical energy. In a gas turbine there are smaller pressure and temperature differences but the velocity of the medium is many times greater, which explains why the rotor blades of a gas turbine are of aerofoil shape as compared to the crescent moon shape of steam turbine blades.

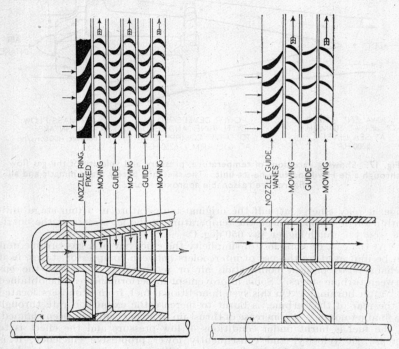

Fig. 15. Diagram of steam turbine with solid nozzle ring and crescent shaped rotor and stator blades.

Fig. 16. Rotor and stator blades of a gas turbine are of aerofoil shape. Nozzle passages are defined by guide vanes.

Several times more air passes through the system than is necessary for complete combustion of the fuel. the excess air being utilized to dilute the combustion products and keep the temperature at the turbine entry down to working limits. With the open cycle turbine, inlet pressures are of the order of 60 lb./sq. in. abs. (45 lb./sq. in. gauge). At such a relatively low pressure gas volume must be large, and therefore large capacity ducts and large blade dimensions are called for. High temperatures are imperative for efficiency but a limit is imposed by the ability of the materials of the turbine to withstand the heat in operation. It must be appreciated that high performance without long working life is unacceptable save in special types of military aircraft.

Apart from the actual combustion zone the highest temperature occurs at the turbine inlet, say 800 deg. C., so that in the case of a multi-stage turbine only the initial row of blading operates under maximum temperature conditions. Since the gas is cooled by performing mechanical work at each

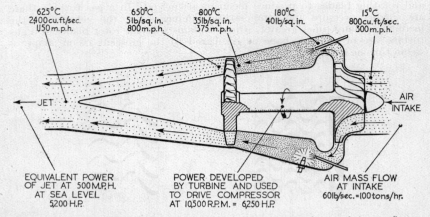

Fig. 17. Showing variations of temperature, pressure and velocity of the gas flow through a de Havilland turbine-jet unit. The sketch is purely diagrammatic and all figures are reasonable approximations.

stage, it may emerge at half the original temperature in a four-stage unit. With a single turbine wheel, the temperature of the jet stream at the nozzle exit would be much higher, say 650 deg. C.

At the cost of some loss of simplicity the efficiency of a gas turbine unit can be improved by the use of intercoolers between compressor stages, heat exchangers to preheat combustion air or regenerators to reheat the gas between turbine stages. Some improvement in performance can be obtained by " after burning." On this system additional fuel, from atomisers located to the rear of the turbine, is burnt to increase the expansion rate through the final jet nozzle. An increase of thrust up to 50 per cent. has been claimed. As the fuel is burnt under conditions of low pressure and the effect is to increase jet velocity, and consequently lower propulsive efficiency, it is relatively uneconomical. Its application will probably be confined to short period operation at take-off and in emergency. A further opportunity of

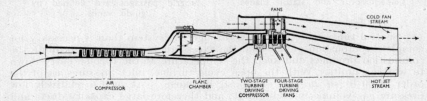

Fig. 18. This diagrammatic section shows the flow path of the Metro-Vick F2/3 turbine-jet unit with ducted fan augmentor.

thrust " augmentation " is provided by the ducted fan or tunnelled airscrew. Taking energy respectively from the gas stream leaving the turbine or from the turbine shaft such systems supply an additional mass flow of air at a lower velocity to supplement the main jet. In Fig. 18 is shown the ducted fan of the Metropolitan Vickers F2/3 unit and the subject of thrust augmentors is dealt with in more detail in Chap. XII.

Component Efficiencies

In 1939 a paper was read by Dr. Adolf Meyer on "The Combustion Gas Turbine" before the Institution of Mechanical Engineers. During the discussion which followed, F. Whittle (at that time Squadron Leader of the R.A.F.) made a notable contribution to the subject.

So far little had been said about the gas turbine in relation to aircraft, which he regarded as a most hopeful field for it, for, as the gas turbine was taken up into the air the reduced atmospheric temperature made possible very much higher efficiencies than could be obtained on the ground. Using a simple formula for the thermodynamic efficiency of a gas turbine, and the usual symbols,

$$\text{Overall efficiency} = \frac{\eta_t K - \dfrac{1}{\eta_c}}{K - 1} \times \text{air standard efficiency}$$

where K was the ratio of positive to negative work in the ideal cycle and was therefore equivalent to the ratio of maximum temperature to compression temperature in the ideal cycle ; η_t was the turbine efficiency, and η_c the compressor efficiency. This formula was slightly defective because it made no allowance for the fuel saved due to the heating effect of the losses in the compressor, neither did it allow for (a) variable specific heat, or (b) the fact that the mass flow through the turbine was greater than the mass flow through the compressor by the amount of the liquid fuel injected into the combustion chamber. Otherwise, however, it gave a close approximation to the overall efficiency of the gas turbine.

The formula could be re-written

$$\eta_0 = \frac{\eta_t \eta_c K - 1}{\eta_c (K - 1)} \times \text{air standard efficiency}$$

in which the relative importance of turbine and compressor efficiencies was more clearly shown, and it could be seen that for a given value of the product $\eta_t \eta_c$ the overall efficiency was inversely proportional to the compressor efficiency.

As an example, assuming a turbine efficiency of 80 per cent. and compressor efficiency of 80 per cent. adiabatic, $\eta_c \eta_t = 0.64$. With a compression ratio of 6.35 and a maximum combustion temperature of 1,100 deg. C abs., the overall efficiency worked out at 19.67 per cent. ; whereas with a turbine efficiency of 90 per cent. and compressor efficiency of 70 per cent. the overall efficiency was 22.8 per cent. for the same compression ratio and maximum temperature. Thus, though $\eta_t \eta_c$ was smaller, the overall efficiency was greater. In the calculations, allowance was made for the heating effect of the compressor losses. Of course the machine with the lower compressor efficiency would require either more stages in the compressor, or higher blade speed to obtain the same pressure ratio. He therefore agreed with the implication that the turbine efficiency was relatively much more important than the compressor efficiency.

The temperature of the international standard atmosphere decreased by 2 deg. C. for every 1,000 feet of height and therefore for a given maximum temperature and a given compressor speed (i.e. a given adiabatic temperature rise of compression) both the air standard efficiency and the ratio K of positive to negative work would increase owing to the lower initial air temperature.

For example, with a turbine efficiency of 85 per cent. and compressor efficiency of 70 per cent., a maximum temperature of 1,100 deg. C. abs., and an adiabatic temperature rise in the compressor of 200 deg. C., the comparative figures between sea level and 35,000 feet were :—

	K	THERMO-DYNAMIC EFFICIENCY, per cent.	AIR STANDARD EFFICIENCY, per cent.	OVERALL EFFICIENCY, per cent.	B.H.P. PER LB. OF AIR per sec.
Ground level...	2.258	45	41	18.45	59.3
35,000 feet ...	2.630	56.5	47.85	27	98.5

Thus there was an increase of 46 per cent. in the overall efficiency, and of 66 per cent. in the power per pound of air per second, on rising from the ground to the stratosphere. Of course the total power fell off, due to the much reduced air density, but so also did the power required for a given flying speed. The overall efficiency of an internal combustion engine, on the other hand, fell off to such an extent that an unsupercharged engine would scarcely be able to turn itself round against its own mechanical losses at heights of the order of 40,000 feet. At 35,000 feet, i.e. the beginning of the stratosphere, the air temperature was about 218 deg. C. abs.

The big flying boat had reached a point where it was limited in development by its power plant ; at present no suitable engine would produce more than 2,000 h.p. in one unit, although power units with an output of 5,000–10,000 h.p. were needed. Moreover, there were, as was well known, strong arguments in favour of flying at very great heights. The combination of these two factors resulted in a demand in the aeronautical world for efficient gas turbines.

Some speakers appeared to be pessimistic about turbine efficiencies, and the figure of 85 per cent. had been discussed. He had never been able to find a satisfactory reason why efficiencies should not be higher than that. If the methods of the aeronautical engineer were applied to turbine design, he could see no fundamental reason why turbine efficiency should be below 94 per cent., taking account of the boundary layer theory and other factors.

Air Commodore Whittle's Current Views

In response to an invitation by the author to contribute to this fourth edition a note on the present stage of development and future prospects of gas turbines, Air Commodore F. Whittle, C.B.E., whose basic patents are embodied in many types of gas turbines in use today, kindly expressed the following views :

1. The aircraft gas turbine has undoubtedly come to stay. In the space of a few years I expect to see it displace the reciprocating engine in all aircraft except possibly the light types. I make the reservation about light aircraft because at present it seems more difficult to design for lower powers than for much higher powers than we use at present, but it is possible that the gas turbine will invade the light aircraft field also.

2. For very high speeds and moderate range the turbo-jet is the appropriate application but for lower speeds and long range the gas turbine driving a propeller will be used. Personally I think there is a strong case for the use of a gas turbine driving a ducted fan for moderate speeds. Although no strong claims can be made for it on the basis of fuel consumption, it has important advantages in respect of noise reduction and absence of vibration when compared with a turbine-airscrew combination. Further, for civil aircraft the elimination of visible " whirling lumps " is a not inconsiderable psychological factor in its favour.

3. The speed possibilities inherent in gas turbines have been clearly shown by the establishment of the World's Air Speed Record at over 600 m.p.h. Much higher speeds will undoubtedly be achieved in the fairly near future. There is no speed limit imposed by the power plant. In fact, the higher the speed the greater the efficiency and power. The attainment of higher speeds therefore depends more upon the aircraft designer than on the turbine designer, though power plant developments will naturally play their part. I do not think that we shall have to wait very long before aerodynamic developments make possible the attainment of supersonic speeds.

4. If long range is to be combined with high speed, flight at great heights will be necessary, and hence the development of the pressure cabin is of great importance. In the not very distant future I expect to see passenger aircraft covering long distances at speeds of approximately 500 m.p.h. at altitudes of the order of 40,000 ft., as a result of the parallel development of the gas turbine, the aircraft, the pressure cabin, and radio and radar aids to navigation.

5. The advent of the aircraft gas turbine makes necessary some important changes of outlook on the part of the designers. Hitherto it has been the practice to develop engines and aircraft virtually independently of each other, but this procedure will not do if we are to get the best out of gas turbine powered aircraft. The performance of the turbine is very dependent upon its installation in the aeroplane and the installation has a very large influence on aircraft drag characteristics. It follows that power plant and airframe must each be " tailor-made " to suit the other. The short development time required for gas turbines should make this procedure easy to follow, more especially as the nature of the engine is such that any successful basic design can be scaled up or down without introducing a host of fresh development troubles. This indeed is a very valuable characteristic.

6. We are as yet only at the beginning of this field of engineering and immense possibilities lie before us. The variations possible with a reciprocating engine are limited by the fact that the processes of compression, combustion and expansion take place in the same organ—the cylinder. In the gas turbine these processes take place in separate components. We can perform the compression process with axial flow compressors, centrifugal compressors, or combinations of these. The combustion chamber can take one of several forms, and there are a large number of variations possible in the turbine. There are many ways in which the major component units can be arranged in combination, and in addition there are the possibilities involved in the use of ducted fans, heat exchangers, after-burning, and other developments.

7. Up to the present two clear lines of development have been apparent in aircraft gas turbines, characterised by the use of either centrifugal compressor or the axial flow compressor. I am frequently asked whether one or the other will be ultimately dominant. My view is that there is a field for both, and that there will be many types in which both wil lbe used in combination.

8. Much has been said about the high fuel consumption of turbo-jet units. It is true that they use a lot of fuel, but that is because they develop a lot of power. In fact, at speeds of the order of 600 m.p.h. the fuel consumption in proportion to effective thrust horse-power is less than it would be for the piston engine and propeller combination at that speed. It is true, however, that at much lower speeds the turbo-jet unit compares very unfavourably with the conventional power plant in respect of fuel consumption, but the gas turbine/propeller combination does not suffer from this disadvantage to anything like the same extent.   In whatever form the gas turbine is used the very low power plant weight is an important compensating factor.   Very low fuel consumptions can be shown for complex engines, i.e., combinations of reciprocating engines and turbines, but though I have been amongst those who have proposed such schemes I am doubtful whether the low fuel consumption is a sufficient compensation for the increased weight, complexity, long development time, and difficulty of installation, etc., except possibly for certain very specialized purposes.

9.   At present Britain leads the world in the field of the aircraft gas turbine, but hard work will be necessary to maintain this lead.   As a nation we must not be parsimonious in our expenditure on research and development nor on engineering training.   Investment in both of these directions can produce very handsome dividends in the future.

10.   In recent months there has been ample evidence of intense interest in jet propulsion and the aircraft gas turbine.   I have no doubt that much of this interest has been aroused by the earlier editions of this book and Mr. Geoffrey Smith's writings in *Flight* and elsewhere.   The first edition appeared in 1942, and though it was of necessity severely limited by considerations of security it served a most useful purpose.   Since then two further editions appeared under wartime conditions, and though correspondingly handicapped have been eagerly snapped up.   The recent releases of hitherto secret developments and the great demand for information on the subject have already made necessary a fourth edition, to which it is a pleasure for me to contribute this note.

CHAPTER III.

EARLY PROJECTS : ATHODYDS AND THRUST AUGMENTERS

SUPPORTING the contention of the old adage, " There is nothing new under the sun," jet reaction, jet propulsion and the turbine may be cited as some of the earliest mechanical ideas. Class-room students will recall the æolipile demonstrated by Hero, the Alexandrian philosopher, at about the commencement of the Christian era. This apparatus consisted of a hollow sphere mounted to rotate between two pillars, one of which, being hollow, served to transmit steam from a closed vessel supported over a fire. Two pipes with right-angle ejecting nozzles were affixed to the sphere on opposite sides and the reaction created by the escape of the jets of steam caused the sphere to revolve.

Sir Isaac Newton, the Lincolnshire scientist, as long ago as 1687, had recognised the possibilities of jet propulsion by the formulation of his third law of motion that action and re-action are equal in magnitude and opposite in direction, but he did not originate the experiment illustrated by Fig. 20. Newton's philosophy in " Principia " was the subject of a later work by Gravesande entitled " Natural Philosophy," which had for its sub-title " An Introduction to Sir Isaac Newton's Philosophy." A contrivance of the nature depicted was therein mentioned as an illustration of Newton's law but not as having been devised by him. As a result many textbooks which followed contained pictures of a carriage propelled by jet reaction loosely captioned " Newton's steam carriage." It showed a four-wheeled vehicle with a spherical boiler, mounted over a fire, the top of the boiler having a rearwardly directed nozzle. By the reaction of the jet of steam thus created the carriage was to be propelled in a forward direction. Speed was to be regulated by the driver's control of a steam cock in the issuing pipe.

Fig. 19. Hero's aeolipile is reputed to be the first apparatus converting steam pressure into mechanical power. It was probably the earliest demonstration of the principle of jet reaction.

In the British Museum is a model of a machine ascribed to Giovanni Branca, an Italian engineer, who in 1629 suggested a form of steam turbine. His idea was to direct a powerful jet of steam tangentially against open vanes formed on the circumference of a fan wheel

Fig. 20. The illustration of a jet-propelled carriage which appears in many early textbooks on the evolution of the horseless road vehicle.

mounted on a vertical spindle. From this spindle other mechanisms were to be driven at reduced speed through a crude cogwheel gearing. The sketch (Fig. 21) shows the machine arranged to drive a stamp mill.

In 1791, that is to say over 150 years ago, an Englishman, John Barber, took out the first patent for a gas turbine. The sketch which accompanied it was, perhaps naturally, very rudimentary and certainly it provided no clue to the technical possibilities of the design. The proposed plant comprised a gas producer, gas receiver, gas and air compressors, a combus-

Fig. 21. Possibly the first proposal for a turbine was made by an Italian engineer, Giovanni Branca. The value of high rotational speed and reduction gearing was apparently realised in 1629.

tion chamber, a turbine wheel and speed-reducing gearing. About that time the substitution of mechanical power for human energy had become an economic necessity; the steam engine was the only known machine capable of producing motive power. There is no definite information regarding the aims of the inventor or what influenced him to devise an alternative to the ubiquitous steam engine. Relative efficiency would not arise

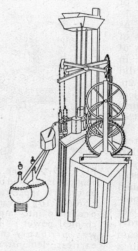

Fig. 22. Diagram of the first gas turbine proposed and patented by John Barber in 1791.

at that early period, and it can only be assumed that it was desired to produce a prime mover less complicated than the boiler, engine and condensing equipment of the steam plant and to obtain rotary motion without the need for the crank and connecting rod mechanism.

A concluding example of inventive vision is the "flying machine" embodying the principle of Avery's rotary engine.

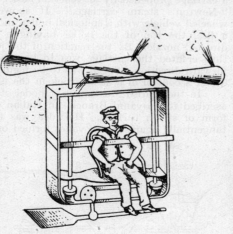

Fig. 23. Suggested in 1903—a helicopter using Avery's rotary engine (steam jet reaction).

The illustration is from " Flying," an early Iliffe periodical of 1903. Even as this edition goes to press the National Advisory Committee for Aeronautics, U.S.A., announces its interest in airscrews rotated by jet reaction.

At the beginning of the present century the practical realisation of the age-old dream of mechanical flight was delayed by lack of an efficient and reliable power unit. Steam plants were too heavy and cumbersome and the internal combustion engine was in its infancy. With little design or operational experience to draw upon, with quite elementary production facilities and with unsuitable and untested materials, the pioneers were obliged to build their own engines as well as the airframes. They developed their technique as they experimented and suffered many bitter disappointments. It was inevitable that in looking ahead such men sought alternative means of power production and methods of propulsion.

For a brief period the Gnome engine, that ingeniously conceived, beautifully made, but temperamental combination of rotary and reciprocating motion, met current requirements and made possible tremendous progress in aeronautics. However, since the advent of practical mechanical flight the demand has been for more and still more power from smaller and lighter units. It is of more than passing interest to record that jet propulsion, gas turbines, athodyds, thrust augmenters and thrust spoilers were visualised

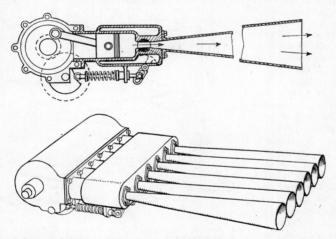

Fig. 24. The Lorin scheme of 1908. A conventional engine is employed solely to produce a propulsive jet. The lower sketch shows a proposed multi-cylinder layout for wing installation.

by the pioneers. Moreover, it is only as the result of successful development of the gas turbine and jet propulsion that engine manufacturers are able, for the first time in history, to supply more powerful units than the builders of airframes can at the moment usefully employ. The relative position has been reversed.

It was probably inevitable that the earliest efforts should be made in conjunction with the orthodox internal combustion engine.

Perhaps the simplest illustration is given by the 1908 scheme, Fig. 24, of the French engineer, Lorin. In this a conventional engine exhausts directly through a divergent nozzle to produce a propulsive jet. Air is compressed in the cylinder, there is combustion of fuel and the effluent expands in the discharge duct. Apart from the energy used in driving the usual auxiliaries, the engine functions solely to produce the jet and no power is taken off the engine crankshaft. Lorin visualised multi-cylinder units of this type, as shown in perspective, installed in the wings of aircraft.

By modern standards this design is only of historical interest. Nevertheless it deserves an honourable mention, as it was the original suggestion to employ a reciprocating engine and use part of the combustion energy to compress the air. It suffered, of course, by reason of the quite inadequate mass of air handled, which could not be more than that required to produce a combustible mixture in the engine cylinder.

Thrust Augmenters

Early efforts to overcome this handicap led to ingenious schemes to increase the mass of air and thus " augment " the thrust.

In 1917 O. Morize, of Chateaudun, France, proposed the plant shown diagrammatically in Fig. 25.

An engine A drives a compressor B which delivers air through an equalising chamber C to the combustion chamber D, the walls of which are lined with refractory material. The air inlet surrounds the jet E supplied with liquid fuel from tank F by an engine-driven pump G. A suitable means of ignition, electric or incandescent, is provided, and the combustion products are discharged through the combustion chamber nozzle into the convergent forward end of the " ejector " tube H. This creates a region of low pressure and air is induced into the end

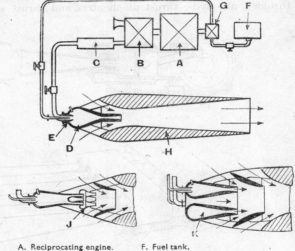

A. Reciprocating engine.
B. Air compressor.
C. Equalising chamber.
D. Combustion chamber.
E. Fuel injector.
F. Fuel tank.
G. Fuel pump.
H. " Ejector " tube.
J. Multi-nozzle combustion chamber.
K. Annular combustion chamber.

Fig. 25. In the Morize " ejector " scheme, fuel and air are supplied to a combustion chamber which discharges into a convergent-divergent tube.

of the tube H to join the rapidly moving gas stream. In the divergent portion of the tube H the velocity is diminished, thus imparting increased pressure to the stream as it is discharged.

Control of the thrust is effected by varying the quantity and pressure of the fuel and the charging air which supports combustion. Modified types of " ejectors," of which two are shown, had a series of air intakes, a plurality of combustion chamber nozzles, J, or an annular combustion chamber K.

In the same year H. S. Harris, of Esher, devised a propulsion plant of considerable interest, although it was not developed to a practical stage He also sought to induce air into the discharge tube in order to increase the mass of the jet. Instead, however, of achieving this aim by allowing the combustion gases to expand in a tube of increasing cross-sectional area, he inverted the process adopted by Morize.

The combustion gases enter the discharge tube at high velocity and low pressure (approximately atmospheric pressure) in the form of a cylindrical stream or jet. As this jet is cooled and contracted on its way to the discharge nozzle a " depression " is produced which induces the inflow of air at the open forward end of the discharge tube. The tube is of a considerable length in order to ensure that the stream of gas and air issuing from the discharge nozzle is completely cooled. Consequently, no rapid expansion will occur at the nozzle which might give a pressure drop and induce a reverse flow. To compensate for the continued cooling and the corresponding decrease in volume of the stream, the discharge tube is of decreasing cross-sectional area, thus maintaining the velocity.

It is somewhat remarkable that the scheme contains no suggestion of utilising the effluents of the engine which drives the blower supplying air to the combustion chambers. On the other hand, it appears ahead of its time in the proposal to employ powdered coal for fuel, as an alternative to liquid hydrocarbons such as petrol or paraffin. It is noteworthy as being one of the earliest, if not the first, to employ a radial compressor.

Petrol is used for the twin-jet plant shown in the diagram Fig. 26. A twin-cylinder engine A drives directly a low-pressure blower B, which draws air from a forward axial intake and delivers to combustion chambers C. Fuel from tank D is supplied to jets E and mingles with the air to form a combustible mixture. Each combustion chamber is positioned axially in a long discharge tube F open at both ends. The issuing gases, on cooling in this tube, produce a partial vacuum which draws air into the tube in the direction of flow and increases the mass of the rearwardly flowing stream.

A number of modified arrangements were suggested. Instead of two jets, a single large discharge tube with a plurality of combustion chambers may be provided. Or a series of combustion chambers may be fitted in each discharge tube and additional air be admitted at several points along the tube at successive stages. The charging blower, it was suggested, could be driven by means of a rotor mounted in the discharge tube ; in which case, presumably, the engine would be used only for starting. Either the complete discharge tube or a

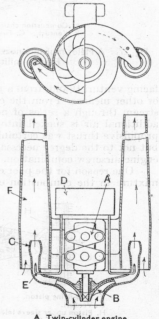

A. Twin-cylinder engine.
B. Low-pressure blower.
C. Combustion chamber.
D. Fuel tank.
E. Fuel injector.
F. Discharge conduit.

Fig. 26. The Harris plant also uses induced air, but the combustion chambers discharge into divergent-convergent tubes.

terminal portion may be mounted to swivel horizontally and vertically to
effect or assist the control of the aircraft.   Furthermore, means of temporarily closing the discharge end of the tube may be provided to cause the
gas stream to issue from the forward end of the tube to produce a braking
effect when landing.

Many schemes have been proposed in which a stream of gases issuing
from a combustion chamber creates an area of negative pressure in a tube
or duct and induces a supply of air to augment the mass of the propulsive
jet.   One of the best-known and most widely quoted is that invented by
Mélot and patented in 1920.   Previously it had been submitted to the French
military authorities who, during the war of 1914-18, experimented with
the device.

Referring to the diagram, Fig. 27, of the Mélot multiple-nozzle device,
the combustion chamber A is charged by relative wind entering by a forwardly

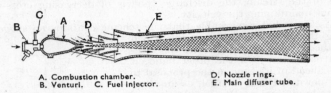

A. Combustion chamber.   D. Nozzle rings.
B. Venturi.   C. Fuel injector.   E. Main diffuser tube.

Fig. 27.   A Mélot multiple-nozzle " thrust augmenter " of the type tried out by the
French military authorities in the last war.

facing venturi B and, from a jet C, carrying in fuel which is ignited by electric
or other means.   From the chamber the combustion gases are emitted as a
stream through a series of nozzles D of increasing diameter through which
additional air is sucked into the main diffuser tube E as indicated.   The
propulsive thrust was certainly " augmented " by the additional mass of air,
but not to the degree necessary to enable it to challenge the efficiency of the
engine-airscrew combination.

One reason for the poor efficiency was the low compression of the fuel-air
mixture in the combustion chamber.   This was apparently appreciated by

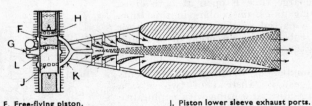

F. Free-flying piston.   J. Piston lower sleeve exhaust ports.
G. Venturi.   K. Exhaust conduit.
H. Piston upper sleeve inlet ports. L. Piston lower sleeve inlet ports.

Fig. 28.   Later Mélot design in which a two-stroke engine is employed to furnish a
higher compression cycle for the more efficient combustion of the fuel.

Mélot, for later he produced the relatively high compression, combustion
engine design, which is illustrated in Fig. 28.   The air-cooled two-stroke
engine had two opposed cylinders in axial alignment, and a common, free-
flying piston F having ported sleeve extensions.   In the position shown a
charge of air and fuel has been admitted through the venturi G, the common

cylinder inlet duct and the piston inlet ports H and compressed in the upper cylinder, which is at the point of ignition. The lower cylinder has discharged its effluents through piston exhaust ports J and the lower branch of the exhaust conduit K which delivers to the multiple-nozzle device. A new charge is simultaneously being aspirated by the lower cylinder by way of inlet ports L. Starting is effected by compressed air and electric ignition, but compression ignition is relied upon for continuous running.

An American Investigation

In 1927 two American investigators, E. N. Jacobs and J. M. Shoemaker, undertook a series of tests at the Langley Memorial Aeronautical Laboratory to determine to what extent the Mélot type augmenter would increase the thrust reaction of a jet. The apparatus used, shown in Fig. 29, followed as closely as possible the Mélot design with a pressure chamber, three annular nozzle rings, and a main convergent-divergent diffuser tube. Instead of burning a fuel to raise pressure, however, the chamber was supplied with compressed air at ordinary temperature. The venturi-shaped nozzle of the pressure chamber had a throat of $\frac{3}{8}$in. diameter, and the main diffuser tube was about 3ft. 9in. in overall length. Mathematically it would appear that the thrust of a free jet would need to be increased several times in order to make jet propulsion a feasible proposition. Accordingly, the reaction thrusts of a free jet and a jet with Mélot and other type augmenters at various pressures were weighed on the scale.

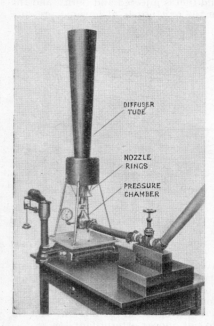

DIFFUSER TUBE

NOZZLE RINGS

PRESSURE CHAMBER

Fig. 29. Mélot type thrust augmenter on test at the Langley Memorial Aeronautical Laboratory, U.S.A.

The tests showed that the Mélot design gave the best results and represents a very creditable advance. Quantitatively, however, although the performance could possibly be improved by careful design, these results provided no evidence that the efficiency could be raised to the degree necessary for the successful propulsion of aircraft. The diffuser tube was designed to expand air from 185 lb./sq. in. gauge to atmospheric pressure at the mouth, but the best results were obtained at approximately 100 lb./sq. in. gauge. At this pressure the thrust was 137 per cent. of the theoretical thrust of a free jet (which was used as a basis for comparison), while a free jet was only 88 per cent. With a pressure of 185 lb./sq. in. gauge, the thrust of the Mélot augmenter fell to 122 per cent., while the free jet slightly improved to 90 per cent. This would seem to indicate that the diffuser employed was unsuitable in conjunction with the Mélot nozzles and did not provide for adequate expansion of the jet from the pressure chamber. It was found that variation of the distance from the mouth of the pressure nozzle to the entrance of the diffuser between two inches and nine inches produced no substantial effect on the thrust. A spacing of six inches, approximately that used in the Mélot system, gave the best results.

A Compressorless Design

The French engineer, René Leduc is mainly associated with projects for compressorless jet-propelled aircraft, so-called " athodyds," in which the main fuselage structure forms a continuous air duct from nose to tail. It is slightly barrelled to produce a divergent (compression) intake and a convergent (expansion) outlet. Due to the forward speed of the aircraft air is rammed into the intake, the velocity is lowered and pressure increased by the divergent shape of the duct, liquid fuel is injected and burnt, and the combustion gas and air discharges from the exit nozzle at lowered pressure

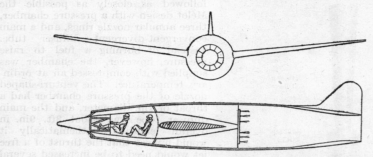

Fig. 30. A model of this Leduc design was shown at the Paris Salon, 1938.

and increased velocity to form the propulsive jet. Such aircraft would need to be launched at high speed by some means as it would seem quite impracticable to obtain sufficient thrust for take-off by air induced whilst on the ground and either stationary or moving at a relatively slow speed.

In 1938, at the Paris Salon de l'Aviation, a model of a Leduc aircraft, shown in Fig. 30, was exhibited. A notice suggested that this " machine of the future " would have an output of 14,000 h.p., a speed of 1,000 kilometres per hour and a ceiling of 30 kilometres. Nothing further was heard of this design. It is, however, significant of progress in the interval that the suggested performance figures to-day do not appear utterly fantastic.

The First Whittle Patent

On January 16th, 1930, Frank Whittle filed the application for his first jet propulsion patent. It is a quite brief but extraordinarily interesting document which, in the cautious phraseology of the patent specification, reveals the inventor's aims, objects and opinions. It refers to a method of propulsion in one direction by the reaction caused by expelling fluid in the opposite direction, and is deemed to be particularly adapted for aircraft, but not necessarily limited to this use.

The heat cycle is described as " consisting of one or more stages of compression, one or more stages of expansion and a heat addition between the end of compression and the beginning of expansion, part of the work done in expansion being employed to do the work of compression, and the remainder to provide the fluid reaction."

Characteristic of the inventor is the unequivocal expression of the belief
" that an embodiment of this invention will provide a large thrust in proportion to its weight, that it will perform at greater altitudes than are at present
obtainable, that it makes possible higher speeds than have up to the present

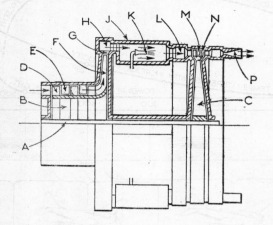

A. Shaft.
B. Compressor rotor.
C. Turbine rotor.
D. Compressor rotor blades.
E. Compressor stator blades.
F. Radial blades.
G. Diffuser vanes.
H. Air collector ring.
J. Combustion chamber.
K. Fuel jet.
L. Gas collector ring.
M. Turbine stator blades.
N. Turbine rotor blades.
P. Discharge nozzle.

Fig. 31. The plant suggested
by F. Whittle in his first patent
specification embodied a combined axial-radial compressor
and a plurality of combustion
chambers.

been obtained, that it will operate with any fuel now in use, and that it will
have a reasonably low fuel consumption. Further, that simplicity and
convenient external form is achieved."

The propulsion unit proposed is shown diagrammatically in Fig. 31. On
a common shaft A are mounted the rotor B of an axial-radial air compressor
and the gas turbine rotor C. The compressor rotor has axial flow blade
rings D, working in conjunction with stator blade rings E on the casing, and
terminal radial blading F. Air is delivered past diffuser vanes G to a hollow
collector ring H and thence to a plurality of combustion chambers J. These
chambers may be lagged to conserve heat and lined with refractory material,
and liquid fuel is introduced and burnt at jets K.

From the combustion chambers the heated gas/air mixture passes into
a collector ring L and expands through the turbine, which has a single stator
blade ring M between two rotor blade rings N. After leaving the turbine
the gases enter a third collector ring and are finally expanded to atmosphere
through a plurality of axially disposed nozzles P.

It is stated in the specification that " It can be demonstrated that the
efficiency of this device conceived as a propulsive engine will not be reduced
by reduction of the density of the atmosphere, and owing to the low temperature of the upper atmosphere may actually be enhanced." Also, " Controlling
means may include fuel control, gas flow control, or mechanical control of
the speed of the blower and/or its mover. The final emission of gas may
perhaps be directionally controlled for manœuvring purposes."

The first Whittle, single-jet plant to be constructed had only one combustion chamber and the turbine casing and bearing housing was jacketed
for water cooling.

The radial compressor has two air intakes, arranged one on each side
of the plane of rotation of the impeller A. This component is rotated at
such speed that the air leaves the tips of the blades at super-sonic velocity.
The air is delivered first into the radial primary diffuser chamber B,

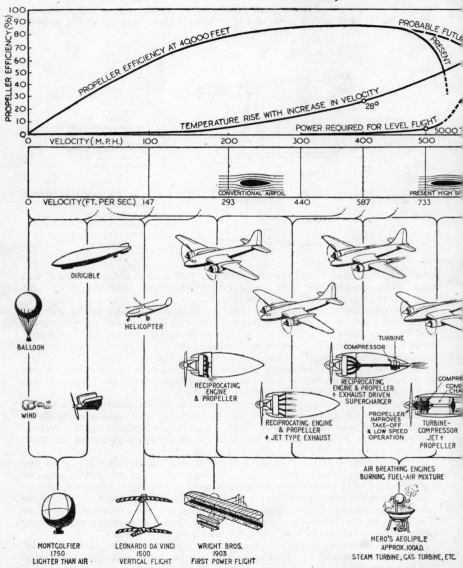

Fig. 32. This pictorial diagram of the evolution of aircraft and means of propulsion, prepared in 1944, lacks the German V-I intermittent impulse duct and the V-2 liquid rocket projectiles. The latter would extend

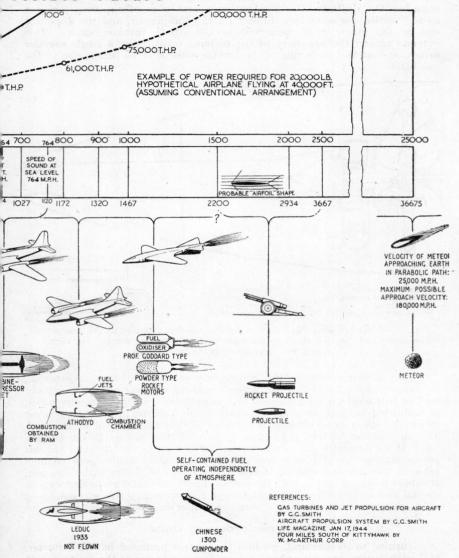

EXAMPLE OF POWER REQUIRED FOR 20,000 LB.
HYPOTHETICAL AIRPLANE FLYING AT 40,000 FT.
(ASSUMING CONVENTIONAL ARRANGEMENT)

SPEED OF SOUND AT SEA LEVEL 764 M.P.H.

PROBABLE AIRFOIL SHAPE

VELOCITY OF METEOR
APPROACHING EARTH
IN PARABOLIC PATH:
25,000 M.P.H.
MAXIMUM POSSIBLE
APPROACH VELOCITY:
180,000 M.P.H.

METEOR

FUEL
OXIDISER
PROF. GODDARD TYPE

FUEL
JETS

POWDER TYPE
ROCKET MOTORS

ROCKET PROJECTILE

PROJECTILE

TURBINE-COMPRESSOR JET

ATHODYD

COMBUSTION CHAMBER

COMBUSTION OBTAINED BY RAM

SELF-CONTAINED FUEL
OPERATING INDEPENDENTLY
OF ATMOSPHERE

LEDUC
1933
NOT FLOWN

CHINESE
1300
GUNPOWDER

REFERENCES:
GAS TURBINES AND JET PROPULSION FOR AIRCRAFT
BY G.G.SMITH
AIRCRAFT PROPULSION SYSTEM BY G.G.SMITH
LIFE MAGAZINE JAN 17, 1944
FOUR MILES SOUTH OF KITTYHAWK BY
W. McARTHUR CORP.

the velocity of rocket-driven projectiles to 3,400 m.p.h. The upper curves
relate to aircraft powered by conventional engine and airscrew units and
suggest a speed of about 550 m.p.h. as the practical limit for this type.

From "Douglas Airview"

which discharges into the delivery scroll, C, of increasing cross-sectional area. At its outlet, the scroll is directly connected to a helical combustion chamber D. Initially the combustion chamber is of tapering form so as to constitute a secondary diffuser for the compressor, and the discharge end of the chamber is connected to the volute turbine nozzle. This extends around the periphery of the turbine, constituting a single annular orifice, so that the blade ring of the turbine rotor is at all times open to the gas blast.

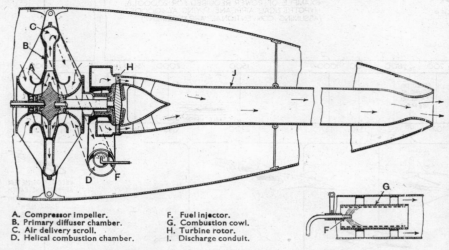

A. Compressor impeller.
B. Primary diffuser chamber.
C. Air delivery scroll.
D. Helical combustion chamber.
F. Fuel injector.
G. Combustion cowl.
H. Turbine rotor.
I. Discharge conduit.

Fig. 33.   A Whittle propulsion plant in which air is first admitted to the interior of the casing and then picked up by the high-speed rotary compressor.   The turbine casing and rotor bearings are fluid-cooled.

Fuel is introduced to the combustion chamber through injector F, surrounded by a cowl G. To ensure continuous combustion, the inner wall of this cowl may be covered with a perforated metal or a wire mesh, as indicated in the small detail drawing, to produce a boundary layer of air travelling at a velocity below that of the flame speed of the fuel. The air and combustion gases give up part of their energy to the turbine rotor H to drive the air compressor. After leaving the turbine, the air passes into an annular collecting chamber formed as a divergent channel between the discharge conduit J and a cone mounted on the turbine casing. It should be noted that in both the patent specification and in the first experimental unit to be built, a straight-through combustion system was employed although reverse-flow chambers were used on certain subsequent designs.

Swiss Reciprocating Units

Turning to Switzerland, we find the system proposed by W. Schurter, of Zürich, makes exclusive use of compressor aggregates of the reciprocating type. Single-piston or opposed-piston, high-compression, two-stroke engines are employed, and both types are illustrated in Fig. 34.

Dealing first with the smaller unit, the single-acting engine piston is rigidly combined with a double-acting, annular compressor piston. Groups of admission and discharge valves are provided at each end of the compressor cylinder. One end of the compressor delivers scavenging and charging air, at approximately twice atmospheric pressure, to the engine cylinder by way of duct A and the scavenge ports. From the other end air is discharged into conduit B, where it mixes with the combustion gases as they are leaving the engine cylinder by the exhaust ports. The engine piston is of the crosshead type and by means of a stationary abutment with a gland for the piston rod, a cushioning cylinder is arranged below the piston at C.

Of similar design, the opposed-piston unit is virtually self-balanced, and the engine has the more satisfactory end-to-end scavenging action. The upper side of the lower compressor delivers air to chamber D, whence part is taken for scavenging and charging the engine, and the remainder is passed through the shallow annular passage E to the mixing chamber F, thereby cooling, and absorbing heat from, the combustion zone of the cylinder. Air from the outer ends of both compressors passes through conduit G to the mixing chamber into which the lower side of the upper compressor discharges directly. Although the compressors work at only a relatively low pressure, the large number of automatically operated admission and discharge valves will scarcely be regarded with favour by aircraft engineers, particularly as a high engine speed is essential for the treatment of large volumes of air.

For a complete installation a plurality of compressor aggregates would be employed, as shown diagrammatically in Fig. 35. Not all of these need to be continuously operative, and one or more could be cut off from the main distributing conduit H by the valves J to serve as reserve sources of power. Obviously, with such an arrangement it would be necessary to regulate the pressure and volume of the gases in conduit H, and valves K are provided for this purpose. These are spring-loaded and automatically vary the cross-sectional area of the discharge nozzles according to the pressure prevailing in the conduit.

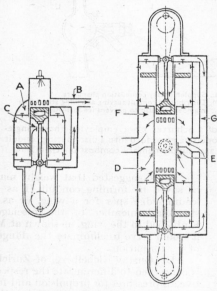

A. Scavenging air trunk.
B. Combustion gas and air conduit.
C. Cushioning cylinder.
D. Scavenging and cooling air trunk.
E. Annular air passage.
F. Gas/air mixing chamber.
G. Upper and lower air conduits.

Fig. 34. Schurter single-piston and opposed-piston compressor aggregates. A double-acting compressor piston is directly attached to each single-acting, two-stroke engine piston.

As the gases in conduit H contain an adequate supply of oxygen and the temperature is relatively low (approximately 200 deg. C.) "after-burning" can be employed to increase the power output. The efficiency of combustion at this stage is admittedly low, but the added propulsive effort could be of advantage when taking off or climbing. Supplementary combustion chambers L may be provided in conduit H and additionally, or alternatively, between the conduit and the discharge nozzles.

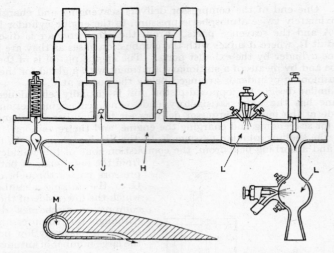

H. Main distribution conduit.
J. Cut-off valves.
K. Discharge nozzle control valves.
L. Supplementary combustion chambers.
M. Distribution conduit serving as a wing structural
   member and also to prevent ice formation.

Fig. 35. Diagrammatic arrangement of a Schurter plant employing three single-piston compressor aggregates. The propulsive gases feed into a distributing conduit having controlled discharge nozzles and supplementary combustion chambers.

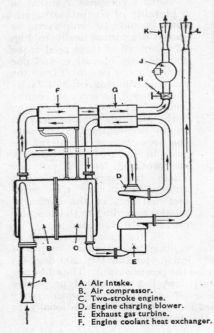

A. Air intake.
B. Air compressor.
C. Two-stroke engine.
D. Engine charging blower.
E. Exhaust gas turbine.
F. Engine coolant heat exchanger.
G. Charging air heat exchanger.
H. Regulating valve.
J. Supplementary combustion chamber.
K. Main discharge nozzle.
L. Turbine effluent discharge nozzle.

It is suggested that weight may be saved by forming conduit H as a leading-edge spar for a wing, or as a structural member of the fuselage. Embodied in the wing, as shown at M, it would serve to eliminate the danger of ice formation.

Dr. Gustav Eichelberg, of Zürich, is concerned to differentiate the respective air pressures for propulsion and for charging the motive unit driving the compressor. For efficient operation the pressure at the discharge nozzles should be about 2 atm., and as the flying

Fig. 36. A Swiss design, the Eichelberg, has an independent engine-charging system operated by a separate exhaust gas turbine. Effluent from the turbine is not mixed with the main air supply but discharged from a separate nozzle to assist propulsion.

altitude is increased this should be reduced in approximate proportion to the fall in atmospheric pressure.

On the other hand, an absolute pressure of from 4 to 5 kilograms per square centimetre (57 to 71 lb. per square inch) may be required for charging in order to keep the weight and dimensions of the engine at a minimum.

A diagram of a complete unit is given in Fig. 36. Air enters through a diffuser intake A, which is located either to take advantage of the dynamic pressure set up by the aircraft in flight or to suck in the boundary layer from a suitable point of the fuselage or wing. The compressor B is either mechani-

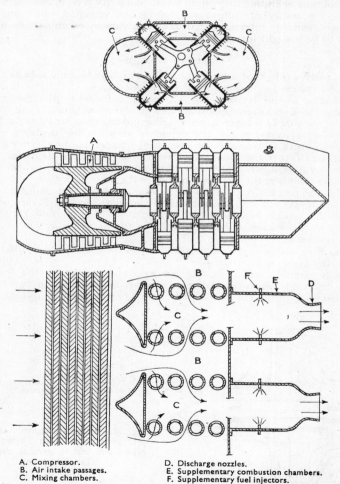

A. Compressor.
B. Air intake passages.
C. Mixing chambers.
D. Discharge nozzles.
E. Supplementary combustion chambers.
F. Supplementary fuel injectors.

Fig. 37. Junkers jet reaction plant employing a multi-bank, air-cooled, two-stroke engine to drive the rotary compressor. Additional fuel may be injected into the final expansion chambers to increase the propulsive effort.

cally coupled or, as indicated, structurally combined with a two-stroke engine C. From the air leaving the compressor a supply is drawn off by the charging blower D driven by the exhaust gas turbine E. Cooling fluid from the engine cylinder jackets is circulated through heat-exchanger F, and the charging air is passed through exchanger G on its way to the engine intake manifold. After traversing the heat-exchangers, the main propulsion air passes a regulating valve H and combustion chamber J, into which supplementary fuel can be injected to furnish additional power for peak loads, to the discharge nozzle K. The waste gases from turbine E are discharged from the nozzle L.

To obtain operational flexibility and reliability a complete plant would comprise a plurality of compressor aggregates, charging units and heat-exchangers, suitably interconnected to enable various combinations of components to be brought into co-operative function.

German Designs

An early project of the Junkers Co. employed a multi-bank, radial, two-stroke engine to drive an axial compressor.

Referring to the drawing, Fig. 37, the air is forced by the compressor A into passages B between opposite pairs of cylinder banks, from which a portion of the supply is taken as scavenging and charging air for the cylinders. The remainder passes round the cylinders as a cooling medium into the mixing chambers C arranged between the cylinder banks alternate to the passages B. Into these chambers the exhaust gases are delivered to mix with the by-passed air, which has been pre-heated by the cylinder walls. From these chambers the mixture expands to the outer air by way of nozzles D. To enable the propulsive effort to be increased, combustion chambers E, into which additional fuel can be introduced through injectors F, are provided between the mixing chambers and the nozzles. The air flow through the complete unit is shown diagrammatically in the plane projection of a longitudinal section of the plant.

The firm of Ernst Heinkel sponsored a compact jet propulsion unit, Fig. 38, designed by Max Hahn.

In a circular casing having an axial air intake at the front and coaxial discharge orifice at the rear, a shaft is mounted in two bearings supported on spiders. On this shaft is a single rotor which is divided to form

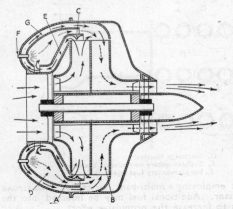

A. Blower impeller.
B. Turbine wheel.
C. Air flow guide ring.
D. Annular combustion chamber.
E. Combustion air passage.
F. Fuel injector.
G. Insulation passage.

Fig. 38. A self-contained all-rotary jet propulsion unit patented by Max Hahn and assigned to the firm of Ernst Heinkel.

a box-type blower impeller A and a boxed turbine wheel B. Air drawn into the unit through the forward central aperture leaves the impeller at its periphery and the stream is here divided by a projecting guide C on the enshrouding wall of the annular combustion chamber D.

The main supply is diverted to the rear to the turbine wheel, whilst a smaller portion passes along passage E between the main casing and the combustion chamber wall. At the point of smallest diameter, surrounding the intake aperture, this portion of the air-stream is again divided. Part enters chamber D into which fuel is injected by nozzles F and burnt to furnish additional heat for the final jet. The remainder continues around the combustion chamber in space G and joins the initial air-stream and the effluent from the combustion chamber to form a common stream which expands through the turbine and furnishes the motive power for rotating the blower. By passing a portion of the airstream completely round the combustion chamber this is effectively insulated and heat from the chamber is not completely lost by radiation to the atmosphere but is largely carried off by the air to perform useful work in expansion through the turbine.

Some Swedish Systems

Streamlined units for wing installation, to the designs of A. Lysholm, are suggested by Milo Aktiebolaget, of Stockholm. In one of these, shown in part-section in Fig. 39, the air enters by an annular orifice, is compressed in a

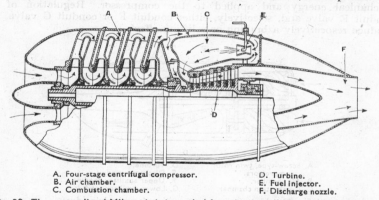

A. Four-stage centrifugal compressor.
B. Air chamber.
C. Combustion chamber.
D. Turbine.
E. Fuel injector.
F. Discharge nozzle.

Fig. 39. The streamlined Milo unit is intended for wing installation. All the air compressed by the multi-stage blower is passed to the combustion chamber and, with added fuel, is expanded through the multi-stage gas turbine.

multi-stage blower A and delivered to chamber B. This chamber houses an annular combustion chamber C and the gas turbine D which drives the blower. The air, preheated in its passage over the walls of the combustion chamber and the turbine stator casing, at the rear reverses its direction of flow and enters the combustion chamber past fuel nozzles E. From the combustion chamber the flow is again reversed, and the gases expand through the turbine and pass with an accelerating velocity through an outlet conduit of diminishing cross-sectional area to the discharge nozzle F.

Plants of similar type are proposed by Aktiebolaget Ljungströms Angturbin. In addition to a unit constructionally resembling the Milo design previously described, the one illustrated in Fig. 40 is of interest, as it employs a pair of twin-rotor, screw-type compressors A, gear-driven from

the turbine shaft.   Air taken in at the forward end is delivered by the
blowers through the receiving chamber B to combustion chamber C.   Fuel
is delivered by a pump driven from the forward end of the turbine rotor
shaft to a series of shrouded injectors in the mouth of the combustion chamber.   The combustion gas and air mixture expands through the multi-stage
turbine D and discharges by way of a convergent conduit E.

To permit rapid acceleration without ill-effects, that part of the
energy available for propulsion is temporarily reduced, and thus the
power input to the compressor is increased simultaneously.   The compressor
speed is thus accelerated, the quantity of air delivered increases to an excess
over that required for the fuel supplied, and the temperature of the propulsive
gases is lowered.   Thereafter it is permissible rapidly to increase the supply
of fuel to correspond with the increased quantity of air, the normal fuel-air
ratio is re-established, and the aircraft is accelerated.

Normally the gases leaving the turbine are discharged through conduit E,
which is furnished with a valve.   From points adjacent to the turbine
outlet two auxiliary conduits, F and G, are fitted, each provided with a
valve.   Extending to the exterior of the casing, the outlets are directed
forward and downward respectively.   For normal operation the three valves
are positioned as shown in full line, but if the valve of either conduit F or G
is opened, the back pressure will be reduced.   This results in an increased
heat and pressure drop in the turbine, which is transformed into additional
mechanical energy and applied to the compressor.   Regulation of the
conduit E valve and, selectively, either conduit F or conduit G valve, will
produce respectively a braking or a lifting effect.

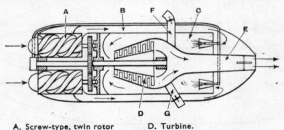

A. Screw-type, twin rotor   D. Turbine.
      compressors.   E. Discharge conduit.
B. Air chamber.   F. Upper auxiliary conduit.
C. Combustion chamber.   G. Lower auxiliary conduit.

Fig. 40.   Ljungströms Angturbin unit embodying dual
twin-rotor air compressors.   Special arrangements
are made for speeding-up of the compressor to
permit rapid acceleration in emergency.

Italian Investigations

Previous editions of this book gave some prominence to the work of
Signor Campini.   This is now largely of historical interest, but it is
proposed to retain some account of Campini's early efforts and to refer to
Italian designs subsequent to the C.C.2, the aircraft which first flew in August,
1940 and was widely publicised in 1941 after its Milan-Rome flight.

The C.C.1 design, which never materialised, is shown in Fig. 41.   This
project was naively described by its designer as being intended for operation
at either subsonic or supersonic speeds.   The cabin A is of ovoid form and
constructed as a pressure unit for high-altitude operation.   Air is admitted
where the annular space between cabin A and the enshrouding cylinder B

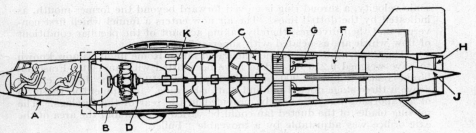

A. Ovoid cabin.
B. Enshrouding cylinder.
C. Two-stage centrifugal com-
pressor.

D. Radial engine.
E. Rectifier-radiator
F. Combustion space.
G. Annular mixing channel.

H. Discharge nozzle.
J. Cone for varying nozzle orifice.
K. Controlled lateral orifices.

Fig. 41. The Campini CC1 design of high-altitude craft intended for operation at either sub- or supersonic speeds. The control cabin is pressure charged. A petrol engine is used to drive the compressor.

has its smallest cross-section. This ram-compressed air then passes through a two-stage centrifugal compressor C driven by a radial engine D or, alternatively, a gas turbine. Beyond the compressor it passes a radiator E, which also acts as a rectifier, into the wide combustion space F. Here, in an annular channel G of venturi shape, the air is supplied with fuel and, after expansion, discharges through the nozzle H. The nozzle unit is arranged to swivel and the cross-sectional area may be varied by means of the cone J. On starting, there will be a negative pressure in the inlet chamber between the cabin and the enshrouding ring, and air can be admitted by way of lateral orifices K.

The air-admission arrangement outlined above is that employed for operation at sub-sonic speeds. If the speed of flight is increased to a super-

Fig. 42. The Caproni-Campini jet-propelled cantilever monoplane in the air. Known as the CC2, it weighed about 9,250 lb.

sonic velocity, a shroud ring is moved forward beyond the former mouth, as indicated by the dotted lines.   The air now enters a funnel which first converges and then diverges, thereby taking account of the peculiar conditions of flow which are associated with supersonic velocities.

The C.C.2, which made the celebrated Milan-Rome flight, is now known to have weighed 9,250 lb. and to have been fitted with an Isotta-Fraschini liquid-cooled engine of 900 h.p.   The span was 52 ft.   The Isotta engine drove a three-stage ducted fan and " after-burning " equipment in the form of a vaporising burner could be provided in the rear of the fuselage.   The moving blades of the ducted fan could be varied in pitch and the area of the exit orifice was adjustable by a moveable " bullet."

In view of the conjectures concerning the performance of the C.C.2 the following figures may be of interest.   The maximum speed was 205 m.p.h. at 9,800ft., but this could be increased with after-burning to about 230 m.p.h. at the same height.   The climb to 13,000ft. took 53 minutes.

It is clear from information obtained in Italy during the war that the C.C.2 was not regarded as a success.   Nevertheless, Campini persevered and produced a number of designs for the Italian Air Ministry for fighter and bomber aircraft utilising ducted fan power units located in the wing and driven remotely from one or two reciprocating engines in the fuselage.   With " afterburning " one of the Campini fighters was estimated to have a speed of 450 m.p.h. at 33,000ft.   The reciprocating engine was to be a German DB 605 of 1,300 h.p.   A bomber type was to have two of these engines.

Campini also submitted to the Italian Air Ministry a proposal for a gas turbine-airscrew unit utilising a nine-stage turbine and an eight-stage centrifugal compressor, with intercooling on the last two stages.

The Caproni concern, which had collaborated with Campini, suggested a development of their Reggiane Re 2005 single-seat fighter with an additional reaction propulsion device.   It was proposed to use a twelve-cylinder engine of 370 h.p. to drive two centrifugal compressors, one for supercharging the main DB 605 and the auxiliary unit, and the second for providing reaction propulsion.   The proposed layout is shown in Fig. 43.

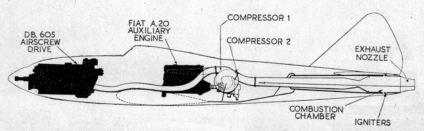

Fig. 43.   Reggiane Re 2005 fighter project with airscrew and jet propulsion.

CHAPTER IV

GAS TURBINE COMPONENTS : RADIAL AND AXIAL COMPRESSORS : TYPES OF TURBINES

ROTARY air compressors are mainly one of two types differentiated by the line of flow in either a radial or axial direction. The radial type, more commonly described as a centrifugal compressor, may have one or more stages but the axial type is invariably a multi-stage unit. Units exist in which an initial radial stage is followed by a number of axial stages and, conversely, axial stages with a terminal radial stage.

The compressor on the Heinkel-Hirth jet engine has an initial stage which is not specifically axial or radial, but embodies characteristics of both. The mechanical engineer would probably term this a " mixed flow " but on aircraft units it is aptly designated as a diagonal or semi-axial stage. A further type meriting attention is the Lysholm twin helical screw compressor which is included in Swedish aircraft designs and employed on large gas turbine stationary power plants in America. Whilst of the rotary type it has the advantage of positive air displacement. It is employed as a supercharging blower but, as far as is known, has not yet been in practical use for jet propulsion.

Radial Compressors

Due to its long use as an engine-driven blower for pressure-charging reciprocating type aircraft engines, the radial compressor has received many years of intensive development. Performance and reliability are well established so, despite certain inherent limitations, it was adopted for gas turbines. Whilst it could satisfactorily furnish the volume of air required by a piston engine operating with a fuel-air ratio of about 1 : 15 it was less well suited for the turbine-jet unit which requires a fuel-air ratio of from 1 : 60 to 1 : 70. The volume of air to be handled necessitated an impeller of large diameter and a high speed of rotation, resulting in the linear speed at the periphery being markedly increased. It is not uncommon for the tip speeds of impellers to exceed the speed of sound but in a jet plant it is most desirable to maintain a smoothly accelerating flow and to avoid surging or wave effects.

The diameter of a radial compressor is necessarily greater than an equivalent one of axial type and thus the overall diameter of the unit is greater. This constitutes a disadvantage, particularly in the case of wing installation. At the high air speeds of jet-propelled aircraft, a reduction in diameter and consequent lowering of installation drag may well yield an improvement in propulsive efficiency which will outweigh the advantage of a better specific consumption or a higher thrust. This is well exemplified by a comparison of the basically similar German B.M.W. and Junkers plants, both of which employ axial compressors. The Junkers 004 develops a thrust of 1,984 lb. but the B.M.W. 003, 4 in. smaller in diameter and 200 lb. less in weight, which has a thrust of only 1,786 lb. gives the same flight speed when installed in an aircraft.

There are, however, compensating advantages when it is compared with the axial type. It is cheaper to produce, more robust, can be run at higher speeds and is less prone to icing under unfavourable atmospheric conditions. Furthermore, it has a wider effective operational range than the axial type, and in this respect is more suitable for the duty in a variable speed, variable load propulsion unit. In a gas turbine, as in all heat engines, design is a compromise between favourable and unfavourable characteristics, and the radial compressor is successfully employed, for instance, in the Rolls-Royce, de Havilland and American G.E.C. units.

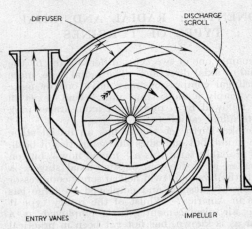

Fig. 44. Diagram of radial compressor with twin discharge outlets.

Air enters the compressor casing by way of the relatively small intake eye around the hub to be picked up by the radial vanes of the rotating impeller, rapidly accelerated and discharged from the periphery into a diffuser. This annular chamber is provided with a number of vanes defining a series of divergent passages, the function of which is to build up pressure in the air stream at the expense of velocity. From the diffuser the air passes to a discharge scroll having one or more outlets, see Fig. 44.

Drawings of three different types of impeller are given in Fig. 45. A simple single-entry "web" type A has radial vanes supported on one side by a disc. The radial, divergent passages between the vanes are thus defined on three sides by the impeller and completed by the adjacent casing wall when the impeller is mounted in position. Small curved vanes around the hub are "entry" vanes to facilitate the change of flow from the axial to the radial direction and thus reduce the so-called entry shock.

The double-entry type B is a variation of the web impeller with radial vanes on each side of the single central disc. Air enters at each side and is delivered to a common collector duct. It is, in effect, two single-entry impellers arranged back to back. The third impeller C is designated the "closed" or "shrouded" type. This resembles type A, but has additionally an annular wall on the entry side, and thus the radial passages are completely defined.

Pictorial representations of the three

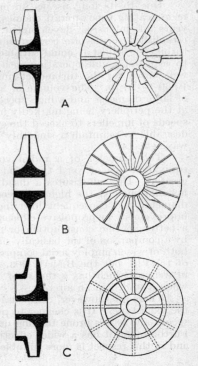

Fig. 45. Three commonly-used impellers for radial compressors:
A. Single-entry web type.
B. Double-entry web type.
C. Closed, or shrouded, type.

different types, in the order referred to, are given in Fig. 46. Actually these show the impellers of turbine-driven supercharging blowers for normal aircraft engines. There is no essential structural difference for either duty.

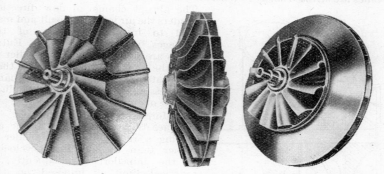

Fig. 46. These views of single-entry web, double-entry web and shrouded impellers clearly show the curved entry vanes.

The web type A is that in common use as a supercharging blower on piston engines. Type B has the obvious advantage of being subjected to approximately equal forces on both sides of the central web and thus is axially balanced. An example in this category is the impeller of the Rolls-Royce Derwent turbine jet engine, Fig. 47. The fully shrouded type C is more difficult to manufacture, but can usually be designed to produce an efficiency 2 or 3 per cent. higher than type A. A variant of this type is the Junkers design with separately boxed passages resembling tubular spokes of a wheel.

It is practical to design radial compressors for a

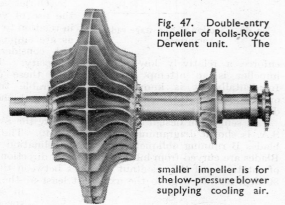

Fig. 47. Double-entry impeller of Rolls-Royce Derwent unit. The smaller impeller is for the low-pressure blower supplying cooling air.

pressure ratio approaching 4 : 1 in a single stage and possible, at some lowering of efficiency, to achieve a higher pressure. Consequently it may be preferable to keep the stage ratio reasonably low and obtain the desired pressure by increasing the number of stages. This substantially increases the axial length of the unit as it necessitates interstage passages to transfer the air from the diffuser of one stage to the intake eye of the next stage, as will be seen in the diagram of a two-stage unit, Fig. 48. Interstage losses will to some degree lower the overall efficiency.

The pressure ratio per stage increases approximately with the square of the peripheral velocity of the impeller and development in the past has mainly been obtained by raising rotational speed. When the peripheral velocity approaches or exceeds that of sound the mechanical stressing of the impeller is of such magnitude that it becomes almost imperative to arrange the vanes truly radial. Bending stresses in the metal sections are thus avoided and the vanes are stressed solely in tension, but there are concomitant drawbacks.

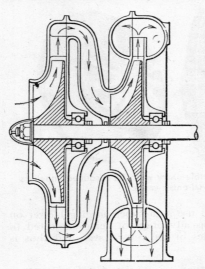

The abrupt change of flow direction renders the air intake difficult and may lead to incomplete filling of the passages between the vanes. Entry vanes are provided on the impeller to ease the change of flow, and as they are located near the hub, the mechanical stressing is not sufficient to preclude the use of curved vanes.

More important, however, is the fact that the velocity of the air leaving a radially vaned impeller is higher than the peripheral velocity of the impeller. Consequently, a practical limit is imposed on the peripheral velocity of the impeller by the absolute velocity of the air which is susceptible, at speeds in excess of the speed of sound, to compressibility factors which reduce efficiency.

Outlet velocity can be reduced by the use of vanes curved backwardly in relation to the direction of rotation, as are employed in pumps and fans, but considerations of strength will enforce a relatively low peripheral velocity. The semi-axial form of impeller is an attempt to circumvent these opposing characteristics. Incidentally, it is known that considerable trouble was encountered on the Heinkel-Hirth design owing to the attached blades coming adrift during operation.

Fig. 48.   Section of two-stage radial compressor.

A semi-axial design of some promise by the Swiss firm of Sulzer Freres S.A. is shown diagrammatically in Fig. 49. The impeller A has integral blades B running obliquely and at an inclination with respect to the axis. Blades are curved from inlet to outlet in a direction opposite to the direction of rotation and the resultant passages between the blades may vary from 30 deg. and 60 deg. to the axis. At least at the outlet edges, the blades in service have a peripheral speed higher than the velocity of sound, but the velocity of the compressed air at the outlet will not exceed the velocity of sound. Consequently it becomes possible to arrange a relatively high ratio of compression in a single stage without suffering a disturbance of flow at the outlet by pressure waves due to supersonic velocity.

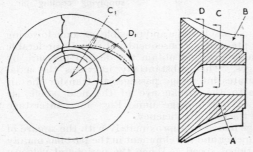

Fig. 49.   Sulzer   Semi-axial or "diagonal" compressor rotor.

The shape of the blades is such that at any plane normal

to the axis, say C and D, the cross-section is truly radial, as shown at C_1 and D_1 in dotted outline, in order to withstand centrifugal stressing without being subjected to bending loads. Modifications of this design have additional intermediate blades at the outlet or interrupted and staggered blades, all with the aim of producing a non-turbulent flow of air at uniform pressure.

At present the method of varying the output of a radial compressor usually entails the use of some form of throttling device and is apt to lead to an undesirable back pressure effect. There are, however, projected schemes for varying the output which avoid this disadvantage. Blackburn Aircraft Ltd., in their variable output compressor, Fig. 50, form the impeller in two parts. Part A, consisting of a plurality of radially disposed blades shaped on the entry side to conform to the contour of the casing, is positively located on the driving shaft. The dish-shaped part B is slidably splined to the driving shaft and is slotted to permit it to be moved axially over the radial blades of part A. In the position shown in the upper half of the diagram, part B is in the limit position exposing the maximum area of the impeller blades for maximum output.

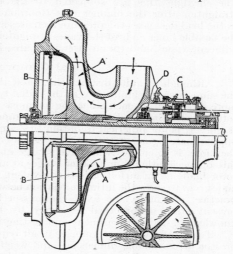

Fig. 50. Variable output radial compressor by Blackburn Aircraft Ltd.

In the lower half, part B has been moved to the opposite limit reducing the operative area of the blades for a minimum output. Control is effected by means of an annular pressure cylinder C which, through the medium of a plurality of rods and a yoke engaging ball thrust races on an extension sleeve, axially moves part B to determine the effective area of the impeller blades and consequently the output. This particular design was intended for a supercharging blower for conventional engines.

An automatic control arrangement, Fig. 51, is proposed by the British Thomson-Houston Co., Ltd., to maintain the operating efficiency of radial compressors under varying load. It is known

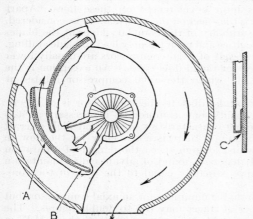

Fig. 51. Flexible diffuser vanes for automatic control of B.T.H. compressor.

that the pressure increases as the flow decreases, and this characteristic is exploited to adjust the diffuser vanes and thus vary the shape of the diffuser passages. The diffuser vanes A are hollow and constructed with the closed inner ends in the form of curved, flexible tips B which are unattached to the casing wall, as shown at C. At the outermost ends the vanes are open to the region of higher pressure in the discharge scroll. The flexible tips are subjected to the pressure produced and tend to straighten after the manner of a Bourdon tube in a pressure gauge. Thus, as the load decreases the pressure increases at the discharge ends of the vanes. the flexible inner ends of the vanes straighten somewhat to move closer to the adjacent vanes, and the diffuser inlet area is thereby lessened.

Axial Compressors

Although of quite distinct character, the axial compressor is subject to the same laws and limitations as the radial type. The line of flow is relatively more direct but at each stage the air must be accelerated in the direction of rotation and then re-directed to the appropriate angle of attack for the next stage. It is not practical to obtain the same pressure ratio per stage and an approximate figure of 1 : 1.25 may be noted for the axial type. The trend, therefore, is to employ a relatively large number of stages and maintain the rate of acceleration in individual stages at an efficient level. Regarding each rotor blade as an airfoil, this is equivalent to avoiding a high lift coefficient and serves to show the intimate relation between mechanical and aerodynamic practice. Actually, the axial compressor has been brought rapidly to its present state of practical efficiency by the application of aerodynamic knowledge and by experiment and testing in aerodynamic laboratories.

To transfer the huge volumes of air required for turbine plants in a compressor of reasonable dimensions and weight the blading demands as much care in design as the wing or airscrew blade of a high-speed aircraft. Entry shock must be avoided, Mach numbers must be kept down and every effort made to prevent boundary layer separation and turbulence. As in the normal airscrew blade, the compressor blade must have a varying angle of attack to compensate for the increasing linear velocity from root to tip.

The Germans claimed an efficiency on test of 85 per cent. for their axial compressors, but probably 77 to 78 per cent. was realised in operation. Delivery volume can be raised by increasing rotational speed and axial velocity but important factors limit development on these lines. Apart from mechanical problems there is the effect on the air stream to be considered. Centrifugal force may upset the stability of the boundary layer at the blades and thus create operational difficulties and even possibly lead to blade stalling. It will be noted that rotational speeds of axial compressors are usually lower than those successfully employed for radial flow types. An exception is the Westinghouse Yankee jet unit in which the axial compressor rotates at 18,000 r.p.m.

The profile of the annular intake duct to the compressor is of specia importance. As in other components some compromise is necessary as it is difficult to reconcile the conflicting characteristics at low and high aircraft speeds. When stationary or taking-off there is a tendency for the flow to separate from the inner cone, whilst at high speed the danger of separation occurs at the outer contour. It has been found of advantage to maintain a constant cross-sectional area approximately equal to the area of the compressor intake.

Three stages constitute a probable minimum for an axial compressor, but at the other extreme the number of stages may run to double figures. The German Junkers jet plant has an eight-stage compressor and the B.M.W. a seven-stage unit. The same firms had projected designs with eleven- and twelve-stage compressors. (See Chapter VII). In Britain the Metropolitan-Vickers and Armstrong-Siddeley jet engines have respectively nine and fourteen-stage axial compressors.

A diagrammatic section, Fig. 52, shows the disposition of parts in a five-stage axial compressor. The casing is usually cylindrical and reduction of the annular working space is achieved by the use of a rotor drum increasing in diameter from entry to discharge. Eleven rows of blading are shown as both entry and discharge guide vanes are provided, although discharge vanes and, less commonly, entry vanes may be omitted in certain designs. The rotor is built up of five discs, but in an alternative type discs are employed only at each end and intervening blade rows are carried on a series of rings

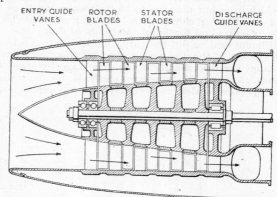

Fig. 52. Diagrammatic arrangement of a five-stage axial compressor.

Fig. 53. Assembled rotor of Westinghouse six-stage axial compressor.

registering on each other and the end discs to form a hollow rotor drum.   A
completely assembled and balanced rotor for the six-stage Westinghouse
compressor being checked for truth of shaft diameter, is shown in Fig. 53.

Rotor discs may be of steel or light alloy and will probably decrease in
width from low-pressure to high-pressure stages as they accommodate blades
of diminishing chord.   Steel or light alloy blades are machined to profile
from individual forgings.   Methods of fixing the blades to the disc vary in
different designs but they are commonly fitted into tee or dovetail slots in the
periphery of the disc and secured by pins, wedges or screws.   The number of
blades per disc usually diminishes stage by stage from intake to discharge.
Figs. 54 and 55, showing methods of mounting Junkers and B.M.W.
compressor blades, respectively, are self-explanatory.

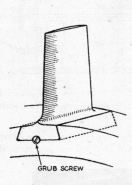

Fig. 54.   Junkers blades are
axially located by grub
screws.

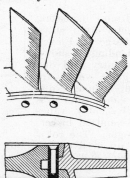

Fig. 55.   B.M.W. duralumin
blades pinned in magnesium
disc.

Stator blades to direct the air flow between stages will also be of either
steel or light alloy and probably be assembled in half-rings for mounting in
the longitudinally-divided light alloy compressor casing.   They may be
machined from forgings, folded from
sheet material, developed from tubes
or, in the case of steel, even cambered
from a single sheet.   The casing of the
B.M.W. compressor is not divided and
the pressed duralumin stator blades
are built up in inner and outer rings
of magnesium alloy.   Both rings are
slotted to receive the blades, which
are bent and spot-welded to the inner
ring, but allowed freedom to expand
in the outer ring, as shown in Fig. 56.
The stator rings are loosely positioned
on the rotor assembly, inserted in the
casing and located by radial set
screws.

Earlier reference was made to
the relatively narrow operational characteristics of the axial compressor.
It is this factor which makes desirable

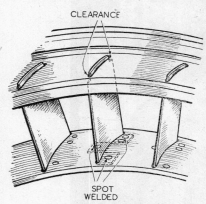

Fig. 56.   Method of fixing stator
blades of B.M.W. compressor.

a " bullet " to control the effective cross-sectional area of the terminal jet orifice. The blades of an axial compressor tend to stall at low thrust and consequently a bullet, which would probably be a disadvantage if used in conjunction with a radial compressor, becomes of practical value. German jet engines employ bullet control devices which, severally, have two positions for idling and power, four positions for starting, take-off, cruising and high speed, and continuous variation determined by the throttle lever and the pitot head pressure.

A too-rapid opening of the throttle from idling to maximum position may lead to violent acceleration of rotational speed and stalling of the compressor blades. Should this occur complications may follow rapidly as air delivery falls, air/fuel ratio is changed, combustion conditions become unstable and gas temperature at the turbine becomes excessive. In Germany governed control devices have been fitted, ensuring that the period of acceleration from low to maximum r.p.m. is not less than a predetermined minimum of several seconds to avoid this contingency and the consequent danger of loss of flying speed and damage to the power unit.

Such a limitation, not necessary on a unit embodying a radial compressor, constitutes a handicap in combat performance. To lessen the tendency to stalling by increasing the number of stages and lowering the blade loading, implies an increase in the inertia of the rotor, which militates against rapid acceleration. Doubtless the handicap will be removed as a result of continued development of the axial type.

An axial compressor with fixed blading has only a limited range of air

Fig. 57. Brown-Boveri experimental axial compressor with adjustable pitch blading.

delivery volumes. With adjustable rotor blades, however, it could be regulated to deliver any volume from zero to maximum, and pressure from zero to maximum at constant speed. Such an innovation would be as important as the variable pitch airscrew has proved to be in normal aircraft propulsion. Fig. 57 shows the rotor of an experimental three-stage, high-speed compressor of this type, built by Brown-Boveri for test purposes. The blades can be adjusted between 0 deg. and 45 deg., whilst running, and normal maximum air delivery is 6,395 cu. ft. per minute at a pressure of 2.1 atm. (30.9 lb./sq. in. absolute) at 7,800 r.p.m.

Another method of regulating the output of a multi-stage axial compressor is proposed by the Junkers Co. According to this scheme one or more rings of rotor blades are disconnectably mounted on the rotor shaft and are allowed to run idly in the air stream for reduced delivery. Further, one or more sets of stator blades are disconnectably mounted in the casing and similarly may be allowed to rotate idly for reduced output. Disconnectable rotor and stator blade rings may be embodied in the same design. When the rings are uncoupled they assume a speed at which the blades are in the inoperative position in relation to the flow of air through the compressor. The change of speed is relatively small, which is advantageous as the clutching elements have to absorb only small mass forces when brought into operation.

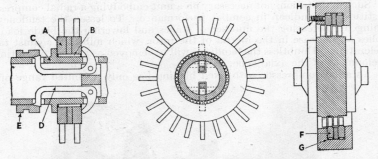

Fig. 58. Junkers proposal for regulating output by disconnectable stator and rotor blade rings.

The principle is shown in purely diagrammatic form in Fig. 58. Rotor blades are built on to rings A mounted for rotation on needle rollers B on rotor shaft C. They may be clutched to the shaft by means of a pair of bell-crank levers D, pivoted inside the hollow shaft and actuated by a slidable collar E.

Stator blades are similarly built on rings F rotatable on rollers G in casing H. One means of clutching them to the casing is by screw clamping devices, as indicated at J. Actuation may be arranged in any suitable manner with mechanical, hydraulic or electro-magnetic clutches.

Turbines

Making use of convenient and not unreasonable approximations, a jet propulsion engine will deliver approximately 50 lb. thrust for every pound of air flowing through the unit per second. To drive a modern rotary compressor approximately 100 h.p. is necessary for each pound of air delivered per second. It follows that in a unit developing 2,500 lb. thrust the turbine driving the compressor must produce about 5,000 h.p. This estimate is revealing, as it shows an expenditure of energy greater than that of a pair of conventional piston engines of high power output and indicates why performance of a jet-propelled aircraft is so outstanding and why the rate of fuel consumption is relatively heavy. In short, the jet engine is a high-powered unit. Furthermore, it makes clear why the respective component efficiencies are so important. Lecturing before the Institution of Mechanical Engineers in 1939 Dr. Adolph Meyer showed that an increase in the overall efficiency of the compressor and turbine from 70 per cent. to 75 per cent. would raise the cycle efficiency from 15 to 18 per cent., representing a 20 per cent. improvement. Every one per cent. increase meant, therefore, an improvement of about 4 per cent. in the cycle efficiency.

Turbines may be of the single-stage or multi-stage type but it must be remembered that a loss occurs at each stage and consequently there is advantage to be gained by using only a single stage providing the requisite output can be obtained. This implies high speed of rotation and will tend to confine the use of a single - stage turbine to units employing a radial compressor. At the present level of development a single-stage turbine can provide all the power necessary to drive a single-stage radial compressor. It is lighter, simpler to manufacture and more efficient. Multi-stage turbines are more applicable to axial flow compressors, which operate at lower speeds of rotation, and are also convenient for turbine-driven airscrews where one stage can be used to drive the compressor and the other the airscrew. A single-stage turbine in conjunction with a single-stage radial compressor is the simplest combination for a jet propulsion engine. The Rolls-Royce and de Havilland designs of this

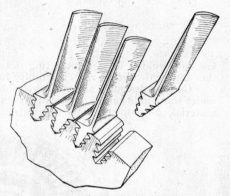

Fig. 59.   " Fir-tree " blade root fixing on de Havilland turbine.

type will demonstrate this when compared with, for example, the German Junkers and B.M.W. jet engines. The performance of these British power units in the record breaking Meteor and the Vampire aircraft respectively will confirm their relative efficiency.

In British practice turbine blades are fully machined from individual forgings to the closest limits for shape and dimensions and each is subject to what is virtually a laboratory examination. Blades are furnished with profile ground "fir-tree" roots which are pressed into slots broached in the periphery of the disc and secured by peening on each side, as on the de Havilland Goblin turbine, Fig. 59. Produced to close limits of weight, each blade is weighed on a momentum balance, marked to the amount plus or minus of the standard and stored accordingly. Sets of blades are selected, greased, inserted in the previously balanced rotor and peened in a fixture equipped with small compressed air riveting hammers. After a final operation to align the blades the assembly is degreased and then dynamically balanced. Balance is redressed by the removal of blades and the substitution of other blades having a corrective weight. Usually the rotor assembly includes the shaft as it has been found that in bolting up the disc to the shaft the balance may be upset. The Rolls-Royce Derwent turbine wheel with shaft and half-coupling is shown in Fig. 60.

Similar materials and methods of production are employed for the guide vanes of the turbine nozzle. As, however, the vanes are stationary and not subjected to stressing by centrifugal force, they may be precision cast by the " lost-wax " process. This is the method used by Rolls-Royce.

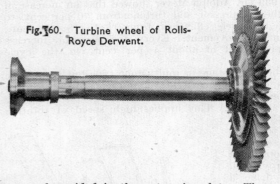

Fig. 60. Turbine wheel of Rolls-Royce Derwent.

Vanes are fitted in helical slots in the periphery of the inner ring and secured by side clamp rings. On the side adjacent to the rotor the clamp ring may incorporate one half of the labyrinth sealing device between nozzle and turbine blades. As the vanes are continuously exposed to the combustion gases at maximum temperature they are permitted freedom of expansion in the radial direction and are only guided in the outer ring slots. These features are to be seen in the Derwent nozzle ring assembly, Fig. 61.

German designers also employed solid blades but, faced with the necessity under war conditions of drastically curtailing the expenditure of vital alloying material, developed blades fabricated from sheet or tubular stock with

Fig. 61. Nozzle ring of Derwent turbine, showing radial clearance of vanes.

considerable success. Junkers, B.M.W. and Heinkel-Hirth each had different designs of fabricated blades and each had a different method of fixing. For the Junkers 004 the blade is pressed from taper-rolled austenitic steel sheet, folded and welded at the trailing edge. The root of the thicker section, of course, is formed into a rhomboidal socket and fits over a projecting stud of the same shape on the periphery of the disc. It is secured by shear pins, as in Fig. 62, and brazed.

The B.M.W. blade is also of tapered sheet, welded at the trailing edge, but furnished with a duplex bulb root which is fitted in a slot in the disc and secured by wedges and pins. Inside the blade is mounted a hollow deflector of similar profile to direct the flow of cooling air along the interior of the blade wall. This air is discharged at the blade tips and joins the main gas flow, so is necessarily at a relatively high pressure. The deflector is retained by a pin fitted in the lower bulb to prevent it collapsing. When slipped into the slot the blade is keyed by two pins at the neck between the bulbs and a pair of triangular section wedges engaging the upper bulb, as in Fig. 63. These, it is claimed, tighten on the bulb under the influence of centrifugal action. Side plates position the blades axially.

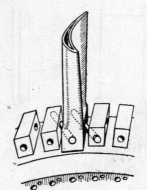

Fig. 62. Hollow blades of Junkers turbine are pinned and brazed to the disc.

What appears to be a more attractive design of hollow blade is featured on the Heinkel-Hirth turbine. It is produced by deep-drawing austenitic steel to form a closed-end tube, which is then profiled and shaped at the closed, root end. The root is reduced in width to permit the passage of the anchor pin and furnish apertures for the admission of cooling air to the interior. Stages in the manufacture of the blade are shown in Fig. 64. When mounted on its anchor pin in the grooved turbine disc, the blade is free to hinge about the pin. Freedom of movement is limited by spacers located between adjacent blades.

Stator blades for the nozzle ring are also hollow and air-cooled in German designs. Usually the cooling air is discharged through slots in the trailing edge. For satisfactory cooling of both stator and rotor blades 5–7 per cent. of the compressor output may be required, and this constitutes a material disadvantage.

Under the stress of their war emergency, the Germans investigated a variety of constructions and materials with the aim of making permissible higher gas temperatures at the turbine. A serious effort made to produce a ceramic blade was unsuccessful, due to the low mechanical strength of the material. There would, however, appear to be a reasonable prospect of developing this type for the less highly stressed entry vanes and interstage stator blades.

The Swiss firm Brown-Boveri has patented a turbine blade which is part metal and part ceramic. By employing the technique of powder metallurgy the material is distributed so that the root of the blade is 100 per cent. metal and the tip 100 per cent. ceramic.

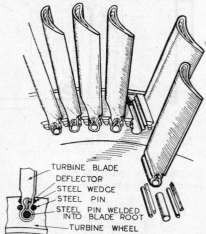

TURBINE BLADE
DEFLECTOR
STEEL WEDGE
STEEL PIN
STEEL PIN WELDED INTO BLADE ROOT
TURBINE WHEEL

Fig. 63. Bulb root fixing of B.M.W. hollow turbine blade.

Details of the practical development of a blade of this type are not yet available. Similar experiments have been carried out in British research establishments.

Although not applied to aircraft units, interesting results were obtained from experimental internally water-cooled turbines. One German single-stage

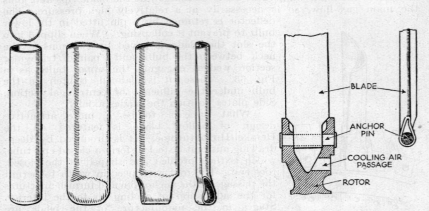

Fig. 64. Development of Heinkel-Hirth tubular turbine blade and method of mounting on the rotor.

unit operated satisfactorily at 12,000 r.p.m. with a gas temperature of 1,200 deg. C. The blades were integral with the drum and drilled with several blind holes, as indicated in the diagram, Fig. 65. The cooled water fed to the interior of the drum is, in operation, flung radially outwards to the blades, the hottest region. As the water in the holes becomes heated it becomes less dense and thus a pressure differential is created. A core of cold water from the drum flows out to the tip of the blade, displacing the hot water in contact with the wall of the hole. If water-cooled stator blades were employed, it has been estimated, a turbine of this type could be operated

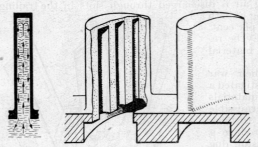

Fig. 65. Schmidt experimental water cooling system for turbine blades.

continuously with a gas temperature of 1,500 deg. C. yet a blade temperature of only approximately 500 deg. C.

CHAPTER V

COMBUSTION SYSTEM : FUEL EQUIPMENT : CONTROL.

So marked is the tendency to regard the gas turbine as a " compressor-turbine " combination that the combustion system commonly receives less attention than is merited. It is fruitless to attempt a precise relative importance as all components are essential and functionally interdependent. Nevertheless, it is a truism that the efficiency and performance of a turbine power unit are materially influenced by the combustion system employed. German compressors and turbines were not markedly inferior to British components but their less highly developed combustion systems were reflected in lower performance, higher specific fuel consumption and decidedly shorter working life.

Basic requirements for a satisfactory system are a high rate of burning, minimum pressure drop, small bulk and light weight. It must be consistent in operation over a wide range of loads and altitudes, with no liability to flood with fuel or conversely to " blow out." Starting must be easy and positive both on the ground and in the air and combustion must be complete to avoid formation of carbon.

Entirely new problems were presented by the aircraft gas turbine. For the release of the necessary heat values at the requisite rate of burning there was no precedent. Steam boilers, industrial furnaces or even heat-treatment

Fig. 66. Component parts of a combustion chamber. A complete assembly is shown on the right.

furnaces are not required to release heat at the rate demanded by the gas turbine and are not handicapped by severe limitations in respect of weight and space occupied. In a light tubular combustion chamber of fabricated sheet steel, which by ordinary furnace standards would be regarded as

65

flimsy, it is already possible to release more than 300,000 heat units per minute. To quote one example only of a power unit in regular production will be of interest. The Rolls-Royce Nene has nine combustion chambers each consuming 81.5 gal of aviation kerosene per hour. The fuel has a calorific value of approximately 150,000 BTU/gal, so each chamber releases more than 200,000 BTU/min. Expressed in another way, the Nene consumes 733.5 gal/hr or 12.2 gal/min. This is an expenditure of potential heat energy at a rate equivalent to 43,000 horsepower.

The combustion turbine may be termed a continuous constant-pressure

Fig. 67. Cascade traverse for measuring airflow pattern at the combustion chamber inlet.

engine. To enable the turbine to expand the gases to the desired level the pressure at the nozzle guide vanes should be as near as possible to the pressure of the air as delivered by the compressor. Fuel cannot be burnt, however, unless turbulence is created, and this is only obtained by a drop in pressure in the primary injection and mixing zones. Thus 100 per cent. efficiency would not appear to be possible of achievement. Further, as applied to aircraft, the system must function with the minimum loss of unburnt fuel over a wide range of conditions, and thus it is frequently operating below the optimum. Despite the difficulties, combustion systems are operating on standard engines with a total pressure drop of only about 2 lb./sq. in.

Lucas Research Work

Following is a brief description of methods employed at the combustion research laboratories of the Joseph Lucas organisation.

In tackling the problem of combustion, four main lines of attack are pursued: chemical and physical; aerodynamic; thermodynamic and mechanical. Knowledge of conditions existing inside the flame tube is only possible by the analysis of samples of gas withdrawn from various points. It is of importance to determine how far combustion reactions have progressed at any point in the flame tube, and consequently care must be taken to prevent these reactions continuing whilst the sample is being extracted. To secure such conditions, the sample is withdrawn through a water-cooled tube, the hot gases are rapidly chilled and the reactions brought to a standstill. Subsequent analysis then shows, as nearly as possible, the composition existing at the sampling point at the time of withdrawal. Main gas analyses are carried out on the Haldane apparatus, which permits an accuracy of ± 0.02 per cent. Complications are introduced when samples are taken from the primary combustion zone as it is possible to have unburnt fuel and " cracked " gaseous products as well as combustion gases.

Air distribution through the chamber is the subject of detailed study. It is intimately dependent upon flow conditions from the compressor, and particular care is taken in the design of the delivery duct. Pulsation, surging or shock from the compressor delivery would, of course, radically affect combustion conditions. A special traversing apparatus has been developed in the laboratory for investigating the airflow at the compressor outlet. This enables yawmeter, pitot-static tube and temperature traverses to be carried out at any position in the passage. The first measurement is of yaw in two

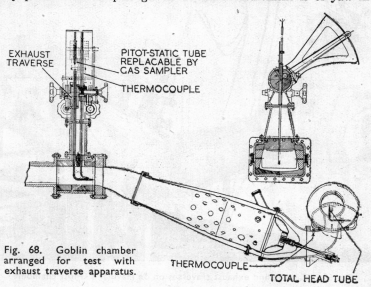

EXHAUST
TRAVERSE

PITOT-STATIC TUBE
REPLACABLE BY
GAS SAMPLER

THERMOCOUPLE

Fig. 68. Goblin chamber arranged for test with exhaust traverse apparatus.

THERMOCOUPLE

TOTAL HEAD TUBE

perpendicular planes.   When this is ascertained a pitot tube having the appropriate droop is set up with the correct yaw.

Velocity diagrams obtained by this system of airflow measurement are
visually demonstrated by so-called " pin-cushion " models.   In a base block
of shape and area corresponding to the section of the delivery passage,
wires of a scale length to show velocity are set at the appropriate angle to
indicate flow direction.   In the case of a reverse flow in turbulent conditions
this is represented by a loop.

Optical methods of investigating airflow are also being developed.   It is
intended to observe flow lines in a cascade box fitted with Perspex sides by
means of a Schlieren set-up and to record them with an ultra-high-speed
camera.

Similar traversing equipment is employed to determine pressure and
temperature at the opposite end of the chamber, where the gases are delivered
to the nozzle guide vanes of the turbine.

Combustion efficiency may be defined as :

$$\frac{\text{Actual Temperature Rise}}{\text{Theoretical Temperature Rise}}$$

It will be appreciated that extremely careful measurements of air supply,
fuel supply and assessment of calorific value are necessary to obtain an
accurate estimate of the theoretical temperature rise.   Traversing instruments
carrying thermo-couples are used to determine the actual mean temperature
at both the inlet and outlet of the chamber.   At the discharge end the gases
have a mean temperature of about 800 deg. C. and a velocity of the order of
500–600 ft./sec.   It is, of course, essential that combustion be complete
before reaching the turbine nozzle ring.   Flame, unburnt fuel, or a stratified
flow at different temperatures would have a most detrimental effect on the
turbine blading.

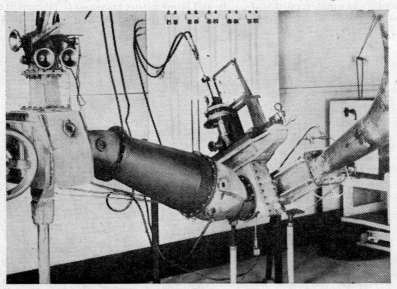

Fig. 69.   Cascade and exhaust traverses on de Havilland Ghost chamber.

Flame tubes are of Inconel or Nimonic 80 nickel-chrome alloys, whilst the outer casing is usually of mild steel. Apart from obtaining satisfactory combustion performance, it is obviously most important to extend the reliable working life of the components. Already the life of flame tubes in fully developed engines is in excess of two hundred hours.

	No. of Chambers	Fuel consumption gal./hour	Air Mass Flow lb./sec.	Air/fuel ratio
Experimental ...	6	17.2	2.3	60 : 1
Derwent V. ...	9	57.0	7.0	55 : 1
Ghost	10	67.0	8.8	59 : 1
Nene	9	81.5	10.0	55 : 1

Test performance of typical chambers is given in the above table.

The trend would appear to be towards fewer individual chambers, as exampled by the change from 16 on the Goblin to 10 on the Ghost ; both

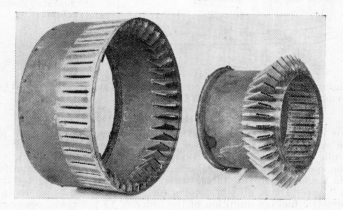

Fig. 70. Main components of B.M.W. 003 annular combustion chamber.

de Havilland units. The only British design to incorporate an annular combustion chamber is the Metropolitan-Vickers. This type is a feature of B.M.W. and Heinkel-Hirth in Germany and Westinghouse in the U.S.A. Inner and outer components of the B.M.W. chamber with the characteristic air mixing slots are shown in Fig. 70, whilst Fig. 71, is a section of the

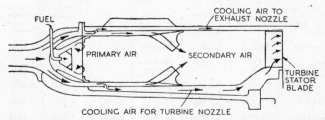

Fig. 71. Diagrammatic section of B.M.W. chamber showing flow path.

assembled chamber and indicates the air flow path. An investigation of the characteristics of this chamber revealed that air at 160 deg. C. enters at 360 ft/sec. In the main combustion zone, prior to dilution, the temperature is 798 deg. C. and velocity 240 ft/sec, but aft of the mixing slots temperature is lowered to 750 deg. C. and velocity increased to 310 ft/sec.

This " slot-mixing " principle is also used on the six individual chambers of the Junkers 004 jet unit. The flame tube, mounted co-axially in the chamber, has vanes at the forward end to impart a swirling motion to the combustion air into which the fuel is injected upstream. Passing rearwardly through slots defined by hollow bars the combustion gases are mixed with the cool dilution air in the main casing before reaching the turbine inlet.

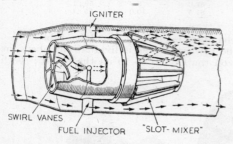

Fig. 72. Diagram showing flow path of Junkers combustion chamber.

Descriptions of the combustion systems of a variety of units will be found in relevant Chapters VI, VII or VIII.

Fuel Characteristics

For aircraft gas turbines fuels having a high calorific value per unit volume are most desirable, as weight can be accommodated more readily than bulk in modern high speed aircraft.

The specific gravity and calorific values of various petroleum fuels are given in the accompanying table. It will be seen that, if a gas turbine could run on " heavy Diesel oil " or " boiler fuel," there would be an improvement in volumetric fuel consumption of the order of 15 per cent., compared with

FUEL	SPECIFIC GRAVITY	CALORIFIC VALUE (net.)		RATIO TO P.B.O.		RATIO TO 100/130 GRADE	
		B.T.U./lb.	B.T.U./gal.	Per lb.	Per gal.	Per lb.	Per gal.
100/130 Grade ...	0.720	18,940	136,580	1.021	0.9081	1	1
Cumene	0.862	17,820	153,600	0.960	1.02	0.940	1.124
Safety Fuel Alk. Bottoms ... RDE/SF/1 ISO	0.750	18,820	141,160	1.014	0.9386	0.9936	1.034
Dodecane ...	0.771	18,740	144,460	1.009	0.9605	0.9891	1.058
Pool Burning Oil...	0.810	18,560	150,390	1	1	0.9802	1.101
Pool Burning Oil...	0.801 – 0.806	18,590	148,950 – 149,880	—	—	—	—
Gas Oil	0.850	18,260	155,230	0.9836	1.032	0.9641	1.136
Light Diesel Oil ...	0.870	18,050	157,040	0.9722	1.044	0.9529	1.15
Heavy Diesel Oil...	0.910	17,980	163,630	0.9684	1.088	0.9492	1.198
Boiler Fuel ...	0.973	17,800	173,160	0.9585	1.1514	0.9395	1.268

the present fuel used, variously termed " paraffin," " aviation kerosene " and " pool burning oil." Unfortunately, apart from undesirable features connected with the combustion of the heavier fuels, it appears that P.B.O. is the heaviest fuel we can expect to get with a freezing point in the region of — 50 degrees C.

Clean fuel is essential for satisfactory operation in view of the fine working clearance of the injection components and the relatively restricted passages in the burners. In Britain the tanker vehicles employed for refuelling jet aircraft are equipped with Streamline filters to prevent the transfer of foreign matter to the aircraft tanks. As paraffin has virtually no lubricating properties and, in fact, has a scouring action, it is customary to make an addition of 1 per cent. of lubricating oil to the fuel to ensure satisfactory operation of the injection system.

Fuel Injection Equipment

There is, of course, a wide range of components employed for the injection, automatic regulation, and control of fuel supply to the various turbine units. Those developed by Joseph Lucas in collaboration with Rolls-Royce may be

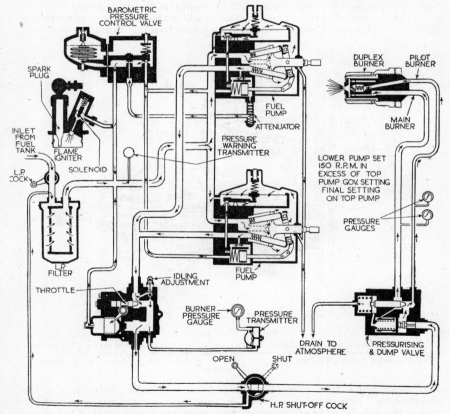

Fig. 73. Diagrammatic layout of Nene fuel system.

cited as typical. A diagrammatic layout and connections of the fuel system
of the Rolls-Royce Nene is given in Fig. 73. The provision of two high-
pressure pumps in parallel is merely to obtain the requisite high rate of delivery
from standardised units and involves no operating principle.

The seven plungers of this positive-displacement pump reciprocate in a
rotor running in a carbon bush and a roller race and driven from the engine
by a splined quill shaft. The bores for the plungers are spaced evenly around
a pitch cone concentric with the rotor axis and converge towards the inner
or pumping end. Reciprocation of the plungers is effected by means of a
cam plate engaging the outer ends of the plungers. The cam plate is carried on
a large-diameter ball bearing mounted in a control ring swivelling on a pair
of trunnion pins set at right angles to the rotor axis. By varying the angle of
the plane of the cam plate relative to the rotor axis from 90 deg. to 81 deg.
the stroke of the plungers is varied from zero to approximately 10.5 mm.
Retraction of the plungers on the inlet stroke is ensured by helical springs
located against the reduced inner ends of the bores.

At its inner end the face of the rotor is ground flat and smooth to make a
pressure-tight seal with a valve insert furnished with two kidney-shaped
ports communicating respectively with the pump inlet and the pump delivery.

Parallel with the rotor axis is a bore in which the pressure-control piston
operates. The piston rod is connected by a link to a lug on the control ring,

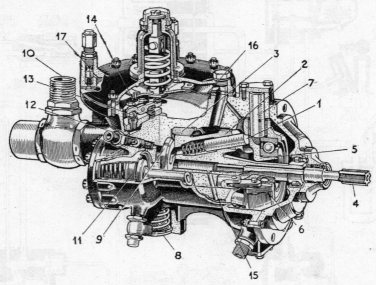

Fig. 74. Fuel pump.

1, Plunger ; 2, Rotor ; 3, Carbon bush ; 4, Quill shaft ; 5, Cam plate ; 6, Control ring ; 7, Trunnion
pin ; 8, Inlet strainer ; 9, Ported valve insert ; 10, Delivery connection ; 11, Pressure control piston ;
12, Restricting orifice ; 13, Plate valve ; 14, Rocker ; 15, Radial holes in rotor ; 16, Diaphragm
17, Bleed valve.

and concentric helical springs bias the piston to move the control ring to the
position for maximum stroke of the pump and consequently maximum output.
From the delivery side of the pump, fuel under pressure is applied below the
piston in opposition to the springs and also, by way of an adjustable restricting

orifice, above the piston. From this space above the piston, fuel can escape by way of a plate valve which is normally held to its seating by a spring-loaded rocker. By this means the fluid forces acting on the piston are balanced and there is no resulting movement. Should, however, the fluid pressure exceed a value determined by the spring loading of the rocker, the plate valve will be lifted from its seating and the flow through causes a pressure drop to occur across the restricting orifice and creates a state of unbalance. Under this influence the piston moves to a new position, reducing the stroke of the plungers and consequently the output of the pump.

Incorporated in the pump is a hydraulic mechanism to limit the pump output, and consequently the engine speed, to a predetermined maximum. In the rotor are seven radial drillings extending from the maximum peripheral diameter to an axial bore which is in free communication with the suction chamber of the pump. In operation, centrifugal force produces in the drillings a pressure difference which results in the fuel in the pump casing surrounding the rotor and also in the space above the diaphragm being maintained at a pressure higher than obtains in the suction chamber. This pressure difference is utilised to move the diaphragm, against the constraint of a helical spring in tension, so that it depresses the rocker and unloads the plate valve. The pump output is then reduced in the manner already described. The spring loading of the diaphragm is readily adjustable so that the engine speed at which the governing action begins may be set with accuracy.

The loading of the springs on the control piston, opposing the movement of the cam plate to the zero position, is so arranged that the minimum pressure at the burners when the governor is in operation is more than adequate to maintain atomisation of the fuel. The possible extinction of the flame due to governor action is thereby prevented. Should the rotational speed of the engine be lowered by " throttling back " and reducing the fuel supply to the burners, the pressure acting on the diaphragm is reduced until contact between

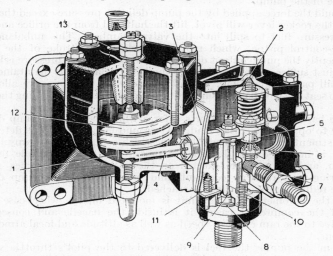

Fig. 75.   Barometric Pressure Control Unit.

1, Capsule chamber ; 2, Valve chamber ; 3, Pivot plate ; 4, Rocker ; 5, Half-ball ; 6, Orifice ; 7, Filter ;
8, Diaphragm ; 9, Piston ; 10, Operating rod ; 11, Eccentric adjusting sleeve ; 12, Barometric capsule ;
13, Vent to atmosphere.

it and the rocker is broken and the plate valve is re-seated ; pressure above the control piston is restored and the cam plate is moved to increase the stroke. It is essential for correct functioning of the pump that no air is allowed to accumulate on either side of the diaphragm, and a ball-type bleed valve is provided to evacuate air from both upper and lower spaces.

Barometric Control Unit

As flying altitude is increased it is necessary to reduce automatically the delivery of fuel. The barometric pressure control unit varies the delivery pressure of the pump in accordance with change of altitude. As the pressure-control piston of the pump is connected to the cam plate, the stroke is varied and the delivery flow of fuel adjusted to specific requirements.

Constructionally, the unit comprises a body divided into a capsule chamber and a valve chamber by a diaphragm which isolates the two chambers and serves as a pivot plate to which is secured a rocker lever extending into both. The barometric capsule is mounted with its lower pivot seated in one end of the rocker lever and its upper pivot located in an adjustable screw mounted in the chamber cover.

The other end of the rocker lever is loaded by a spring and carries a half-ball seating on an orifice supplied with fuel at servo pressure from above the pressure-control piston of the pump. Control of the rocker lever is by fuel at delivery pressure from below the pressure-control piston. Pressure is applied to a rubber diaphragm and transmitted by a small piston and an operating rod, the upper end of which abuts the end of an adjuster screw in the rocker arm. These components are mounted in the base of the chamber in an eccentric sleeve to enable the end of the rod to be moved across the face of the adjuster screw to alter the operative distance from the fulcrum point of the lever. The valve chamber is in open communication with the inlet side of the pump.

Should the force applied by the pump delivery pressure exceed the spring loading the rocker lever will pivot, lift the half-ball from the orifice and allow servo pressure fuel to spill into the valve chamber. This unbalances the pressure-control piston, which moves to reduce the stroke of the pump. Consequently the pump output decreases, and the delivery pressure is lowered until it just suffices to balance the spring load. Balance is maintained by a small spill past the half-ball. A fall in pump delivery pressure allows the spring to seat the half-ball, closing the orifice and, in turn, increasing the pump stroke.

The barometric capsule exerts a force which assists the pump delivery pressure to oppose the spring load. At ground level the force is determined by adjustment of the upper pivot screw which compresses the capsule. As altitude is increased and barometric pressure falls, the capsule tends to lengthen, and the pressure exerted on the rocker lever becomes greater. The spring load remains constant, and consequently the pump delivery pressure reduces until a balance is reached.

As the barometric control unit is mounted on the wheel-case on the front of the compressor casing it is inside the nacelle and consequently responsive to the ram effect at speed as well as altitude and local atmospheric conditions.

From the pumps the fuel is delivered to the pilot's throttle valve, a manually-operated variable orifice, and thence to the high-pressure cock, also manually operated by the pilot to cut the supply to the burners and so shut down the unit. On the throttle valve is an adjustable by-pass through which fuel flows to maintain the engine running at idling speed when only the throttle valve is closed. A pressurising valve is inserted between the high-pressure cock and the ring manifolds supplying the burners. This is merely a spring-loaded, conical-seating plunger which at low pressure and volume is closed to ensure that all fuel is delivered by way of the small-diameter pilot manifold. As pressure builds up the valve is lifted against its spring to admit fuel to the larger diameter main manifold. Incorporated with this unit is the spring-loaded dump valve. In operation, even at idling speeds, the fuel pressure closes this valve, but when the high-pressure cock is shut off and pressure falls, it opens automatically to drain the manifolds.

Duplex Burners

The provision of duplex fuel burners is to ensure, without resort to abnormally high pressures, a completely atomized fuel spray at the low rates of flow occurring when cranking for a start and also under high-altitude conditions. Separate connections from the pilot and main manifolds are taken to each burner. Under reduced flow conditions all the fuel is delivered to the pilot atomizer. It passes through helical grooves cut in the face of a conical plug to reach the swirl chamber, and is projected as a finely atomized conical spray.

At the substantially higher rates of flow during normal operating con-

ditions, the pressurizing valve is lifted and fuel is delivered to both the pilot and the main manifolds. The pilot flow continues as before, whilst fuel from the main manifold passes to an annular space surrounding the housing of the primary swirl cone. Through a series of holes in the ring element in which the primary swirl cone is seated the fuel reaches the swirl plate having a number of tangential slots communicating with the central swirl chamber. Here the primary and main flows mix and pass out of the final orifice. The functions of a particular burner may be readily adjusted by substituting a

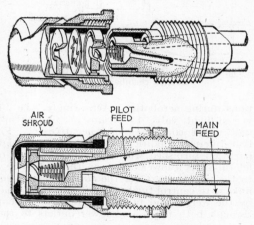

Fig. 76. The duplex burner ensures thorough atomization of fuel at all rates of delivery.

swirl plate of different thickness which, of course, alters the volume of the swirl chamber.

Flame Igniters

A minor problem of ignition is the location of the sparking plug in relation to the fuel spray. To secure an effective position the end of the plug was usually more or less exposed to the heat of combustion and liable to suffer accordingly. The larger diameter of the Nene combustion chambers intensified this problem, but a solution was found in the provision of what is termed the flame igniter. This is a small self-contained unit embodying a special low-pressure atomizer and a sparking plug. Fuel at the low pressure supplied by the booster pump to the inlet side of the high-pressure pumps is piped to the igniter and controlled by a Messier solenoid-operated valve. Normally this valve is closed, but at appropriate timing in the starting cycle the solenoid is energized and fuel flows through the atomizer and is ignited by the sparking plug. A flaming jet of fuel, as from a blow torch, is then projected into the main fuel spray from the burner. The ends of both atomizer and sparking plug are shrouded, and in any case are only exposed to the secondary air in the annular space between the flame tube and the outer casing of the combustion chamber. One igniter is sufficient for a complete engine unit, but two are fitted to cover all eventualities. From the two combustion chambers fitted with flame igniters combustion is propagated to other chambers through the usual connecting pipes. The igniters, of course, only function for a brief period when starting and during normal operation are completely cut off.

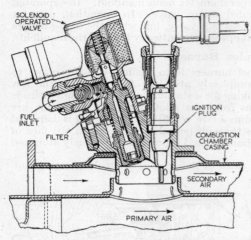

Fig. 77. Flame igniters are fitted to two combustion chambers only.

For military machines it is necessary to make arrangements for exceptional conditions during aerobatics. Accordingly, the fuel tank is fitted with an inverted-flight valve to ensure an uninterrupted supply of fuel to the jet unit under conditions of "negative g." Fig. 78 shows the flow under two different conditions. At about mid-height, the tank has a horizontal partition furnished with flap valves closing on the under side. The outlet tube has a lower orifice on the tank base and an upper orifice adjacent to the partition. Over the tube slides a sleeve actuated by a weight and linkage to control the lower orifice. In normal operation the sleeve is raised by the weight and fuel flows through the flap valves in the partition and through both upper and lower outlets to the Self-Priming booster pump.

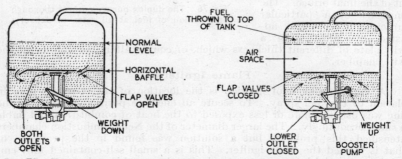

Fig. 78. The inverted-flight valve in the fuel tank. (Left) normal conditions. (Right) "negative g" conditions.

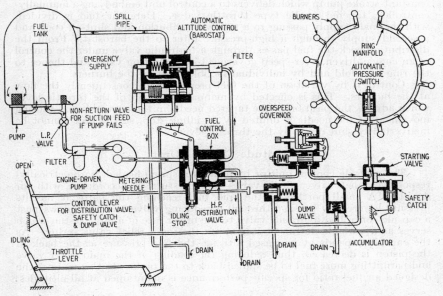

Fig. 79. Goblin fuel and control system.

Under conditions of " negative g," when the fuel tends to surge to the top of the tank, the flap valves close and some portion of the fuel is trapped in the lower compartment. The weight rises, closes the lower orifice which is now exposed, and fuel continues to flow from the upper orifice below the partition.

Starting Cycle

Starting is effected by a 24-volt electric motor and all necessary operations are effected by a timed automatic cycle. When the master switch is closed, current is supplied to the booster fuel pump and a warning light glows until the requisite pressure is built up. With the throttle closed, depression of the starter button brings the clockwork time switch into operation. In timed sequence, current is supplied to the ignition coils, flame igniters and the starter motor. The motor takes up the drive and cranks the engine at a low speed for about 5 seconds, after which a relay closes to allow full excitation of the motor. The time switch completes its cycle in 30 seconds and cuts off all current. If, however, the engine starts and reaches a predetermined speed prior to this, starter, ignition coils and flame igniters are automatically cut out.

The De Havilland System

In contradistinction to the method of automatically adjusting the stroke of the pump to regulate the delivery of fuel in accordance with change of altitude, the de Havilland Goblin employs a constant-stroke pump and an automatic control unit, or barostat, to spill excess fuel back to the tank. The system is shown in a diagrammatic layout, Fig. 79.

From the tank the fuel is fed through a filter to a Dowty, seven-plunger, constant-stroke pump which delivers to a control unit embodying a manually-controlled, tapered needle type throttle valve. Here the fuel is divided, with the main supply passing to a rotary distribution and shut-off cock and a second supply through a high-pressure filter to the barostat. From the distribution cock the fuel passes through a hydraulic valve under the control of an engine-driven, over-speed governor to the starting valve and thence to the ring manifold and by individual flexible pipes to the burners.

Control is by variation of the fuel pressure, and consequently the flow at the burners. This is effected by manual operation of the throttle lever which adjusts the position of the tapered needle in the control box. Closing movement of the needle is limited by an idling stop, so the unit cannot be inadvertently shut down by the throttle lever.

Altitude Control Unit

The altitude control unit or barostat is a spring-loaded, barometrically-responsive relief valve which varies fuel pressure in accordance with air density. A small portion of the spill fuel reaching the barostat has its pressure lowered by passage through a reducing valve and then flows past a capsule-controlled hydraulic valve to the upper face of a large piston which serves as a variable datum abutment for the main relief valve spring. As the capsule expands at increased altitude the fuel pressure at the back of the piston is decreased, thus reducing the loading of the main relief valve and permitting more fuel to be spilled back to the tank. In this manner the designed air/fuel ratio for specific performance is maintained at all altitudes.

Starting Routine

The throttle is closed to the idling position, and by means of a second lever the shut-off cock is opened. Operation of a push-button closes the circuits for the starter motor, the booster coils for the ignition plugs, and the time switch. Thereafter the sequence is automatically controlled. The motor is operated at low speed through two resistances for five seconds to ensure easy engagement. Then one of the resistances is cut out, the motor speed increases and the main jet unit is brought to a speed sufficient to raise fuel pressure against the closed starting valve. A spring-loaded accumulator in the fuel line between the governor and the starting valve is charged with fuel, and when a predetermined pressure is reached the starting valve lifts and is then retained in the open position by a spring-controlled safety catch. Fuel then passes to the manifold and the burners and ignition is effected.

Simultaneously, a pressure-actuated switch in connection with the fuel manifold cuts out the second resistance, thereby releasing more electrical energy for the starter motor which continues the drive and assists the acceleration of the main jet unit. Thirty seconds after operation of the push button the time switch cuts off the motor and the ignition system.

To stop the unit, it is brought down to idling speed with the throttle lever and then shut off by the second control lever. Operation of the shut-off cock releases the safety catch on the starting valve and opens the dump valve, which permits the fuel in the manifold to drain to atmosphere.

In the event of a false start it might be possible for fuel to accumulate in the heads of the three lower combustion chambers. For safety, therefore, the lowest combustion chamber is fitted with a valve which opens automatically when pressure in the chambers falls below 3lb./sq. in. and, through the interconnections, drains the affected three lower chambers.

CHAPTER VI

METALLURGY : PROBLEMS ASSOCIATED WITH
TURBINE DISCS AND BLADES

BY raising the average temperature of the gases, the continuous combustion
cycle, on which the constant pressure gas turbine operates, demands
materials with a higher degree of heat resistance than is necessary in a diesel
or petrol engine which has an intermittent combustion cycle. Moreover,
the speed with which the gases pass through a gas turbine creates special
problems of erosion. The steel selected must not be subject to oxidisation,
corrosion or scaling and not prone to " creep " or " growth " following
cyclic variation of temperature—that is repeated heating and cooling in
service.

Disc Forgings

By reason of the high speeds of rotation the turbine disc is subjected to
particularly high stressing. Centrifugal force, tending to burst the disc, varies
as the square of the velocity, it will be remembered. Thus the centrifugal
loading of a given disc rotated at 15,000 r.p.m. will not be 1.5 times but
2.25 times the loading at a speed of 10,000 r.p.m. The peripheral velocity
of a 12in. diameter disc running at 15,000 r.p.m. is 47,100ft./min. (535 m.p.h.)
whilst at the tips of the blades, say 18in. diameter, the velocity is
70,650ft./min. (803 m.p.h.). Fortunately the design of discs rotating at high
speeds has for years been the subject of intensive study and mathematical
analysis, particularly in regard to the rotors of steam turbines. Shape and
dimensions can be determined to meet requirements with relative precision
but in the case of the gas turbine a new factor is introduced by the higher
temperature of the working medium.

Many grades of steel possess adequate strength in the lower temperature
ranges but cannot maintain it at elevated temperatures. In operation there is a
substantial difference in temperature between the hub and peripheral portions
of the disc, say 300–350 deg. C., which produces a thermal stress in addition
to the centrifugal loading. Usually rotor discs are produced from forgings
of austenitic steel but de Havilland have standardised a disc of ferritic steel.
It was found that a ferritic steel, possessing higher strength at the working
temperature of the central portion of the disc and a lower coefficient of
expansion, enabled a disc of relatively lighter weight and consequent lower
moment of inertia to be employed.

To reduce the thermal stressing of the disc and the transfer of heat from
the disc to the shaft and bearings it is usual to employ some form of cooling.
Designs have appeared and units have been built having a water cooled
disc and water cooled bearings but this system is somewhat anomalous in a
power unit employing such vast quantities of air and it is usual to cool the
rotor by a continuous blast of air passing over the face of the disc from
hub to rim. Rolls - Royce Derwent and Nene and de Havilland Goblin
are examples in which cooling air is applied respectively to one face and
both faces of the disc. Steel such as Jessop's G.18B have been proved
satisfactory for turbine discs. This austenitic steel, developed primarily
by Messrs. D. A. Oliver and G. T. Harris, is being produced for discs of 32in.
diameter, with a maximum boss thickness of 5¼in. The thickness can be

increased to 7in. if required. A typical composition of G.18B steel (suitable not only for turbine discs, but for blades and nozzles) is :—

Carbon	..	0.4 per cent.	Cobalt	.. ..	10.0 per cent.
Manganese	..	0.8 ,,	Tungsten..	..	2.5 ,,
Silicon	..	1.0 ,,	Molybdenum	..	2.0 ,,
Nickel	..	13.0 ,,	Columbium⎱	..	3.0 ,,
Chromium	..	13.0 ,,	Tantalum ⎰		

Basic heat treatment conditions are three, known respectively as (a) " solution treated," (b) " solution treated and aged," and (c) " solution treated and warm-worked," the last in order to achieve the highest values of proof stress and creep properties at temperatures between 1,300 deg. F. and 1,500 deg. F. (700 deg. C. to 815 deg. C.).

Certain types of discs have been forged with a short stub-shaft about 5in. in diameter and 10in. in length, the disc being 22in. in diameter and about 4in. thick. William Jessop & Sons, Ltd., state that there is no limitation within reason to the length of shaft which can be produced by this method, except facilities for obtaining a particular heat treatment. Another notable contribution by the same firm to the technique of gas-turbine construction is the fabrication of G.18B turbine discs flash butt-welded to a lower carbon stainless shaft material, the latter having columbium additions and being known as Special R.20 austenitic steel. This welding technique is a boon where more than one rotor disc is employed and where long shafts are involved.

Another possibility of interest to designers of axial-flow gas turbine units is that of producing solid rotor forgings in G.18B steel, with drum diameters up to 18in., and an axial length of 3ft., increased by integral extension shafts to 7ft. Special methods of heat-treatment have been developed for such large components and the manufacturers report that creep tests have given results within 15 per cent. of the figure claimed for smaller components under precise laboratory control.

The distinguishing features claimed for G.18B steel are high creep strength associated with ductility and " notch insensitivity." It has the following hot fatigue strengths for an endurance limit of 40 million reversals. (The values refer to the material in the " solution treated " condition already referred to).

TEMPERATURE		FATIGUE STRENGTH	
deg. F.	deg. C.	Long tons/ sq. in.	lbs./sq. in.
1,112	600	±18	±40,300
1,202	650	±15	±33,600
1,292	700	±13	±29,200

The 0.1 per cent. proof temperatures range between 31,000 lb./sq. in. and 58,000 lb./sq. in., according to the heat treatment.

Turbine Blades

The blades of the turbine operate under more arduous conditions than the disc. Necessarily of light section, they are exposed to the highest temperature and subjected to the heaviest centrifugal loading. Considering a hypothetical turbine producing 5,000 h.p., this would probably have about fifty-five blades approximately 3in. long, each of which must transmit continuously about 90 h.p. Nevertheless, at the high rotational speed, say 15,000 r.p.m., the tensile stress due to centrifugal force will exceed the bending stress of the load.

For maximum efficiency, the gas should enter the turbine at a high temperature which, obviously, is limited to the capacity of the materials used in the component parts to withstand the effects of such temperature. Dr. Meyer has stated that on a compressor - turbine unit having an overall efficiency of 76 per cent., to increase the gas temperature at the turbine inlet by 20 per cent. from 540 deg. C. to 650 deg. C. would raise the cycle efficiency from 18 per cent. to 23 per cent., representing an improvement of 28 per cent.

Ordinary grades of steel are quite inadequate for turbine blades. In general the special steels are alloys containing high percentages of chromium and nickel and smaller additions of other elements such as silicon, tungsten or molybdenum. A steel having a chromium content of 12–14 per cent. is superior to ordinary steels as regards scaling and the maintenance of mechanical strength up to moderately high temperatures. Above 650 deg. C., however, its strength decreases rapidly and at 850 deg. C. the non-scaling characteristic is lost. The addition of silicon, up to about 3 per cent., has been found to produce marked improvement in the non-scaling properties of high chromium steel and also to impart some improvement in strength at high temperatures. Despite this it has not been possible to maintain these features satisfactorily at temperatures higher than 800 deg. C.

Exhaust gas turbines for driving the supercharging blowers of diesel engines operate at about 600 deg. C. but on petrol aircraft engines the exhaust temperature may reach 1,000 deg. C. These conditions are being satisfactorily met with existing steels. As long ago as 1933 Sir Robert Hadfield was able to report that prolonged research by his firm in collaboration with

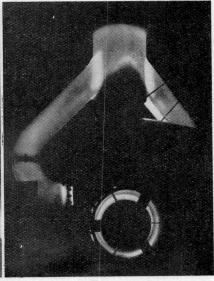

Fig. 80. A Brown-Boveri exhaust turbo blower set on the test bed, running continuously at 30,000 r.p.m. with a gas temperature of 1,000 deg. C.

Fig. 81. The night photograph of the charging set in Fig. 80 shows the turbine operating at full load with the rotor and guide blades glowing at a red heat.

D

S.A. de Commentry Fourchambault et Decazeville, of Imphy, France, had resulted in the evolution of a high-percentage nickel-chromium steel of reasonable cost, possessing exceptional strength and non-scaling properties at high temperatures. Designated " Era/ATV " steel, it was being used at bright red heat and under high centrifugal and other stresses in exhaust gas turbines working at a temperature of 800 deg. C. to 930 deg. C. and at speeds ranging from 30,000 r.p.m. to 50,000 r.p.m. It is of interest to note that when operating at high altitudes certain portions of these rotors are exposed at the same time to atmospheric temperatures which may fall as low as — 50 deg. C.

For a number of years the Brown-Boveri Company in Switzerland has had a large test bed for testing exhaust gas turbine-driven blowers for petrol aircraft engines. The test equipment is designed to withstand temperatures up to 1,100 deg. C. Figs. 80 and 81 show a charging set of their manufacture running with a gas admission temperature of 1,000 deg. C. at the designed full speed of 30,000 r.p.m. In Fig. 80 the equipment is fully illuminated and on the left shows the end of the duct discharging air to simulate the relative wind during flight, and on the right, the collecting funnel for the convenient evacuation of the turbine effluent. The night picture of the same set in operation was taken by the light radiated from the exhaust gas piping and the turbine. The ring of light at the turbine is actually produced by the stationary guide blades which are heated to a bright red. The rotor blades, at a somewhat duller red, cannot be distinguished owing to the high speed of rotation.

Whilst unquestionably there remains much research and development to be done for turbine blade steels, it must be recorded that already substantial progress has been made. To cite only one example, the Rolls-Royce turbine blades of Wiggins' " Nimonic 80 " alloy operate successfully at a continuous gas temperature of 850 deg. C. (1,560 deg. F.).

Nozzle Guide Vanes

The nozzle guide vanes, which receive the hot gases after they leave the combustion chambers, are subjected to particularly high temperatures, although not highly stressed. Again Jessop's G.18B steel has been used

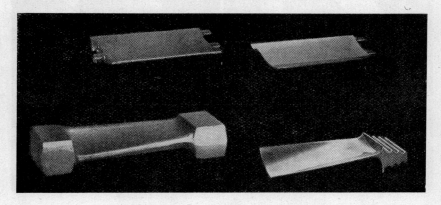

Fig. 82. A Goblin turbine nozzle blade (top) and turbine blade shown "as stamped" and "as finished." Both are of Jessop's G.18B and produced by the B.S.A. Co.. Ltd.

and a vane produced in this material by the Birmingham Small Arms Co., Ltd., is shown in Fig. 82. A high-quality drop forging is made from a flawless ground bar and after the necessary heat treatment the blade is brought to the final form by machining, grinding and polishing operations. The final contour is correct to within a few thousandths of an inch. The same technique is used in G.18B turbine blade production.

An interesting illustration of the progress made in turbine blade material throughout the war years was advanced by Major F. B. Halford during a lecture before the Royal Society of Arts in May, 1946. (See Fig. 83.) Beyond 1946 is mere conjecture, he said, but not altogether based on imagination. There are good grounds for thinking that such materials will be forthcoming, and to the turbine designer it is a very vital matter.

In a given turbine the highest possible thrust will depend on what temperature we dare to run the turbine blades, and he thought a maximum blade

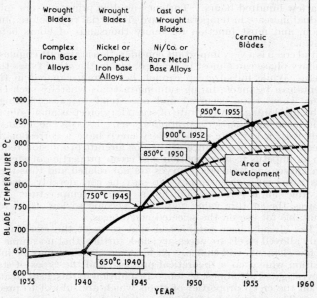

Fig. 83. Trend of development in gas turbine blade materials.

temperature of 850 deg. C.—corresponding to a gas temperature of 1,000 deg. C. at entry to the turbine—should be obtainable by 1950. In practically all their jet units the Germans adopted air-cooled turbine blades owing to their wartime shortage of suitable heat-resisting materials, but they had to pay something in performance for robbing air from the compressor for this purpose. If, however, one could cool the turbine blades and discs without excessive cost in performance, there would be savings in manufacturing expenses, though at the moment it is very difficult to be dogmatic on this subject. Each case must be examined on its own particular merits.

Writing in *Iron & Steel* on the subject of high temperature engineering in relation to gas turbines, Mr. J. Taylor, of Hadfields, Ltd., said :—

" It has been established that the pearlitic types of steel are restricted in their usefulness to a temperature range of below 550 deg. C., since in excess of this value creep strength rapidly decreases, and in addition to this structural changes resulting from prolonged heating have the effect of detrimentally affecting the creep strength. These characteristics necessitate the use of austenitic steels for higher temperature ranges, and the problem becomes more complicated, due to the higher coefficients of expansion of this group of steels as compared with pearlitic. This has the effect of increasing the magnitude of stress engendered by temperature differences.

Two Main Types

" There are, broadly speaking, two main types of gas turbines as viewed from the aspect under discussion, those used for aircraft, on the one hand, and on the other prime movers for generating plant, etc. This classification is associated with the differences in operating conditions. In the case of aircraft engines, frequent and rapid stresses arise due to the relatively short duration of the runs, and the total life between overhauls and examinations is of the order of a few hundred hours. Turbines used as prime movers subject to a more gradual increase in temperature, are given trial runs before putting into commission, and must function for many thousands of hours before being taken down.

" Initial creep is a very important consideration in aircraft engines, whereas the secondary phase can almost be ignored, but in the other types the reverse is the case. While initial creep cannot be entirely ignored in the latter, adjustments can be made during running-in trials whereby such changes in dimensions which have occurred and may tend to cause fouling, can be rectified by machining. A low rate of secondary creep is an absolutely essential requirement for long-service applications. It is by no means the rule that steels with a low rate of secondary creep have a correspondingly low initial creep, and the importance of this for aircraft propulsion requirements has given an impetus to investigation into creep properties of steels. Stress to rupture curves and total creep curves are not related and thus the permissible stress based on a given total creep may be considerably lower than the rupture value for a given period for a certain temperature. At higher temperatures, the rupture value may have become so low as to render the steel unsuitable for use on the selected creep basis.

" It has already been established that to meet the exacting demands very highly alloyed steels are necessary, and, further, that no simple combination of a few elements will suffice. At least ten elements may be involved in a composition which has a theoretical promise, and the types of steel which may be investigated are almost legion. In addition to this, heat treatment has an effect on the creep properties of steels which are subject to precipitation hardening. The magnitude of the task, even if short time creep tests only are involved, will be appreciated. This is further enlarged since, having obtained a promising composition, in actual production variation in the proportion of elements must inevitably occur, and hence it is essential that limits of composition be established to maintain the optimum creep strength. It is equally necessary in certain cases to establish ' load to rupture ' data. The engineer is quite naturally eager to construct gas turbines which will function at the highest efficiencies, which can only be attained by increasing the temperature of the blades and rotors. But, in view of the magnitude of the metallurgist's task, a co-operative and tolerant attitude on the part of the engineer is essential to success.

" The production of a suitable steel for aircraft engines, where relatively short period tests will suffice, calls for enormous effort, but this pales into insignificance where the other types of turbine are involved, and where some proportion of the tests must occupy thousands of hours in order to determine creep and/or rupture values. In rotors, in particular, there are portions which never attain the temperature at which creep operates and where the stress differs considerably from the hot portions."

A Temperature-Recording Alloy

In the development of gas turbines great difficulty has been experienced in accurately recording the temperatures reached during operation at various points of the disc and blades. From America the General Electric Co. reports the use of a new temperature-recording alloy which, substituted for normal turbine parts, undergoes a colour change and thus reveals the local temperature. The alloy is a special chrome-cobalt composition which oxidises so slowly at higher temperatures that it shows a marked change of colour at regular variations of 25 deg. in temperature from 500 deg. C. to 700 deg. C. It possesses the curious characteristic of completing one scale of colours, reverting to its light straw colour and then repeating the scale in a second and higher range of temperature. On the basis of operation for one hour, the alloy turns a light straw colour at 500 deg. C., straw at 525 deg. C., bronze at 550 deg. C., purple at 575 deg. C., and so on. At 700 deg. C. it turns light blue and would normally be expected to then turn to grey indicating that the colour scale was completed. However, at 725 deg. C. it reverts to light straw and the colours progress again. At 900 deg. C. it reaches light blue and at 925 deg. C. greying tendencies become evident. This indicates that the oxide coating has become so thick or irregular that no colour is transmitted and its use as a temperature-recorder is exhausted.

Compressor Impellers

Although the compressor is not thermally stressed to the same extent as the turbine, the impellers of radial compressors for turbine-jet units presented some problems. Their production necessitated the manufacture of a new type of aluminium alloy forging. The material had not to be subject to size effect nor to reduced properties transverse to the grain flow, and at the same time possess good hot strength and creep resistance at temperatures up to 250 deg. C. The impellers required were from 22–33in. diameter and from 10–14in. thick and this implied solid forgings weighing from 400–1,000 lb. each possessing the mechanical properties hitherto expected from a one inch square test bar. Rotors for axial flow compressors necessitated hollow forgings up to 15in. diameter and 20–30in. long with a wall thickness of about 3in.

The Rolls-Royce alloys were considered most suitable due to their good constituent dispersion and to their adaptability to the chilling process without undue skin segregation. RR56, RR58 and RR59 have been used. The nominal percentage composition of RR59 is : copper 2.2, magnesium 1.5, nickel 1.2, iron 1.0, silicon 0.9 and titanium 0.05.

Later study focussed attention on the L42 low silicon alloy. Difficulties had previously been experienced in casting or working this material but special high purity aluminium was employed and a new technique of forging was developed and the manufacturing difficulties were rapidly overcome. A typical percentage composition of this alloy is : copper 2.2, magnesium 1.6, nickel 1.2, iron 1.0, silicon 0.1 to 0.2 and titanium 0.1.

High Duty Alloys, Ltd., proved that impeller failures were mainly due to heavy stresses set up during heat treatment and recommended the provision of a central hole in the forging to reduce the differential cooling rate on quenching. While this method results in increased centrifugal stressing in operation, it has completely eliminated failures in service.

CHAPTER VII

BRITISH GAS TURBINES
A REVIEW OF DEVELOPMENT AND MODERN PRACTICE

A SURVEY of gas-turbine development in all countries (excluding the U.S.S.R., whose research work is unknown) shows Great Britain to be in the forefront of design. True, the axial-flow layout, which must eventually be adopted for the attainment of very great thrusts, has been less favoured than in Germany, but the performance of the De Havilland Goblin and Rolls-Royce Derwent and Nene units has fully vindicated their designers' convictions that, having regard to the thrusts required and the necessary restrictions on development time and mechanical complication, radial flow was the correct choice. Similarly, individual combustion chambers were selected, not because the theoretical superiority of the single annular chamber was denied, but with the realisation that lack of experience might lead to unwarranted delays in production.

In planning layouts and selecting components, British designers

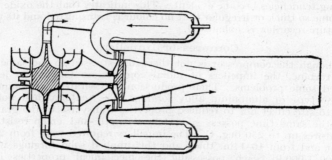

Fig. 84. Diagram of the " return flow " combustion system of the classical Whittle unit.

have displayed nice judgment. The De Havilland Company, for example, while recognising that the double-sided impeller offered smaller overall diameter, higher rotational speeds and easier manufacture, decided upon a single-sided design in order to benefit to the full from ram effect and from direct airflow to the impeller eye, and to reduce eddy and friction losses.

The virtues of the axial-flow gas turbine are not unappreciated in Great Britain. Already Rolls-Royce, Armstrong Siddeley, the Bristol Aeroplane Co., and Metropolitan-Vickers have built some advanced units of this type.

The Early Days

The flow of British gas turbine work, to quote Dr. Roxbee Cox, springs from two distinct streams, one (axial compressors) owing its origin to Dr. A. A. Griffith, and the other (radial compressors) associated with the name of Air Commodore F. Whittle. While a Flight Cadet at the R.A.F. College in 1928, Whittle discussed in a scientific thesis the possibilities of jet propulsion and of gas turbines, but it was not until eighteen months later that he conceived the idea of using a gas turbine *for* jet propulsion. He applied for his first patent in January, 1930, and submitted the idea to the Air

86

Ministry, who declined it on the ground that practical difficulties in the way of development were too great. Firms displayed no more interest, but with some private assistance Whittle succeeded in coming to an arrangement which led to the formation of Power Jets, Ltd., in March, 1936. Three months later this company placed an order for the manufacture of a gas turbine unit with the British Thomson-Houston Company. Whittle was fairly confident in regard to the compressor and turbine elements but felt rather out of his depth with the combustion problem. Early tests proved that his fears regarding combustion were justified ; compressor performance, moreover, was far below expectations. After the first series of tests in 1937 the Air Ministry began to pay more attention to Whittle's work and by 1938 a reconstructed unit was ready for test. After five hours' running severe damage resulted from a turbine blade failure. The Air Ministry had by this time accepted the fact that Whittle had the basis of a practicable aircraft power plant and a contract was placed with Power Jets for a " flight " engine —the W1—for installation in the Gloster E28/39 aircraft. During manufacture certain major components were considered to be unairworthy, and

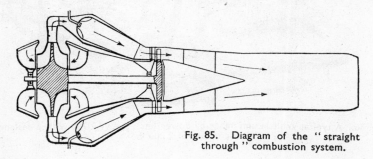

Fig. 85. Diagram of the " straight through " combustion system.

it was decided to use these with some spare components, made for the first experimental engine, to build an " early edition " of the W1, known as the W1X. The Gloster E.28 aircraft, powered with a W1X, left the ground for a short hop during taxying trials in April, 1941, and flight trials with the W1 (850 lb. thrust at 16,500 r.p.m.) began during the following month. The success attained gave a powerful stimulus to gas turbine research.

In the meantime Power Jets had been authorised to go ahead with a more advanced engine, the W2, and the Gloster Aircraft Company was requested to proceed with the design of a twin-engined interceptor fighter, the F9/40, prototype of the Meteor. Moreover direct contracts were placed with the British Thomson-Houston Company and other firms for the manufacture and development of gas turbines and Power Jets became a research and development organisation supplying all other firms engaged with drawings and information.

For historical interest reference is made to various pioneer gas turbine units of Whittle design. The W1(T) was a modified W1 built for bench development from spares ; another modification of the W1 was designated W1(3). The W1A, of 1,450 lb. thrust, incorporated most of the features of the W1 but also had an air-cooled turbine (earlier models had water-cooling) and certain special features of the W2 which it was desired to test in advance. This unit was flown in the Gloster E.28 and was manufactured by the British Thomson-Houston Company to Power Jets' requirements.

Drawings of the ambitious W2 unit were handed over to the Rover

Company for development, and when it was realised that the unit was extremely sensitive to design assumptions, it was changed by stages to bring it nearer to the standard of the W2B. A major and important change was later made by the adoption of straight-through combustion chambers in place of reverse flow.

Complete sets of drawings of the W2B were passed to the several firms by then engaged. This unit was the prototype of the Welland, which subse-

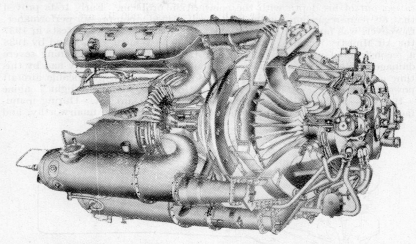

Fig. 86.   A typical Whittle unit made by Power Jets : the W.2/700 with a designed static thrust of 2,000 lb.

quently powered the Meteor IV, and of the " Type I," the corresponding unit made by the General Electric Company in the U.S.A.

By arrangement between the British and American Governments, the W1X turbine unit, a set of drawings of the W2B, and a small team of Power Jets' engineers, were flown to America in the autumn of 1941, and development of the gas turbine at the G.E.C. works was initiated.

The M.A.P. decided to plan for production of the W2B and the Meteor and many sceptics were converted. The firms already engaged increased their activities considerably, Joseph Lucas, Ltd., commenced research on combustion and fuel systems, and firms which had practically ignored the gas turbine began to evince a lively interest.

A Notable Contribution in 1926

In tracing the development of the axial-flow gas turbine in Great Britain it is necessary to refer to the " aerodynamic theory of turbine design " prepared by Dr. A. A. Griffith at the R.A.E. in 1926. This paper indicated that the gas turbine was feasible as a means of aircraft propulsion and ten years later the Establishment obtained authority to build an axial-flow compressor, following its recommendations. In the following year Mr. H. Constant, also of the R.A.E., concluded that a turbine to drive an airscrew could be constructed which would compare in specific weight and fuel consumption with the reciprocating engine, and as the outcome of his work the R.A.E. collaborated with Metropolitan-Vickers in designing the B.10, a unit with a nine-stage axial compressor driven by a four-stage turbine. A series of schemes followed in which the air flowed direct through a single compressor, an annular combustion chamber, the compressor turbine and a power turbine. In the meantime (1938) an experimental turbine compressor, resembling that suggested by Dr. Griffith, had been designed at the R.A.E. and was manufactured and tested by Armstrong Siddeley in 1939–40. Two years later Armstrong Siddeley were given a contract for a unit known as the ASX, the forerunner of the Python later described.

British gas turbine units with a thrust of 5,000 lb. are now available and designs with 8,000 lb. and 10,000 lb. thrusts are under development.

BRITISH GAS TURBINES

Unit	Static Thrust (lb.)	R.P.M.	Consumption (lb./lb./hr.)	Compressor	Combustion Chambers	Turbine	Length (ft.–in.)	Diam. (in.)	W'ght (lb.)
A R'M. S I D D. A.S.X.	2,600	8,000	1.03	Axial-14	11	Axial-2	14–0	42	1,900
Python	3,670h.p. + 1,150 lb.	8,000	359 gal./hr.	Axial-14	11	Axial-2	11–4	42	3,140
Bristol Theseus	1,950h.p. + 500 lb.	9,000	—	Axial-9 Radial-1	—	Axial-2 (Comps.) Axial-1 (screw)	—	—	2,500
De Hav. Goblin II	3,000	10,200	1.23	Radial-1	16	Axial-1	8–11	50	1,550
Ghost II	5,000	—	1.05	Radial-I	10	Axial-I	10–2½	53	1,950
Met.- Vic. F.2. Ser. IV	3,500	7,700	1.05	Axial-10	Annular- 20 burners	Axial-1	13–3	37–11	1,750
F.2/3	4,000	7,600	0.65	Axial-9	Annular- 20 burners	Axial-2 (Comp.) Axial-4 (Aug.)	11–5	47½	2,200
Rolls- Royce Derwent V	3,500- 4,000	14,500	1.0	Radial-1	9	Axial-1	7–4½	43	Under 1,500
Nene	5,000	12,300	1.05	Radial-1	9	Axial-1	8–1	49½	1,550
Clyde	3,000h.p. + 1,200 lb.	6,000	—	Axial-9 Radial-1	—	Axial-1 (Rad.- comp.) Axial-1 (Ax.comp. and screw)	—	—	2,500

ARMSTRONG SIDDELEY

A.S.X. and Python

Reference has already been made to the A.S.X. axial-flow gas turbine designed by Armstrong Siddeley. This first plain jet project was of a size necessary to give a designed sea-level static thrust of 2,500 lb. and a specific consumption of less than unity. It was also to embody an axial-flow compressor having a compression ratio of 5 : 1, which necessitated the use of a two-stage turbine. During the development of the A.S.X. alternative

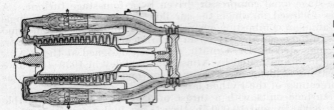

Fig. 87. Gas flow diagram for the Armstrong Siddeley A.S.X. That for the Python is substantially similar.

designs were studied with a view to increasing thrust and producing a power plant suitable for moderate-speed aircraft. As a result, it was decided to develop a turbine-airscrew unit based on the A.S.X. This conversion chiefly entailed provision of a suitable reduction gear and the re-designing of the turbine to provide the necessary shaft horsepower. In other respects the engine remains substantially unaltered; named the A.S.P. or Python, it first ran in March, 1945. During the following month it passed its acceptance test, and since that time it has done some hundreds of hours of development running. The power figures obtained are 3,670 shaft horsepower plus 1,150 lb. jet thrust under sea-level static conditions.

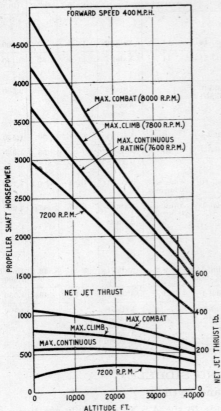

Fig. 88. Estimated shaft horsepower and jet thrust for the Armstrong Siddeley Python at a forward speed of 400 m.p.h. Standard I.C.A.N. atmospheric conditions.

The problem of efficient inhalation of large volumes of air was one of the important considerations during the design studies which led up to the production of the Python. It was considered that the layout adopted, with compressor intake well back from the airscrew spinner, would permit good accessibility and an efficient intake, avoiding disturbances which might be caused by the airscrew blade root sections, and taking advantage of the ram effect produced by the airscrews at positions nearer their outside diameters.

Air for combustion in A.S.X. and A.S.P. units is taken in through either an annulus or two forward-facing ducts, then divided between eleven throats where it is reversed in direction of flow. Next it is passed forward through a multi-stage axial-flow compressor then radially through the diffuser into eleven induction elbows and into the combustion chambers. During the passage from compressor to combustion chamber the direction of flow is again reversed, the combustion chambers being grouped around the compressor casing. To complete its circuit the air, after combustion, passes through extension pipes to the two-stage turbine and out through the tail pipe and jet nozzle to atmosphere.

The main rotating drum of the A.S.X. compressor consists of two forged aluminium alloy sections bolted together on the inside, the division being between the high- and low-pressure stages. Of the fourteen stages five are low-pressure and nine high-pressure. The outer casing, made in two parts, is a light-alloy casting, split horizontally and carrying the fixed, or stator, blades.

The main drives to and from the compressor drum are via front and rear main extension shafts, both of steel and bolted to the drum. At the rear end the drive from the turbine is through a splined sleeve to the stub shaft, which is itself attached by a ring of studs to the turbine disc, the disc having no centre hole. This moving assembly is carried in four bearings, two angular-contact ball races at the front, and one ball and one roller bearing at the rear end. The front shaft provides the drive for the accessories and a means of starting the unit. Arrangements are made to cool both sets of bearings by passing air under the inner and over the outer races. The air for the turbine bearings is bled by external pipes from the fifth stage of the compressor, while for the compressor bearings the

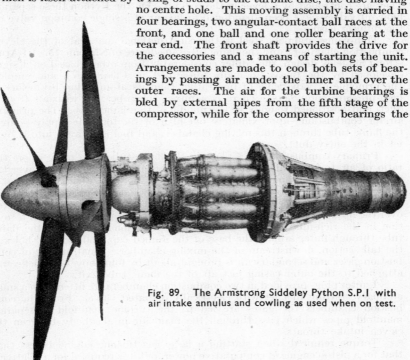

Fig. 89. The Armstrong Siddeley Python S.P.I with air intake annulus and cowling as used when on test.

air is bled from holes in the compressor drum at the seventh stage. The oil feed pipe to the rear bearing passes through the larger-diameter pipe which carries cooling air to the bearing.

Rearward-acting end thrust on the moving assembly is taken mainly by the front bearings, but the load is considerably reduced by a thrust-equalising unit. This comprises a chamber kept at full pressure by a lead from the compressor outlet, and a piston keyed to the front main shaft and exerting on it a forward thrust.

The large single turbine disc is of rather unusual design, incorporating a forked periphery on which is carried the blades for the two stages. Both front and rear faces of the disc are air-cooled. All the rotor blades have " fir tree " roots, which slide into slots in the disc.

The extra power required from the Python turbine to provide the additional shaft horse power for airscrews is obtained by expanding the gases right down to atmospheric pressure, and leaving only the minimum of energy as jet thrust from the exhaust.

After leaving the compressor the air passes through the diffuser casing, the main portion of which carries the concentric diffuser vanes. From the diffuser the air is led to the combustion chambers through eleven elbows containing separate vanes. On each elbow is a blow-off valve, the purpose of which is to aid in starting by releasing to atmosphere a proportion of the air passing through the compressor. The valves also give some aid to acceleration after starting by preventing the compressor blades from stalling. They are controlled by a lever in the cockpit. On the Python these separate blow off valves have been abandoned in favour of a single common valve on the diffuser casing.

Thin-gauge stainless steel is the constructional material of the eleven combustion chambers, and the flame tubes inside are of Nimonic 75. Of Armstrong Siddeley design, they differ considerably from others based on designs developed by the Lucas Company (described in Chapter V), and employ the principle of vaporising of fuel rather than its atomisation by means of high-pressure spray jets. There is a mixing chamber fed with air from a duct, and positioned roughly in the middle of the flame tube. The primary air for combustion—approximately one-fifth of the total air supply—enters the flame tube through this mixing chamber, and fuel is sprayed into it by a jet in the entry duct.

Primary combustion takes place in the flame-tube nose piece where the ratio of air to fuel is about 15-to-1 and the burning gases flow back over the mixing chamber, heating and vaporising the new fuel fed into it. A portion of the secondary air for combustion enters through a hole in the nose of the flame tube, which has a deflector plate on the inside. The cold-air stream is directed over the interior surface of the dome by the plate and prevents carbon formation in the rich-mixture combustion area. Additional air enters the flame tube through flutes around the base of the domed cap, and through holes in the tail section, downstream of the mixing chamber. Final mixing of combustion gases and secondary air is brought about by four shovel-like deflectors attached to the outer casing just aft of the flame tube exit.

Igniter plugs provided in two combustion chambers are fitted with a small auxiliary starting fuel jet with electrically operated valve. From the combustion chambers the gases are led to the turbine manifold by separate manifold pipes which pass through the main air intake body between the eleven intake throats.

Torque required when starting a large gas turbine engine is less than that for a piston engine of comparative power, but it is required for a relatively long period, and this is one of the main problems of starting. A specially designed gas-starter motor is employed on the Python. The automatic starting sequence is initiated by means of a press-button in the pilot's cockpit, or, should it become necessary to re-start in flight, advantage may be taken of the power provided by the wind-milling airscrews. On the A.S.X. an electric starter motor, geared to the front extension shaft, may be used and the special gas-starter is an alternative.

A feature of gas-turbine engines used in conjunction with airscrews is that the power output falls off very rapidly as engine speed decreases, and, to quote the case of the Python, under 100 h.p. is produced at half engine r.p.m. This corresponds with the slow-running speed of the engine, and it will be realised that the airscrew will also be running at half speed. In order to absorb as little power as possible, the airscrew must slow-run with blades in practically zero pitch, and it is therefore necessary to make provision for over-riding the normal fine-pitch stops. In actual fact, these stops are removed, and a device is provided in the reduction gear to ensure that the constant-speed mechanism is inoperative when the airscrews are driving the engine under windmilling conditions.

The reduction-gear unit on the Python is of necessity rather bulky in that an overall ratio of 0.123 : 1 is required in addition to the gearing for contra-rotation of the airscrews.

The S.P.1–1 with annular intake, and the S.P.1–2 with twin-duct intake are both mounted by eleven brackets located at the rear of the intake casing, and all pipes, controls and cables which connect to the aircraft pass between the combustion chambers and the air-intake throats to a bulkhead behind the mounting brackets.

BRISTOL

Bristol's had a general plan for entry into the gas turbine field in 1939, the primary aim being the production of a compound unit of low fuel consumption peculiarly applicable to long-range aircraft. It was necessary, however, to discontinue the project so that attention could be concentrated on sleeve-valve engines for immediate war purposes. Work was eventually resumed and the Theseus I gas-turbine-airscrew unit was announced in 1945. This unit is the first of a family of Bristol gas-turbine units not all of which will necessarily include airscrews and/or heat exchangers.

Theseus I

The Theseus I has an axial and a centrifugal compressor in series, the latter being located between the axial compressor and the combustion chambers. Air is induced through an annular orifice around the airscrew reduction gear, and delivered through a heat-exchanger before passing to the combustion chamber, where its temperature is further raised by the burning

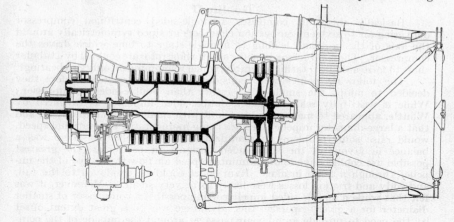

Fig. 90. On the Theseus I airscrew-turbine unit a two-stage turbine drives both axial and centrifugal compressors, while a separate turbine drives the airscrew. A heat exchanger is incorporated.

of injected fuel. The resulting products of combustion pass to a two-stage turbine by means of which the compressors and auxiliaries are driven, and thence to a further turbine stage which, through a forward extension shaft and reduction gearing, drives the airscrew. After leaving the second turbine the gases pass through the heat exchanger, where they give up a measure of their heat to the compressed air on its way to the combustion chambers. From the heat exchanger the exhaust gases are finally discharged through a controllable nozzle, so providing a certain proportion of the total thrust, actually 500 lb. additional to the 1950 h.p. of the unit.

The theoretical advantages claimed for the compound compressor are that the centrifugal component assists the axial compressor over its relatively narrow operating range, particularly during the starting of the unit, thus avoiding instability and promoting flexibility of operation. These advantages, however, are theoretical and experience must be gained before the arrangement can be proved. There is one important advantage in the location of the centrifugal compressor : the air from the discharge of the axial compressor must be turned sharply when separate combustion chambers are used and if a centrifugal compressor is considered necessary for other reasons, it is a very convenient substitute for sharp pipe bends and provides an increase in total pressure ratio.

DE HAVILLAND

In January, 1941, preliminary discussions were held by the De Havilland Company with a view to designing a gas turbine of 3,000 lb. thrust for installation in their Vampire fighter. About sixteen months later the unit—a linear descendant of the early Whittle designs—was ready for testing and by June, 1942, had been operated at its full designed thrust. Production outstripped that of the Vampire and to obtain flight experience two units were initially installed in a Meteor. By Spring, 1944, the Goblin, as the new unit was called, had been flown in both the Vampire and the American Lockheed Shooting Star, both aircraft attaining over 500 m.p.h. An official type-approval test was passed in January, 1945 ; in fact, the Goblin holds Type Certificate No. 1 for a turbine unit for aircraft propulsion. The Series II version of the Goblin is described below.

Goblin II

Basically this unit comprises a single-sided centrifugal compressor delivering air to sixteen combustion chambers grouped symmetrically around the axis of the unit and leading to a single-stage turbine which drives the compressor. The compressor impeller and turbine rotor are coupled by a tubular shaft to form a single rotating assembly, which is mounted on only two bearings.

The following points were considered by the designers before they decided to adopt the single-sided rather than double-sided, compressor : While it was fully realised that a double-sided impeller, as favoured by Whittle, appeared to make possible a unit with smaller overall diameter, and that a large-diameter impeller, besides being more limited in rotational speed, would raise some problems in manufacture, it was felt that there was a balance in favour of the single-sided design. In particular, the greatest possible use could be made of an uninterrupted air flow to the eye of the impeller through a large intake. Ram effect could be employed to the full, and eddy and friction losses were likely to be very small. Moreover, it was felt that while a double-sided impeller made possible a compressor of smaller diameter for a given capacity, this advantage was to a great extent offset by the need to provide annular air passages around the outside of the compressor between the combustion chambers for the supply of air to the rearward facing intake, and by the less compact arrangement of the combustion

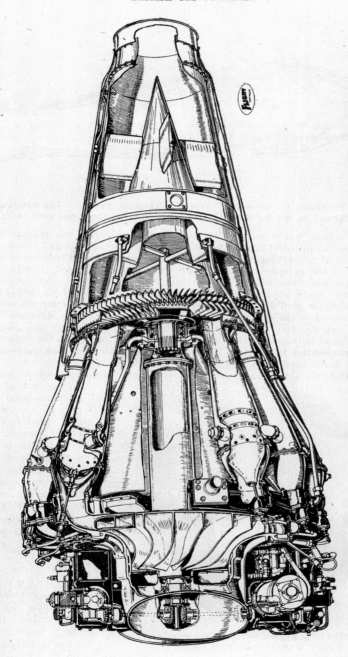

Fig. 91. All the principal features of the De Havilland Goblin II turbine-jet unit, as fitted in the De Havilland Vampire single-seat fighter, are revealed in this sectioned drawing. The Goblin II delivers a maximum static thrust of 3,000 lb. at 10,200 r.p.m. and weighs 1,550 lb.

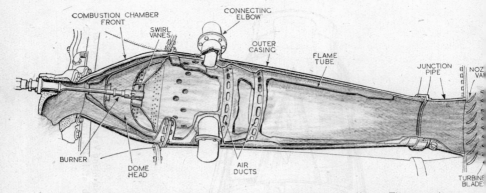

Fig. 92.   The Goblin II "flower pot" type of combustion chamber.   The metering annulus, formed by the burner tube and outer dome, is above the swirl vanes.

chambers which would result.   It was also argued that the rear intake itself, necessitating a 180-degree turn in the air flow, seemed likely to promote some degree of preheating of the air, turbulence and a lack of balance on the two sides of the compressor.   A certain compromise in design, tending to restrict breathing was feared.   For a unit with a single-sided compressor impeller, two more advantages were foreseen : first the inherent simplicity and compactness would permit the use of only two bearings for the main rotating assembly (as compared with three required with a double-sided impeller) and, secondly, the axial load component on the turbine blades could be almost balanced by the forward acting thrust loading on the impeller. A final consideration in selecting the single-sided impeller was that the resulting power unit suited the layout of the Vampire fuselage.

The Goblin's single-stage, single-entry centrifugal compressor provides an air flow of 60 lb. per second at maximum operating speed.   The power required to drive the compressor is a little under 6,000 h.p. and the pressure ratio and temperature rise between inlet and delivery approximate to 3.5 and 150 deg. C. respectively.   At 10,500 r.p.m. the gyroscopic couples are about half those for a comparable piston engine/airscrew installation.

Fig. 93.   The large single-sided one-piece impeller shown as a unit of the main rotating assembly.

The impeller is a one-piece, heat-treated light-alloy forging, anodised and polished. It is thirty-one inches in diameter, has seventeen vanes and reaches a maximum tip speed of 1,430ft. per second. On the back of the impeller a number of concentric labyrinth grooves match up with similar grooves on the sealing plate at the back of the compressor unit to form a gas seal.

The turbine, which provides driving power for the compressor and auxiliaries, is of the single-stage axial-flow type. It has seventy-seven stator blades and eighty-three rotor blades, the numbers having no common denominator to avoid resonance. The moving blades are attached to the turbine disc by the " fir tree " method, that is, evenly spaced serrated slots are broached in the periphery of the turbine disc and the roots of the blades bearing corresponding serrations are slid axially into the slots. The blades

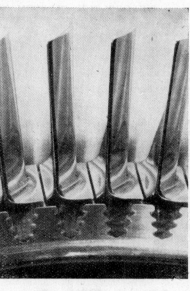

Fig. 94. A section of the turbine disc with serrated slots prepared to receive the blade roots shown in position in the illustration on the right.

are held in position by peening at the roots on each side. On the upstream side the peening is a little heavier to resist rearward thrust.

Bolted to the turbine and the impeller, the large-diameter centre shaft is machined from a steel forging; these three components form the main rotating assembly which is carried in two ball bearings. Any thrust loading is taken by the front bearing which is located on a stub or pivot shaft between the air intake ducts in front of the impeller.

Sixteen combustion chambers are fitted, and on the Goblin II these are of " flower pot " design. Fig. 92. They comprise a flame tube and an outer casing—each of which is made in two basic sections—and a burner. With the primary part of the flame tube, the fuel burner forms an annular space through which passes a metered quantity of air, sufficient for primary combustion. The metering annulus is, in fact, located in the outer dome, between the " snout " and inner dome, and approximately one-quarter of the air to the combustion chamber passes through it. The air for primary combustion also passes through swirl vanes which promote a back vortex round the flame. As a result, the inrush of air helps to promote flame stability instead of blowing the flame out. In addition, a small quantity of air which passes round the outside of the swirl vanes through holes in the inner dome and flared cover plate, produces enough outer turbulence to mix the fuel and air. The remaining bulk of the intake air is admitted to the flame tube in stages as it passes round between tube and outer casing. Its purpose is dilution and cooling of combustion gases. Combustion is completed within one-third of the length of the tapered section of the flame tube.

The main frame or static structure of the Goblin comprises the compressor front casing with twin air intakes ; the two-piece diffuser casing ; the conical centre casing with skirt ; and the nozzle junction box assembly with diaphragm plate and turbine bearing housing.

The starting cycle is automatic, and the starter motor, which is geared to run at about three times engine speed, develops 9–12 h.p. To obtain the necessary air flow, the impeller must be turned at 900 r.p.m. and for satisfactory acceleration to idling speed, 1,500 r.p.m. is required.

The following data for the Goblin II are quoted as they exemplify the characteristics of a modern gas-turbine unit.

D.H. GOBLIN II—PERFORMANCE DESIGN DATA AND DIMENSIONS

10,200 R.P.M. STATIC SEA-LEVEL CONDITIONS

Fuel flow ... 3,720 lb./hr. (465 gal./hr.)	
Maximum fuel pump delivery pressure... ... ... 900 lb./sq. in.	
Blower pressure ratio (overall) ... 3.3 to 1	
Blower pressure ratio (intake-delivery) ... ... 3.75 to 1	
Blower temperature rise... ... 150 deg. C.	
Blower horsepower 5,720	
Air mass flow ... ... 60 lb./sec.	
Air fuel ratio ... ... 58 to 1	

PERFORMANCE

	r.p.m.
Maximum static thrust	3,000 lb. at 10,200
Cruising static thrust	1,850 lb. at 8,700
Idling static thrust	150 lb. at 3,000
Specific fuel consumption :	r.p.m.
Take off ...	1.23 lb./lb./hr. 10,200
Climbing ...	1.23 lb./lb./hr. 9,700
Cruising	1.30 lb./lb./hr. 8,700

Turbine inlet temperature ...	790 deg. C.
Jet velocity	1,610 ft./sec.
Maximum jet pipe temperature...	685 deg. C.
Cruising jet pipe temperature ...	550 deg. C.
Climbing jet pipe temperature ...	630 deg. C.
Maximum rear bearing temperature ...	130 deg. C.
Oil consumption maximum, all conditions	1.5 pt./hr.
Normal oil pressure (cruising)	...40/45 lb./sq. in.
Oil tank capacity	12 pints

DIMENSIONS

Maximum diameter	50in.
Length (engine air intake to propelling nozzle)	107in.
Propelling nozzle diam. (internal)	16in.
Propelling nozzle length	6.25in.
Exhaust cone length (standard)...	43in.
Impeller tip diam.	31in.

WEIGHTS

Total weight	1,550 lb

Ghost II

Resembling the Goblin in layout, but differing in appearance and detail design, the Ghost II gives 5,000 lb. thrust at sea level. The number of combustion chambers has been reduced to ten. Forked pipes lead to the chambers from expansion boxes round the periphery of the compressors.

Fig. 95. The Ghost II, developing a static thrust of 5,000 lb, has an overall diameter of 53 in.

METROPOLITAN–VICKERS
F.2, Series IV

A ten-stage axial-flow compressor and an annular combustion chamber characterise this unit. The maximum diameter is less than 38 inches and the length and dry weight are respectively 13ft. 3in. and 1,750 lb.

Earlier units of similar design were cleared for flight in December, 1943, with a rated output of 1,800 lb. These were the first axial-flow turbine-jet units to fly in this country.

F.2/3

A composite unit of advanced design, the F.2/3 comprises an F.2 axial-flow compressor and turbine with which has been incorporated a ducted-fan thrust augmenter known as the F.3. By this means the thrust delivered has been increased by 67 per cent., for an unchanged fuel consumption and for an increase in weight of only 33.3 per cent. The static thrust rating o 4,000 lb. is, of course, for sea-level conditions, and the proportion of overal thrust contributed by the augmenter decreases with increase in flight speed,

Fig. 96. The Metropolitan-Vickers F.2 turbine-jet unit with axial-flow compressor. Early units of this type were cleared for flight in December 1943 and were the first axial-flow units of British design to be flown.

much in the same way that airscrews lose tractive efficiency. Further, a fall-off in augmented thrust occurs with increased altitude, again in accordance with the laws which cause an airscrew similarly to lose efficiency. However, the thrust drop of the augmenter is not parallel with that of an airscrew and can be largely modified by using a variable-area outlet orifice.

Perhaps the best way of visualising a ducted-fan thrust augmenter is to regard it as something of a half-way measure between pure jet propulsion and airscrew propulsion. It has been shown that smaller losses are occasioned by moving a large mass of air rearward fairly slowly—as in airscrew propulsion—than is the case when a small mass of air is moved rearward at high velocity—as in pure jet propulsion. By including ducted-fans in conjunction with jet propulsion, the thrust obtained from the jet alone is somewhat reduced but a pronounced gain in overall thrust is provided by the fans entraining a

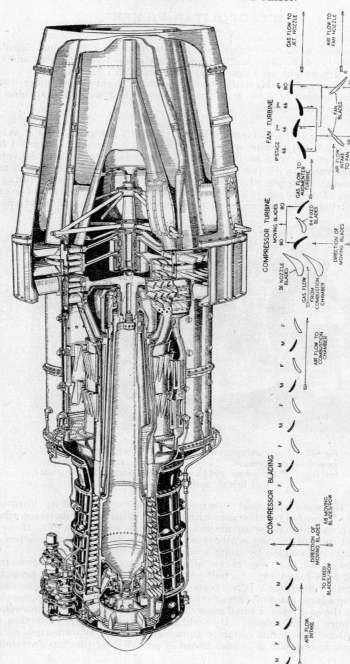

Fig. 97. The layout of the unique Metropolitan-Vickers F.2/3 turbine-jet unit with ducted-fan thrust augmenter may be studied to advantage in this special drawing.

relatively large mass of air and driving it rearward fairly slowly relative to the jet velocity. The streams from the gas turbine and the fans are separated and do not mingle until both have left the jet pipe. Thus at the orifice there is, in effect, a hot high-speed jet from the turbines, and a cold lower-speed annular jet from the fans, the latter stream cylindrically enclosing the jet stream. This has an effect on noise suppression which is most marked, and the unit is the quietest aircraft propulsion engine ever developed.

Air enters the intake to the compressor through a concentrically ringed guard. There are 70 fixed and 68 moving blades respectively on each stator and rotor stage of the compressor. All the fixed blades are similar in detail design, as are all the rotor blades ; that is to say, all blades of one type are

Fig. 98. The main rotating assembly of the Metropolitan-Vickers F.2 turbine-jet unit.

identical in twist, chord, camber, thickness/chord ratio, etc., but are progressively cropped so that, in effect, the moving blades have coarser pitch in the higher stages than in the earlier stages. Since the final ring or stage of blades is a stator, the flow from compressor to combustion chamber is truly axial and has no helical component.

On entry to the annular combustion chamber, the air is divided by a deflector ring into two annular streams each of which flows around the flame chamber. The latter is also annular in shape and is housed concentrically within the combustion chamber. The inner and outer walls of the flame chamber are pierced by 80 wedge-shaped inlets staggered in two rows of 20 each, and the surrounding air stream is admitted to the flame chamber through these wedges downstream of the burners. In the forward end-plate of the flame chamber are small holes through which a governed flow of " primary " air from the compressor delivery is metered to the burners, the amount of air abstracted being merely sufficient to support combustion.

The burners are plain shrouded tubes evenly spaced at 18 deg. intervals, and projecting radially inwards into the flame chamber with forward-facing nozzles. These produce a dense-cored cone of fuel at 650 lb./sq. in. which, meeting the primary air flow in the opposite direction, brings about a high degree of turbulence and facilitates instant and complete combustion. This combusted gas is then tremendously swelled by the relatively large mass flow of cool " secondary " air admitted to the flame chamber through the wedges, resulting in an immediate and very large expansion, with a consequent high velocity flow to the turbine.

The gases pass through a nozzle ring to the turbine blades which are mounted in two rows on the turbine disc and are separated by a ring of stator blades interposed between them. This, then, comprises the first turbine, the sole purpose of which is to drive the compressor.

Immediately to the rear of the first turbine is a second turbine, composed of two contra-rotating wheels, which operate in the gas stream exhausted from the first turbine. This second turbine is for driving the fans, also arranged in two banks which counter-rotate. As the two rings of turbine blades on each wheel are nested together, with one row of each interposed between the two rows of its neighbour, the unit can be regarded as a four-stage component. Additionally, since the nested blades counter-rotate the necessity for fixed rings of stator blades is eliminated. The maximum rotational speeds of the fan-turbine wheels are much lower than that of the compressor turbine, the first fan wheel rotating at 2,850 r.p.m. and the second wheel at 2,300 r.p.m. Having passed through the four blade banks of the second turbine, the gas flows down the tail pipe to the outlet orifice.

The arrangement of the ducted fans and the design of blade mountings is ingenious, the fan blades being mounted on rings carried on the blade crowns of the second turbine. The torque loads on the turbine and fan blades compensate one another, and, since the turbine blades are designed to " windmill " and the fan blades to " screw " this is not particularly difficult ; but the centrifugal loads and bending loads cannot be cancelled out and these must have occasioned the designer no small trouble. The matter is further complicated by the fact that labyrinth seals have to be introduced between fan and turbine blades to preclude untoward pressure losses between the turbine stream and fan stream, and when it is realised that the temperature difference between these streams is of the order of 600 deg. C., the ingenuity and quality of the design may be appreciated.

As already explained, thrust augmentation will fall off with increase in

Fig. 99. This thrust spoiler exemplifies the development work undertaken by Power Jets.

flight speed, since the limitation imposed on the fan stream velocity by the area of the outlet orifice progressively reduces the thrust efficiency of the fan stream. If, by having a variable outlet, the area of the orifice can be reduced proportionally to the rise in flight speed, for a given mass flow the stream velocity will be increased and thus the efficiency of propulsion may be extended to higher speeds with a consequent delay in thrust drop from the augmenter and, proportional to the flight speed, a higher overall thrust.

POWER JETS

Reference has already been made to the early work of this Government-owned establishment, which conducts investigations of general interest to the various manufacturers of British gas-turbines, but mention must be made here of the W2/700, a unit of classical Whittle design with a double-entry centrifugal compressor driven by a single-stage turbine fed by 10 reverse-flow combustion chambers. The W2/700 was designed to give 2,000 lb. static thrust at 16,700 r.p.m. with a specific fuel consumption of 1.13 lb./lb./hr.

One important item on the development of which Power Jets have been engaged is a thrust spoiler which can give negative thrust for braking.

ROLLS-ROYCE

The first active interest in jet propulsion was shown by the Rolls-Royce organisation in 1938 when a department was established for the design of gas turbines. By 1940 test rigs for airfoils, bearings and combustion chambers had been set up and toward the end of the year the Company was manufacturing components for Whittle units. Next an intensive study of radial compressors for these units was undertaken to ascertain the causes of, and the means of eliminating, surging. A special test plant was installed, with a 2,000 h.p. Vulture engine driving the compressors. Late in 1941, under Air Ministry direction, the Company undertook to build a Whittle-type engine known as WRI, designed with low blade stresses to demonstrate that the gas turbine could be made completely reliable.

Early in 1943 Rolls-Royce took over research on the W2B/23 unit from the Rover Company whose engineers had developed straight-through combustion. Units of this type, with the name Welland (Rolls-Royce having decided to standardise river names for their gas-turbine nomenclature) were supplied for installation in the Gloster E.28. In June 1943 two units were fitted in the Gloster F9/40, prototype of the Meteor. This unit had a reverse-flow combustion system, a maximum diameter of 43 inches and could develop 1,700 lb. thrust, although for the F9/40 it was de-rated to 1,450 lb. By May 1944 the Welland was being regularly delivered to the R.A.F.

Whilst all these activities were proceeding Rolls-Royce were engaged on a new design to utilise experience gained from development work. The new project was to be of the same maximum diameter for installation in the standard Meteor engine nacelles but to develop a static thrust of 2,000 lb. Drawings were commenced in April, 1943, and by July the unit was ready for test, and in November, 1943, it passed its 100-hour type-test at 2,000 lb. thrust. In April of the next year it completed its first flight tests in the Meteor with a service rating of 1,800 lb. thrust and a weight of 920 lb.

The new engine was known as the B37, R-R Derwent, Series I. The Series II engine gave an increased thrust of 2,200 lb. Series III was a special unit for experiments to provide suction on aircraft wing surfaces for boundary layer removal and Series IV gave a further increase in thrust to 2,400 lb.

The Derwent Series V, whilst retaining the maximum diameter of 43in., was an entirely new unit developing twice the thrust of the original Derwent I. It is this unit which enabled the Gloster Meteor to achieve 606 m.p.h.

Fig. 100. The compact design of the Derwent V is well shown in this view.

Derwent V

This modern unit is, in effect, a scaled-down version of still another new type, the Nene. Its development was prompted by the promise shown by the Nene and the proof that the Meteor could utilise thrusts greatly in excess of the original estimates.

A double-entry radial compressor of increased capacity as compared with previous Derwents, with an impeller about 21 in. diameter and twenty-nine radial blades on each side, is used on the Derwent V. At the other end of the shaft is a single-stage turbine. The main shaft is mounted in two roller bearings and a central ball-thrust bearing. Air is induced on both sides of the impeller and fed past the diffuser necks to the combustion chambers.

Means are provided to cool the internal mechanism, including the centre and rear bearings and the front face of the turbine disc. A small centrifugal fan mounted in front of the centre bearing induces atmospheric air through short stub pipes on the front end of the engine housing and forces it through the cooling air manifold to the exhaust outlet at the rear. When it is realised that the turbine rotor runs in a gas temperature of about 850 deg. C., and that the 54 individual

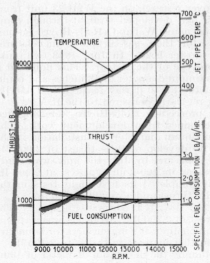

Fig. 101. Graph illustrating sea level static performance of the Derwent V.

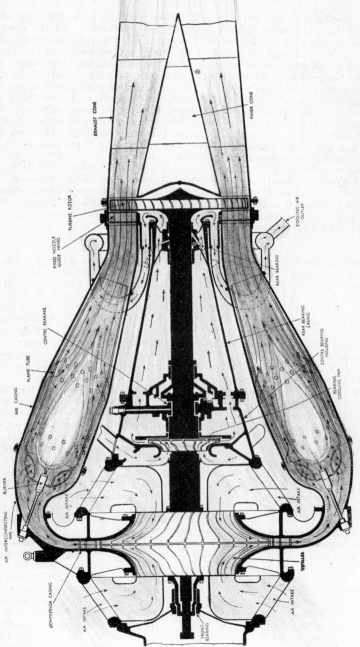

Fig. 102. The gas flow and principal structural features of the Derwent.

blades, measuring about 3in. long and 1.25in. wide, have to transmit about 75 h.p. the importance of the metallurgical problems and the need for internal cooling will be understood. Apart from the anti-corrosive nature of the nickel chromium alloys used, non-creep properties are of the highest importance. A high-tensile strength must be maintained even under high working temperatures, as centrifugal force due to high speed of rotation imposes a heavy mechanical stress. Because of this high speed of rotation the compressor impeller and turbine rotor each needs to be statically and dynamically balanced, both individually and collectively as a single assembly. This explains the fact that the two shafts carrying compressor and turbine are connected by a quickly detachable toothed coupling. The impeller, which has the larger diameter, has a tip velocity of approximately 1,500 ft./sec.—that is considerably in excess of sonic speed.

The installed weight of the Derwent V engine is under 1,500 lb. and it delivers 4,000 lb. thrust—a power/weight ratio never previously attained. For the world's speed record, two of these units in the Meteor developed sufficient power to attain 606 m.p.h. when throttled down to 3,600 lb./thrust. Fuel consumption on the record was high, as full throttle low altitude conditions are the least favourable to thermal efficiency.

Nene I

Early in 1944 the Ministry of Aircraft Production issued a specification for a jet propulsion unit having a maximum overall diameter of 55in., a minimum static thrust of 4,000 lb. and a weight not exceeding 2,200 lb. The Rolls-Royce Nene I is the fulfilment of this requirement in generous measure. Units at present in production are 49½in. diameter, develop a thrust of 5,000 lb. and weigh only 1,550 lb. Thus the realisable performance is 3.2 lb. thrust per lb. weight and 375 lb. thrust per square ft. of frontal area instead of 1.8 lb. and 242 lb. thrust respectively as originally stipulated.

In the remarkably short period of 5½ months the design was completed, all drawings prepared, the first unit built and the proving run of one hour at 5,000 lb. thrust successfully accomplished.

The single stage, double-sided, radial flow compressor of the Nene delivers air at four times atmospheric pressure to nine straight-flow combustion chambers. Aviation kerosene under high pressure is sprayed downstream into the chambers, to form a combustible mixture having an air/fuel ratio of about 18 : 1, and burnt continuously. The major volume of the air, diluting the mixture to a ratio of approximately 60 : 1 is expanded by the heat released by combustion of the fuel.

The complete rotating assembly comprises the compressor impeller, cooling fan, and turbine rotor on two coupled shafts supported in three bearings. End bearings are of the roller type whilst the centre one is a deep groove ball bearing to support axial loads. It is of interest to note that at speeds up to about 8,000 r.p.m. the axial thrust is directed forward, but above that figure it is exerted rearward.

The impeller is 28.5in. diameter and machined with 29 radial vanes each side from a single light alloy forging. Curved entry vanes, approximately 17.75in. diameter, for each side are separate components machined all over. On the 13in. diameter cooling air fan the 30 vanes have integral entry sections which are bent cold in two stages with an intermediate annealing operation.

The compressor casing is built up of front and rear members attached to a central diffuser ring by bolts passing through the diffuser vanes and the intermediate splitter vanes. To facings at the nine outlets from the diffuser ring are bolted the cast elbows conducting the air to the combustion chambers. In the bend of the elbows are three cascade vanes formed of lengths cut from an extruded section and cast in position. A pair of trunnions providing the main supports for the complete unit are also mounted on the diffuser ring. The front bearing housing forms the outer member of the front air intake and also serves to support the wheelcase containing the auxiliary drives and the oil sump.

Bolted up to the turbine shroud ring and nozzle box is the exhaust cone with its inner cone supported by four transverse bolts enclosed by streamlined fairings. The base of the inner cone masks the rear face of the turbine disc. While the exhaust cone is of fixed length, approximately 33in., the jet pipe extending from the exhaust cone to the propulsion nozzle can be varied to meet installation requirements providing a suitable length/diameter ratio is maintained. These parts are double walled and packed

Fig. 103. On the Rolls-Royce Nene engine auxiliaries are mounted on the wheel case forward of the compressor. Gauze screens cover the compressor intakes.

with heat insulating material. Standard length of jet pipe is about 44in. and the weight is 9.5 lb. per foot.

Combustion chambers are similar in general design to those of the Derwent V but of larger capacity.

Nene units at present in production are rated at 5,000 lb. thrust. This is neither the maximum at present available nor the ultimate possibility. A thrust of 5,500 lb. has already been obtained on the test bed. Average figure during development was 5,150 lb. which represents the following component efficiencies :—Compressor 76 per cent., Combustion 98 per cent., Expansion (turbine and tail cone) 93 per cent.

A compressor having a double-sided impeller was chosen because output of a jet unit is largely determined by the amount of air consumed and this is conditioned by diameter of the compressor entry. Obviously two intakes will admit more air than one. Conversely, for a given quantity of air, the overall diameter of the impeller and consequently the complete unit can be relatively smaller than on a single-sided design, which is advantageous particularly with wing installations.

There are, of course, other reasons influencing the choice. The increased air flow for any given diameter necessitates relatively long turbine blades and a smaller diameter turbine disc and permits an advantageous stressing of these parts. A wing nacelle or a fuselage enclosure forms a plenum chamber from which air is drawn to the compressor intakes. Velocity is lowered and any object sucked in may well fall to the bottom of the enclosure instead of passing into the compressor.

The first aircraft to be powered by the Nene was a Lockheed XP80 Shooting Star and recently tests have been conducted on a De Havilland Vampire. In both instances an improvement in performance was obtained. With the American aircraft speeds of the order of 580 m.p.h. and an excellent rate of climb to 42,000ft. were achieved.

Trent

This pioneer Rolls-Royce turbine-airscrew unit was tested in March, 1945, and in September of the same year two Trents were installed in a Meteor. Experimental work with this unit dates back to May, 1944, when a compressor-turbine unit was equipped with a spur-type reduction gear and tested for shaft horse-power. The present Trent engine, which was produced purely to gain experience with a unit combining jet and airscrew propulsion, is still virtually a Derwent with reduction gear and small-diameter five-bladed airscrew added. Approximate weights during early development were as follows :—Weight of turbine unit, 1,000 lb., airscrew 250 lb., and reduction gear 250 lb. (total 1,500 lb.).

Clyde

Comparable in output with the Armstrong Siddeley Python, this R.R. turbine-airscrew unit has a nine-stage axial compressor and a single-stage centrifugal compressor. There are two turbines, the forward (high pressure) one driving the radial compressor and the rear (low pressure) one the axial compressor and counter-rotating airscrews. The gas flow may be studied in Fig. 104.

Power figures for the Clyde are : 3,000 shaft horse power plus 1,200 lb. static jet thrust at 6,000 r.p.m. The dry weight without airscrew is 2,500 lb.

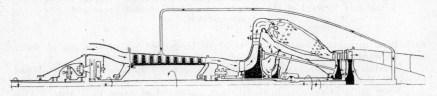

Fig. 104. On the Rolls-Royce Clyde the forward turbine drives the centrifugal compressor and the separate rear turbine the axial compressor and counter-rotating airscrews. The Clyde gives 3,000 shaft h.p. and 1,200 lb. static jet thrust at 6,000 r.p.m.

CHAPTER VIII

AMERICAN GAS TURBINES

VISITING England in 1941 General H. H. Arnold, C.-in-C., U.S. Army Air Forces, was so impressed with progress in aircraft gas-turbines that he arranged for a Whittle unit to be shipped to the U.S.A. This subsequently became the prototype of the General Electric units installed in the Bell XP-59A experimental fighter. By April, 1943, the General Electric I-16, based upon Whittle patents, was rated at 1,650 lb. static thrust at 16,500 r.p.m., and a small production order was placed. Since that date, American manufacturers have produced a variety of turbine units, many of which, as a result of the close technical liaison during the war, bear evidence of the influence of British practice.

GENERAL ELECTRIC
I-40 (J-33)

Work on this single-stage radial compressor unit, Fig. 105, which now powers the Lockheed P-80 Shooting Star, was initiated early in 1943. It was the first U.S. unit to adopt direct flow combustion chambers.

Air enters through circumferential inlets at the front and rear of the double-sided compressor, the inlets having screens to prevent ingress of foreign

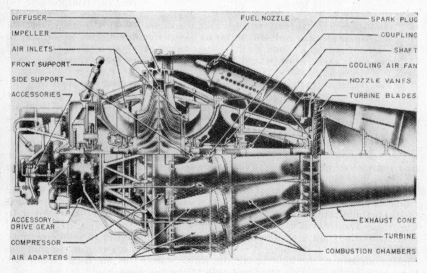

Fig. 105. General Electric I-40 radial-compressor, turbine-jet unit as installed in the Lockheed Shooting Star. It will be seen that the design strongly reflects British practice.

bodies. The air is turned into the annulus of the impeller by guide vanes and a single splitter vane.

There are fourteen straight-through combustion chambers, each furnished with a coaxial flame tube. Fuel is sprayed into the forward end of the flame tube and combustion is controlled by air admitted through holes in the tube. The temperature of the combustion gases is reduced by a progressive dilution of air and a layer of air traverses the length of the outer casing and joins the main stream at the turbine nozzle. Two spark plugs mounted in diametrically opposite air adapters provide starting ignition and combustion is propagated to the other chambers through connecting tubes. The forty-eight blades of the turbine nozzle ring direct the hot gases on to the turbine wheel, which has fifty-four blades.

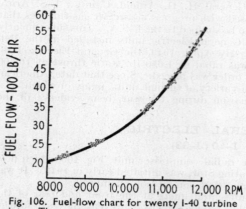

Fig. 106. Fuel-flow chart for twenty I-40 turbine jets. The curve passes through 4,740 lb./hr. at 11,500 r.p.m.

Structurally, the I-40 consists of five major sub-assemblies (1) the accessory drive, (2) compressor, (3) air adapters, (4) combustion chambers and turbine, and (5) exhaust cone. Each sub-assembly is a complete operable unit in itself, so far as its particular function is concerned, and is interchangeable among all I-40 gas turbines. Assemblies (1), (2) and (4) have their own bearings and rotors, so that they can be tested independently if desired.

Two horizontal trunnions and a front support are used for mounting the unit. The two trunnions are placed between air adapters at the rear air inlet to the compressor, very near to the centre of gravity while the front support can be mounted on either the top or the bottom of the accessory drive casing, depending upon the installation.

A double-sided impeller with stub shafts bolted to each side comprises the compressor rotor. The front shaft is carried by a ball bearing and the rear shaft by a roller bearing, axial clearance being adjusted by a sliding ring which carries the outer race of the ball bearing.

The turbine and combustion assembly consists of a turbine-bearing support, the turbine rotor, and a set of combustion chambers. The shaft of the turbine rotor is flash-welded to the disc and blades are dovetailed to the rim. The rotor is carried by a roller bearing at the rear end and a ball bearing at the front end, axial clearance being adjusted in the same manner as for the compressor rotor. A shroud covers the bearing support so that the cooling air can be brought along the inner wall; this air then passes out through a cooling fan on the front side of the turbine wheel.

Arranged around the turbine shaft the combustion chambers join at the turbine inlet to provide an annular flow of hot gases. At the entrance end of each combustion chamber, a piston ring joint is used in order to allow for thermal expansion. Lubricating oil passes through a filter and is delivered to the four main bearings, to the coupling sleeve between the turbine and compressor rotor shafts and to the quill-shaft splines which turn the accessory drive. Oil from the three main bearings between the rotor and from the coupling sleeve drains into a sump from which it is drawn by the scavenge pump and returned to the reservoir. At a turbine speed of 11,500 r.p.m., the supply pump has a displacement of about 3 g.p.m., and the scavenge

pump about 10 g.p.m. Gears and bearings in the accessory drive are lubri
cated by splash from the gear which drives the oil pump.

Operating data for the I-40 are :—

Fuel flow	4,740 lb./hr.
Specific fuel consumption	1.185 lb./lb./hr.
Exhaust temperature	632 deg. C.
Compression ratio	4.126
Compressor discharge temperature	212 deg. C.
Combustion pressure drop	3.18 lb./sq. in.
Turbine inlet temperature	811 deg. C.
Air flow	79 lb./sec.

TG–100

Installed in the Consolidated Vultee XP-81 fighter, this unit is designed
to drive an airscrew. Detailed information has not yet been released, but it is

Fig. 107. General Electric TG-100 turbine-airscrew unit showing the arrangement
of the reduction gear and the formation of the tail pipe.

evident from the accompanying photograph, Fig. 107, that air enters the axial-
flow compressor behind the reduction gear casing. The turbine drives the
compressor direct and from the compressor the drive is transmitted through
a reduction gear to the airscrew. Not all the energy is extracted from the
gases by the turbine, and the efflux is projected rearwards as a jet to provide
a supplementary thrust.

J–35

A later development by the General Electric Co. is a unit known as
J-35 or TG-180 having an axial-flow compressor and seven straight-through
Halford-type combustion chambers, Fig. 108.

Fig. 108. General Electric J-35 axial compressor, turbine-jet unit, intended for
civil and military aircraft.

WESTINGHOUSE
9.5-B (Baby)

Designed to power an American flying bomb this unit, Fig. 109, as the designation implies, is only 9½in. in diameter, and yields a thrust of 275 lb. Because of its small diameter the rotational speed is exceptionally high,

Fig. 109. Westinghouse axial-flow turbine-jets ; on the left the 19-B (" Yankee ") and on the right the " Baby " (9.5-B). The " Baby " was designed to power an American flying bomb.

namely, 34,000 r.p.m.   The manufacturers have suggested that it might be used for the propulsion of light aircraft but except, possibly, for experiment it is doubtful if such installations will materialise.   There would appear to be more likelihood of a small unit of this type being developed as an auxiliary plant for pressurising the cabin of a large civil aircraft.

19-B (Yankee)

Built to the requirements of the U.S. Navy, this turbine/jet unit, Fig. 109, is installed in the McDonnell FD-I (Phantom) fighter. The six-stage axial-flow compressor has blades with " bulb " type roots held in place in milled slots by wire locking keys which are turned up into the grooved sides of the blade root. Though having the same section, the blades in the first compression stage are of deeper chord than succeeding stages, all of which are identical except for blade length. At the maximum speed of 18,000 r.p.m. the centrifugal stress on the first stage is stated to be some 50,000 g. The cast aluminium compressor casing is made in halves which bolt together along axial flanges. The casing has six grooves, five to take stator blade shroud rings and one for straightener vanes. In most cases the stator blades are cast, though some are rolled. The complete straightener vane assembly consists of three rows, resembling in construction the stator assemblies.

The main structural component of the unit is the fuel manifold and thrust-bearing support, a built-up stainless steel unit consisting of three concentric rings joined by eight hollow streamline struts. It is located between the compressor and the combustion chamber assembly.

In the annular combustion chamber are 24 fuel nozzles. In some installations the spray angle is 45 deg., but in most others at 80 deg. Complete details of the combustion chamber have not been disclosed, but it can be said to include a perforated conical burner ring, so designed that the turbulence created gives complete combustion at the high velocities developed. A layer of cooling air is directed along the inner surface of the casing shell so that temperatures do not exceed 400 deg. F.

The single-stage turbine disc, shaft and coupling flange are machined from a single forging. Thirty-two turbine blades having bulb roots fitting into slots in the disc are held in place by peening the shanks of the roots into chamfers at each end of the slots. Inside the exit nozzle casing are four hollow streamline struts supporting a movable tail cone. As on the German units the " cone in " position is for starting and idling, with reduced pressure behind the turbine, while the " cone out " position reduces the outlet airflow and increases back pressure on the turbine, thus reducing available energy to the turbine so that higher temperatures and more fuel are required to maintain rotative speed. The additional energy thus delivered to the jet is realised in the form of an increase in flow velocity through the reduced nozzle area.

Accessories include electric starter, generator, fuel pump, oil pump, governor, vacuum or hydraulic pump, and tachometer generator, all mounted on a gear box containing a train of twelve gears, and located on top, bottom, or either side of the unit.

Operating data for the 19-B are :—

Air flow, static, sea level, maximum	.. ..	28 lb./sec.
Air flow, 500 m.p.h., maximum	.. ..	38 lb./sec.
Temperature at turbine nozzle, maximum	..	815 deg. C.
Temperature at turbine nozzle, normal	.. ..	649 deg. C.
Turbine inlet temperature (1,800 r.p.m.)	.. ..	538 deg. C.

WRIGHT

Long noted for its radial type piston engines, the Wright Aeronautical Corporation has now embarked on a gas-turbine development programme and has announced its intention to specialize on high powered units.

AMERICAN GAS TURBINES

Unit	Static Thrust (lb.)	R.P.M.	Consumption (lb.lb.hr.)	Compressor	Combustion Chambers	Turbine	Length (ft.–in.)	Diam. (in.)	Wt. (lb.)
General Electric I-16	1,670	16,500	—	Radial-1	10	Axial-1	5–10	41½	825
General Electric I-40	4,000	11,500	1.185	Radial-1	14	Axial-1	8–5	48	1820
Westinghouse 19-B	1,365	18,000	—	Axial-6	Annular-24 burners	Axial-1	8–8	20¾	847

E

CHAPTER IX

GERMAN GAS TURBINES : DETAILS OF UNITS PRODUCED AND PROJECTED

WITH the aim of discovering means to counter the heavy Allied bombing offensive, Germany pushed forward the development of a number of unorthodox methods of reaction propulsion for aircraft. Apart from turbine-jet engines and turbine-airscrew units, work was in progress at the termination of hostilities on bi-fuel liquid rockets, turbine-jet and rocket combinations, intermittent impulse ducts such as powered the V-1 weapon, athodyds or ram-jets, and athodyd and rocket combinations. Even solid fuel rockets were under consideration, not only for assisting take-off, but for the propulsion of specialised aircraft. The steam turbine was being investigated for airscrew propulsion.

It is outside the scope of the present work to discuss all these novel systems ; in any case, they were largely in the nature of expedients and, except by their more fanatical protagonists, were not regarded as solutions in themselves to the problem of powering standard types of military aircraft. Thus, in all probability the rocket-propelled Me 163 and its later development the 263 would eventually have been displaced by special interceptor versions of the jet-propelled Me 262 with a pair of liquid rocket units to supplement the main gas turbines. Factors militating against the general adoption of the liquid-rocket system for main propulsion were the excessive consumption rate of the special fuels required and the difficulty of supply and handling. Only with the general introduction of anti-aircraft missiles and new forms of pilotless weapons would these and other new propulsive systems finally have come into extensive use. As the power units of supersonic research aircraft, however, they would undoubtedly have played an important part in Germany's development programme.

Towards the end of the war, jet propulsion became very attractive to the Germans because of the ease and speed of production of a turbine-jet unit as compared with a high-powered reciprocating engine and airscrew. In general, their designs were more advanced and necessarily more complicated than contemporary British units. However, they were heavier on a power/weight basis, less efficient as regards fuel consumption, and not so reliable in operation as British units. Their axial compressors were prone to stall and instability of combustion rendered the unit liable to cut out unless carefully handled by the pilot. In service operation the period between complete overhauls was as low as 25–50 hours.

Materials of suitable quality, in most instances denied to them by reason of constant bombing and the urgency of the deteriorating situation, would have provided much improved results. Panic decisions by Nazi leaders led to frequent changes in leading personnel and their production plans, which seriously handicapped German output. " Hitler was our best ally " is a good method of describing the final phases of the war, after studying the ever-changing Nazi plans which hampered production. Co-ordination and strong direction was completely lacking, and high Nazi officials frequently over-ruled the judgment of experienced technicians.

By contrast, this country pursued a definite policy without deviation or interruption, and scored thereby. This did not prevent desirable modifications and up-to-the-minute changes dictated by experience to ensure the finest aircraft for Service use. The larger German factories were gradually driven underground by persistent bombing but, curiously, this was not a bar to production as it was found that due to more settled mentality, even temperature and better conditions generally, more work was achieved. Metal stocks were large. The largest underground factory was at Nordhausen, Saxony, now in the Russian Zone. Here in a tunnel over a mile in length, with shafts on either side, some 30,000 workers—Russians, French, Italians, Poles and Germans—were employed on V-1 and V-2 weapons and Junkers and B.M.W. turbine-jets.

These views were formed by the author during an officially sponsored visit to Germany and Austria in August and September, 1945, and talks with German technicians and British Service personnel.

Although Daimler-Benz and Focke-Wulf had designed units of their own, German gas-turbine development was principally in the hands of B.M.W., Heinkel (at first, alone, and later in collaboration with Hirth) and Junkers. Reference may be made to the pioneer Heinkel HeS3B and HeS8 units with maximum thrusts of 1,100 lb. and 1,500 lb. respectively, but these were completely outmoded by the HeS011, work on which was begun in 1941 and which had reached a fairly advanced stage of development when hostilities ended.

Junkers did some preliminary work on gas turbines as long ago as 1936, but little progress was made until late in 1939, when the design of the Jumo 004 was put in hand. After the war, it was revealed that the first unit of this type was tested about a year later and underwent flight tests in 1941. This early model gave a thrust of about 1,760 lb. The Jumo 004B, the sub-type selected for quantity production, was designed at the end of 1941, and was first run about 12 months later. A prototype Me262 with two 004B units was flown early in 1943.

The B.M.W. concern, although engaged in jet research during 1937, lacked the background of Junkers. Work began on their 003 project in 1939, the designed static thrust being 1,300 lb. The first unit was tested in 1940, but delivered only 990 lb., with a specific consumption of 2.2 lb./hr./lb. thrust. Originally, the compressor had six stages, but the production version, rated at 1,760 lb. thrust, had seven.

Whereas all the early production-type gas-turbines produced in Great Britain and, later, America, had radial compressors, German designers decided —quite independently, it would appear—to employ axial-flow compressors. This fact is interesting in view of Germany's wide experience with radial compressors for various purposes, apart from engine superchargers. The designers were convinced of the paramount necessity of ensuring the smallest possible diameter and thereby low drag, and were confident that, despite its liability to stall, the axial compressor would ultimately prove to be the more efficient.

It is obvious from an examination of Germany's gas turbines that design was adversely affected by the need to conserve vital alloys. One of the most outstanding efforts to overcome this handicap was the production of hollow turbine blades with internal passages for cooling air, fabricated from austenitic steel sheet. There was, of course, some loss in performance through diverting air from the compressor to cool the turbine in this way. Interesting experiments were being conducted on hollow water-cooled rotors and blades and also on blades of ceramic material. Variable area jet nozzles controlled by a " bullet," the use of a light Diesel oil (J2), as fuel and twin-cylinder two-stroke engines for starting, are features common to the three main types of German gas turbines (B.M.W. 003, Jumo 004 and HeS011).

It is worthy of mention that Germany's early development of jet propelled aircraft was greatly facilitated by the existence of numerous lavishly equipped experimental and research stations distributed around the countryside. The Luftfahrtforschunganstalt of the Hermann Goering Institute at Volkenrode had a staff of 1,200 scientists, technicians and engineers during the war. There were seven tunnels for investigation of aerodynamic problems, as well as supersonic wind tunnels for the study of laminar flow airfoils and of problems of rigidity and strength of materials. Equipment included four interferometers for the visual examination and recording of air flow on models under ultra high speed conditions.

In Munich, adjoining the B.M.W. works, there is a unique high altitude test chamber, 3.8 metres diameter and 7 metres long, suitable for testing large turbine or piston engines. In the autumn of 1945 the author was conducted over this test plant by the resident R.A.F. engineer officer and the German designer, Dr. C. L. Soestmeyer. With complete disregard for cost it was equipped and fully instrumentated for engine tests under simulated conditions at altitudes up to 50,000 ft. Air temperatures can be lowered to —65 deg. C. and wind velocities up to 560 m.p.h. are possible. (See also Chapter X). At the time of the visit British technicians had just arrived by air with a De Havilland Goblin jet propulsion unit for special tests under high altitude conditions and a Rolls-Royce Derwent followed. Apparatus of this character will be available in Great Britain in the course of a year or two.

B.M.W.

The 003 unit is smaller and lighter than the Jumo 004 and the thrust rather less (1,760 lb.). In layout it differs chiefly from the Junkers in having

Fig. 110.   B.M.W. 003 turbine-jet unit with seven-stage axial compressor.

a single annular combustion chamber with sixteen burners, a feature which permitted an overall diameter appreciably smaller than that of the Jumo (27.1in. against 30.4 in.). The single-stage turbine has hollow air-cooled stator and rotor blades and the adjustable " bullet " has internal cooling. Early experimental 003 units had six compressor stages but seven were standardised for production units and a new series was under development with eight stages (003D).

Figures from the B.M.W. works show that air to cool the hollow stator and turbine blades consumed about five per cent. of the compressor capacity. The compressor efficiency was said to be 78 per cent. and that of the turbine 79 per cent. A life of 50 hours between overhauls was claimed, after which the turbine required careful inspection. The writer counted 22 replaced blades in a single turbine wheel. The turbine rotor could be withdrawn and replaced in two hours without removing the complete unit from the aircraft. The total life of the combustion chamber was quoted as 200 hours.

It will be seen from the accompanying table of characteristics that developments of the standard B.M.W. 003A would have increased thrusts, but for use in special interceptor aircraft requiring immense power for climb a special unit, designated 003R, was developed. This was basically a standard 003A with the addition of a B.M.W. 718 bi-fuel liquid rocket giving a thrust of 2,700 lb. for a period of three minutes.

018

Designed in 1940 on the same general lines as the 003 this unit was to have a twelve-stage axial flow compressor, an annular combustion chamber and three-stage turbine running at 6,000 r.p.m. The thrust was to be 7,520 lb. Progress was delayed by our bombing but eventually a compressor was made and tested. As the Allied armies advanced this unit was deliberately destroyed.

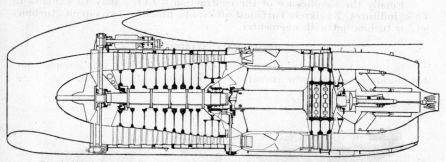

Fig. III. Arrangement of B.M.W. 018 designed to produce 7,520 lb. thrust.

028

It was proposed to modify an 018 unit to drive contra-rotating airscrews through planetary reduction gears from the main compressor shaft. A fourth turbine stage was to be added and 7,000 h.p. was expected at the airscrew.

Project 3306

Under design was a unit intended to develop a static thrust of 3,760 lb. It resembled the 003A as it had a 7-stage axial compressor and a single-stage turbine. Diameter was increased from 27 to 33½in. and weight from 1,344 to 1,980 lb. It was scheduled for testing in the summer of 1946.

Project 3307

This was a special expendable unit designed for very low cost of production and intended for the propulsion of large calibre projectiles. The designed thrust was 1,109 lb. and it had a total weight of 1,433 lb. Overall dimensions were 27in. diameter and 9ft. 5in. long.

DAIMLER–BENZ

Professor Leist developed the Daimler-Benz 007 (ZTL). It was tested in the autumn of 1943 but work was stopped by the German Air Ministry on the grounds of its over-complexity. Nevertheless, the unit was of great technical interest. A compressor and ducted fan were mounted on two contra-rotating drums, the inner directly driven by the turbine and the outer through gears at about half speed. The inner drum carried nine stages of compressor blading while the outer drum had eight stages of compressor blading internally and three stages of fan blading externally. The turbine rotor was cooled over 30 per cent. of its circumference by air drawn from the ducted fan circuit, the remaining 70 per cent. of the circumference receiving the working gases. Four tubular combustion chambers were used, and provision was made for a fifth in case it were found possible to reduce the amount of turbine cooling air.

The unit, which weighed 2,870 lb., was 15ft. 2in. long and $33\frac{1}{2}$in. in diameter. Under the designed conditions of operation, 550 m.p.h. at 19,000ft., the thrust was calculated as 1,363 lb. Other data are :—air mass flow through compressor, 17.6 lb./sec. ; air mass flow through fan, 35.2 lb./sec. ; fuel consumption 0.55 lb./lb./hr. Speed of turbine and inner compressor rotor, 12,000 r.p.m.

Finally the significance of the contraction " ZTL " may be explained. This indicates Zweikreis-Turbine-Luftstrahl—literally two-circuit turbine jet, or turbine jet with augmenter.

HEINKEL–HIRTH

Designed by Herr Ohain, the Heinkel-Hirth HeS 011 was intended for installation in several new aircraft types of widely differing design and is of

Fig. 112.   HeS 011 jet unit with two-stage turbine.

interest in that the compressor has three axial stages preceded by one " diagonal " stage which is partly axial and partly radial. An axial-flow inducer at the intake is another novel feature. The annular combustion chamber has sixteen " fingers " and sixteen injection nozzles ; the two-stage turbine has hollow blades. The adjustable " bullet " in the tail pipe has two positions only : fully " in " for idling and fully " out " for all other conditions. Thrust was 2,860 lb., speed 10,000 r.p.m., and weight 2,090 lb.

HeS 021

A reduction gear and propeller assembly had been developed for the 011, the new designation being as above. The output at the propeller was expected to be 3,300 h.p. at 560 m.p.h.

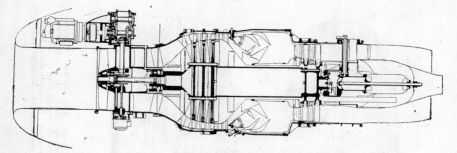

Fig. 113. General arrangement of Heinkel-Hirth HeS 011 turbine-jet.

JUNKERS

The most famous of all the German gas-turbines, Jumo 004, was backed by between 25,000 and 30,000 hours of bench-testing. When Germany collapsed over 5,000 units had been made and production was at the rate of 1,500 per month. The ultimate target was 3,000 per month.

It was claimed the efficiency of the compressor was 85 per cent. and of the turbine 79 per cent. To cool the turbine blades and guide vanes 7 per cent. of the compressor output was diverted.

After 30 hours service the whole power unit would be stripped for cleaning and overhauling of the compressor and for detailed inspection of the turbine wheel and combustion chambers. This work was remarkably simple and very cheaply carried out by women and slave workers. On about half the number of units overhauled a number of compressor rotor and stator blades needed replacement, due to damage from foreign bodies passing through the unit. Turbine blades were frequently cracked as a result of overheating occasioned by unskilled handling on the part of the pilots.

It was asserted by the Junkers firm that a new engine could be assembled in 50 man-hours and that a complete overhaul required 100 man-hours.

The Jumo 004 has an eight-stage axial-flow compressor and a large diameter single-stage turbine. The compressor casing, divided on an axial plane, is of

Fig. 114. Assembled rotor of Jumo 004 eight-stage axial compressor.

Fig. 115. Port side view and longitudinal section of Junkers Jumo 004 unit.

1, nose cowling. 2, oil tank. 3, entry casing. 4, auxiliary gear box. 5, compressor casing. 6, servo motor. 7, ignition apparatus. 8, control lever. 9, outer casing. 10, attachment points. 11, bullet control shaft. 12, exhaust casing. 13, annular fuel tank. 14, Riedel starter. 15, injection pump. 16, auxiliary drive. 17, oil pump. 18, oil filter. 19, front compressor bearing. 20, speed regulator. 21, compressor rotor. 22, fuel filter. 23, rear compressor bearing. 24, flame tube. 25, combustion-chamber muffle. 26, diffusing grill. 27, combustion chamber. 28, injection nozzle. 29, turbine entry casing. 30, turbine stator blades. 31, turbine. 32, forward turbine bearing. 33, rear turbine bearing with oil scavenge pump. 34, bullet-operating gears. 35, movable bullet. 36, bullet support.

cast magnesium, and stator blades are assembled in half rings and bolted into each casing half. The duralumin blades of the compressor are dovetailed into staggered grooves on the periphery of light-alloy discs and are fixed by grub screws through each root. Stagger of the blades increases and the chord decreases in successive stages through the compressor.

The entry guide vanes and first row of stator blades are of fairly thick airfoil-section light alloy, the second stator row being of thinner airfoil section, and the remainder of cambered sheet steel. The rotor is built up with two steel shafts attached to the outside faces of the first and last discs. The front compressor bearing comprises three ball races, each capable of supporting end thrust. The rear bearing consists of a single roller race.

Cooling air is bled off between the fourth and fifth compressor stages, and is led into the double skin surrounding the combustion chamber assembly. A small amount of air is allowed to pass into the space between the combustion chambers and the inner wall. Most of the air passes down a strut to circulate inside the " bullet " and to pass through small holes to cool the downstream face of the turbine disc. Some of this cooling air also passes into a double skin which extends to within about two feet of the final nozzle. After the last compressor stage air is bled off internally and is taken through tunnels in two of the casting ribs to cool the upstream face of the turbine disc. More air is taken through three tunnels in the central casting into the space between the two plate diaphragms in front of the turbine. Most of this air then passes into the hollow turbine nozzle guide vanes, emerging through slits in the trailing-edges of the vanes.

There are six combustion chambers, with interconnectors, disposed parallel to and evenly spaced aı)und the central casting carrying the rear

Fig. 116. Jumo 004 combustion chamber dissembled.

compressor bearing and the turbine shaft bearing. They are of aluminised mild steel sheet and are numbered 1 to 6 from the rear, No. 1 being horizontal on the left. Igniter plugs for initial combustion are in chambers 1, 3 and 5. A fuel injector in each chamber injects fuel upstream. Swirl vanes are fitted to the forward end of each chamber, with baffles at the rear, the hot gases passing through " slot mixers " formed in the rear side wall. The hot gases then mix with the air which by-passes the combustion chambers.

There are sixty-one sheet steel blades on the turbine rotor. Hollow air-cooled blades were adopted only because of the time factor in evolving suitable material to withstand the extremely high temperatures, and the necessity of conserving strategic alloying metals. These blades have forged box section roots and are fitted over lugs formed on the periphery of the disc and secured by a 5 mm. pin and a special soldering process.

Mounted in the tail pipe is a movable " bullet " operated by a servo-motor controlled from the throttle lever. A rack and pinion device moves

it longitudinally.   On the ground or idling in the air the " bullet " is fully
forward while the turbine is running up to 30 per cent. of the maximum
r.p.m.   Between 30 per cent. and 90 per cent. of maximum r.p.m. it is
moved rearwards to re-
duce the area of the jet
orifice.   At take-off it
is near the end of its
backward travel.   For
maximum performance
in flight, above 20,000ft.
and at 400 m.p.h., it is
moved to the extreme
rearward position to
provide maximum
thrust. The servo-motor
control is interlinked
with a capsule sensitive
to ram pressure, so that
the position of the
" bullet " is adjusted
according to the ram
pressure and conse-
quently to the forward
speed of the aircraft.

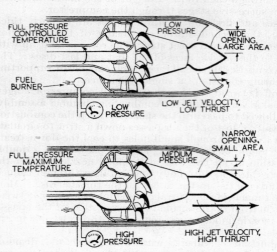

Fig. 117. Diagram showing influence of " bullet "
control of jet pipe orifice.

Oil is carried in an
annular nose tank.
There are two pressure
pumps, one of which
supplies oil to the
r.p.m. governor servo motor and compressor front bearing while the second
delivers oil to the rear compressor bearing and the two turbine rotor
bearings.

A Riedel flat twin two-stroke petrol engine for starting is mounted in
the air intake co-axially with the compressor shaft. From the cockpit it can
be started electrically, but on the ground manual starting by means of a cable
and pulley is possible. Particulars are :—bore 70 mm., stroke 35 mm.,
capacity 270 c.c., max. r.p.m. 10,000, output 10 h.p., weight 36 lb.

The complete propulsion unit is fixed at three pick-up points, two above
the rear compressor bearing, and one above the combustion chamber housing.
All pipe lines and electrical connections are brought to a small panel above
the compressor casing to facilitate installation. The simplified aircraft
instrument panel includes gauges for fuel injection pressure, exhaust gas
temperature, exhaust gas pressure, oil pressure, and an r.p.m. indicator.

The following table should be studied in conjunction with the main
particulars of the Jumo 004B included in the Table of data at the end of
the chapter.

HEIGHT (ft.)	SPEED (m.p.h.)	THRUST (lb.)	CONSUMPTION (lb./hour.)
0	273	1,605	2,920
0	560	1,890	3,680
8,200	273	1,300	2,290
8,200	560	1,600	2,920
36,000	335	572	1,080
36,000	560	715	1,275

Fig. 118. The 270 c.c. Riedel flat twin two-stroke engine for starting turbine units.

Jumo 012 and 022

In common with other firms, Junkers aimed to produce units of much greater output. The Jumo 012 was intended eventually for installation in the Ju 287 bomber. It had an 11-stage axial compressor and a two-stage turbine. Measuring about 17ft. in length this unit was to have a thrust of over 6,000lb. and to weigh about two tons. With contra-rotating airscrews and appropriate reduction gearing the 012 was to be designated as 022.

GERMAN GAS-TURBINES

UNIT	STATIC THRUST (lb.)	R.P.M.	CONSUMPTION (lb./lb./hr.)	COMPRESSOR	COMBUSTION CHAMBERS	TURBINE	LENGTH (ft.–in.)	DIAM. (in.)	WT. (lb.)
B.M.W. 003A	1,760	9,500	1.47	Axial-7	Annular-16 burners	Axial-1	10–5	27	1,344
003C	1,990	9,500	—	Axial-7	Annular-16 burners	Axial-1	9–1	27	1,344
003D	2,760	—	—	Axial-8	Annular-16 burners	Axial-2	10–5	27½	1,366
018	7,520	6,000	—	Axial-12	Annular-24 burners	Axial-3	13–11	49¼	5,080
HE-HIRTH HeS 011	2,860	11,000	1.31	Semi-Axial-1 Axial-3	Annular-16 burners	Axial-2	11–6	34	2,090
JUNKERS Jumo 004B	1,890	8,700	1.4	Axial-8	6	Axial-1	12–8	30½	1,585
Jumo 012	6,000	—	1.2	Axial-11	—	Axial-2	17–0	—	4,400

CHAPTER X

TESTING AND MAINTENANCE

IT may have occurred to the reader that some problems would be presented by the air-testing and development of early British gas turbine units. These were largely solved by converting a Wellington bomber to house a jet unit in the tail, in place of the turret. Later a Lancaster " Universal Test Bed " was also adapted to carry a unit in what was previously the bomb bay, the advantage being that any of a variety of units of different shape and dimensions could be slung very conveniently. The first unit to be tested in the Lancaster was the A.S.X. Fig. 119 shows a Metropolitan-Vickers axial-flow unit installed in the tail of a Lancaster. A feature of turbines is the rapidity with which they may be installed or removed.

Gas Turbines on the Test Bed

At least three different types of test houses are used by the De Havilland Company at Hatfield for their gas turbine engines. These include the early production beds, a later design, and the experimental test houses. In each case the arrangements are similar but the houses differ in detail and in type and quantity of instruments and equipment. Each production test

Fig. 119. A Lancaster flying test bed with a Metropolitan-Vickers turbine-jet in the tail. The intake is above the fuselage.

house is separate and self-contained and comprises basically the engine compartment, the control room and the exhaust tunnel, while in addition there are pump, filter, rectifier, tank and fan rooms. A turbine on its stand is wheeled in through a door in the near end of the exhaust tunnel, positioned on the floating test platform which is supported on rollers, and secured. A forked flexible air-intake duct is attached to the elephant's ears, pipe lines and controls are connected up and exhaust detuner duct and tail pipe guard are brought into position. It is a great deal simpler to install a jet engine and measure the thrust it produces than to set up a comparable airscrew unit for the measurement of shaft horsepower. The time taken for Goblin units is about two hours and removal takes 1½ hours.

Thrust is measured directly through the reaction of the unit or mounting against a statimeter transmitter button. The movement is very small—about ⅜in.—and the button on production beds is connected by capillary tubing to a Bourdon gauge registering in pounds thrust. A plate for contact with the button is now provided on the intake casing of the power unit ; previously this was placed on the engine cradle (a still later design provides for the transmitter button on the engine bearers). In connection with thrust measurement, a very simple dead-weight direct calibrating device has been installed. On the most modern beds Goblins are secured to a floating platform connected by a system of levers to a large Vandome and Hart weighing machine from which a direct thrust reading in pounds is obtained. The dial is large and carries two scales. A capacity-change lever selects the loading for the zero to 3,500 lb. or the zero and 6,000 lb. scale.

When the unit is running, temperatures, pressures and consumptions are observed and recorded in a sound-proofed control room in the same way as for any other type of engine. The particular system of stroboscopic engine-

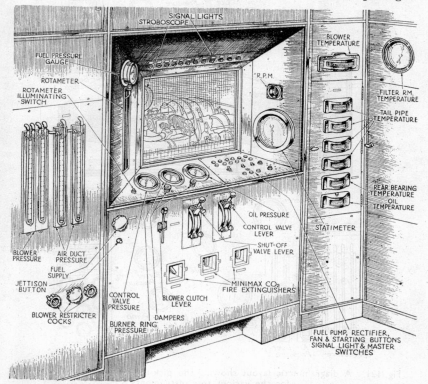

Fig. 120. The control room of the De Havilland test house described in the accompanying notes.

speed measurement on some beds is interesting and a little out of the ordinary. The set-up is the work of the De Havilland Company, and incorporated are a master tuning fork with electrically-controlled frequency and a three-aperture scanning disc, both in the engine compartment. The r.p.m. are indicated electrically in the control cabin and the scanning disc is observed through the double window to the engine compartment. When testing any power unit, the requirement is usually to run at predetermined engine speeds (as opposed to measuring r.p.m. for example at given throttle settings or combustion temperatures). The stroboscopic scanning disc gives accurate readings through its three apertures for thousands, hundreds and fractions of one hundred r.p.m.

Temperatures observed include those of the air-intake duct, compressor delivery, combustion chambers, jet pipe (at four points), rear and front bearings, oil sump, Heywood compressor, and for instrument correction, the control cabin and filter room temperatures. Among the pressures measured are those for diffuser, turbine, intake duct, impeller tip, tail pipe and vacuum

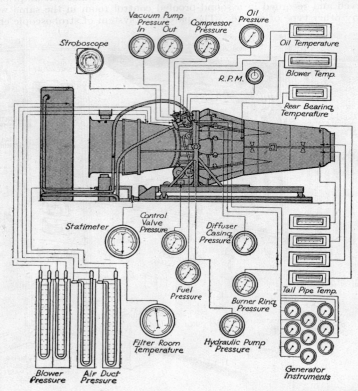

Fig. 121. A diagrammatic layout showing the pick-up points on a D.H. Goblin for the various test instruments.

pump. The main hydraulic pump is checked in conjunction with a loading valve up to 3,000 lb./sq. in., and the Marshall blower for pressure cockpit or cabin has a large receiving tank in the filter room.

With the exception of the exhaust tunnel the test houses are very compact. Intake air is conveniently drawn in through a large duct over the test cubicle and passes through " splitter " panels before entering the filter room. In that the engines must often inhale non-filtered air when installed in an aircraft they are expected to do so on test. The name filter room is, therefore, something of a misnomer for what is in effect a large intermediate compartment in the intake-air duct system.

At the end of the exhaust tunnel a brick blast wall is provided to deflect the jet vertically upwards.

The test schedule laid down for Goblins is as follows :—

(1) Preliminary adjustments and starting test.

(2) Non-stop run of two hours, consisting of 5 min. at idling speed, 1 hr. 45 min. at maximum cruising speed, 5 min. at climbing speed, and 5 min. under take-off conditions.

(3) Acceleration tests from idling speed to maximum r.p.m.

On completion of the preliminary tests the engine is stripped down, inspected and rebuilt.   It then goes through a final test consisting of :—

(1) A run of 15 min. at maximum cruising speed.

(2) Accelerations from idling speed to take-off r.p.m.

(3) Complete thrust calibration over the whole speed range.

High–altitude Test Chamber

The German B.M.W. " Herbitus " high-altitude test plant at Ober-weisenfeld in Austria, which, in its existing form, cost 6,000,000 marks, and was to be developed at a total cost of 9,000,000 marks, was inspected by the author on a visit to Munich after the war.

The layout of the piping associated with the plant is shown diagrammatically in Fig. 122 (top) and below is a chart indicating the corresponding pressure and temperature variations of the air as it passes through the unit.   A three-stage centrifugal compressor delivers air at about 2.5 atmospheres absolute, and expansion down to desired altitude conditions take place in a single-stage axial turbine, the corresponding temperature drop being controlled by two large water and brine coolers forming part of the plant.   Power recovered by the turbine is returned to the compressor so that the driving motor of the latter has only to make good the circuit losses.

The exhaust system comprises two four-stage centrifugal pumps which can be operated either in series or in parallel, depending on the altitude conditions required.

Illustrated in the centre of the diagram is the test chamber proper which consists of a steel cylinder about 12ft. in diameter and 30ft. long which can be evacuated to a static pressure equivalent to an altitude of 50,000 ft.   Air can be supplied to the intakes at 550 m.p.h. and temperatures down to — 65 deg. C. maintained.   The rear end is detachable to enable the unit on test to be wheeled in or out and a special cylindrical nose-piece, which slides freely inside elaborate packing on the main intake nozzle is provided.   An air supply of 11 lb./sec. under ground-level conditions keeps the exterior of the unit cool and prevents overheating of the auxiliaries and electric cables.

The recording room is entirely separated from the test house proper, and is a model of ingenuity and neatness.   Engineers in the control room adjoining the sealed engine chamber are able to peer through the periscope and to note frost encrustations on the exterior of the unit.

Service Notes

Hitherto there has been no authoritative statement on the subject of servicing gas turbines. The following notes by Squadron Leader R. Cracknell, M.B.E., A.M.I.Mech.E., were prepared for a talk before B.O.A.C. maintenance engineers.   The interest they aroused prompted considerable discussion and in reply to criticisms the author pointed out that they were written as a generalization on a variety of gas turbines and were not confined to any particular design. He found it difficult to accept a suggestion that "practically every defect " falls under the heading of " power losses," maintaining that

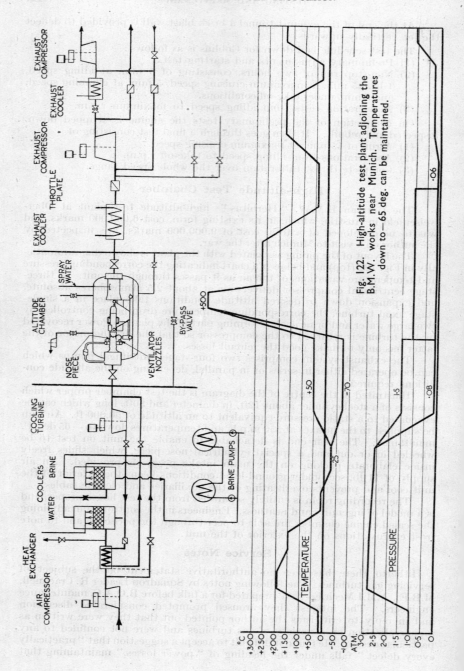

Fig. 122. High-altitude test plant adjoining the
B.M.W. works near Munich. Temperatures
down to −65 deg. can be maintained.

there are many defects which may arise, though seldom do, that have no direct bearing on power output. On the subject of propelling nozzle distortions he agreed that these were very rare on British gas turbines.

The gas turbine is very considerably simplified compared with the piston engine by virtue of the smaller number of moving parts. Absence of such components as magnetos, plugs, ignition harness and carburettors, together with the mechanical side including pistons, connecting rod bearings, valve gear, supercharger, airscrews and reduction gears confers obvious advantage.

In general, operating experience has proved this type of engine to be exceptionally trouble free and reliable. During the early days of development there were customary teething troubles, chiefly confined to the fuel system and bearings. There was also a period when the cracking of impeller blades was not an uncommon occurrence. The combustion assembly has remained fairly reliable throughout the development life of the engines which were cleared for flight, the chief trouble being confined to flame-tube distortion and, in the earlier days, carbon formation and coking troubles, customarily due to faulty burners. Turbine failures have, fortunately, always been very remote. Usually this only happened when the engine was undergoing trials of a severe character in the test chamber, when results were not unnaturally catastrophic.

The operating costs of a power plant take into account the primary costs attributed to labour and materials, plus the overhead charges pertaining to servicing and maintenance. When comparing these costs with those of the reciprocating power plant, it will be seen that the jet has many inherent advantages including appreciably reduced labour expenditure, due to the simplified maintenance, cheaper and safer fuels and, relevantly, insurance reductions concerning fire risks and compulsory precautions, quicker turn-arounds, representing increased flying hours available per unit period, and in addition high reliability.

The compressor and turbine rotor assembly and also the wheelcase drives for the various auxiliaries are now virtually trouble-free. The only remaining source of trouble is the fuel system, where periodically such components as the fuel pump or A.C.U. may need replacement, due to failure or internal maladjustment. (It has already been stated that the gas turbine is exceptionally trouble-free and reliable).

Jet engines are installed in airframes as complete units with the jet pipe detached from the exhaust cone, depending on the particular design. The engine mountings normally consist of two or three main trunnion bearers, and one front or rear mounting pick-up point with a tail support for the jet pipe, of hinge design, to allow for longitudinal expansion under running conditions. The following is a typical list of components to be connected.

(I) *Engine.*—(a) Fuel pipe to the engine pump and Altitude Control Unit or " over-speed " governor return; (b) fuel drain pipes from the fuel system; (c) electric starter motor and booster coil electrical connections ; (d) auxiliary drive to the accessory gear box (if fitted) ; (e) accessories and connections (where auxiliary gear boxes are not used); (f) fire extinguisher ring.

(II) *Controls.*—(a) Throttle and H.P. cock.

(III) *Instrumentations*—(a) Jet pipe temperature thermocouples ; (b) R.P.M. tachometer connections; (c) burner pressure fuel gauge connection ; (d) oil pressure and temperature connections.

It is normal to take a series of readings at cruising, climbing and maximum take-off r.p.m. conditions during the proof run for flight clearance after installation. The only adjustment normally found necessary during this proof run is the governor setting to give the desired maximum r.p.m. and the idling r.p.m. stop on the throttle by-pass.

Engine Changes

It is invariably quicker to change an engine installed in an aircraft than to rectify any major defects.   A typical period of installation life laid down for a gas turbine of centrifugal design at the present time is up to 180 hours. This, however, does not represent the life of the engine by any means, but rather a safe conservation pending further experience.   The useful life of a gas turbine may very well ultimately reach 1,000 flying hours without

Fig. 123. By reason of the absence of an airscrew the undercarriage of a jet-pro-pelled aircraft is exceptionally low and most servicing operations can be effected conveniently from ground level.

difficulty, particularly when not subjected to sudden inertia changes, as in the case of fighter aircraft.

Time-study investigation reveals a substantial saving in man hours for engine changes compared with the piston engine.   Broadly speaking there is about 70 per cent. saving in labour costs.

Daily Inspection

Daily servicing of a gas turbine compared with the orthodox reciprocating I.C. engine power plant is also in every way far simpler and less involved. The two chief sources of trouble experienced on the reciprocating engine are considered to be attributable to ignition and carburation.   Both these factors are non-existent in the gas turbine, while in the case of the simple jet engine there is the further elimination of the airscrew and its controls.

From the labour aspect a pronounced saving of man-hours is effected. To quote experience, the average time to complete a D.I. on a modern reciprocating power plant takes an experienced crew approximately 3½ man-hours (including all trades), whereas a D.I. on a Derwent, installed in a Meteor, for instance, can be completed in about 15–20 per cent. of this time, representing approximately 83 per cent. labour saving. The figures given are only an average and do not take into account any exceptional troubles which may be experienced.

A normal daily inspection on a jet turbine may be summarised to consist of an external examination for oil and fuel leaks, checking the correct level of the lubricating oil in the oil reservoir, viewing up the jet pipe (by torch or mirror reflection) for any signs of turbine blade damage or heat effect, and a " motoring " check for freeness of rotation (by operating the engine through the normal method of starting with the H.P. cock " off "). It is not normal to remove the main engine nacelle cowlings for D.I.s, and in certain instances ground run checks are not considered essential.

Minor Inspections

These are arranged to synchronise with the airframe inspection periods. This system has a direct reflection on the operating costs and flight planning of the aircraft. The average time taken to carry out a minor inspection on a centrifugal installation represents approximately 10–12 man-hours per power plant and does not necessitate removing the engine from the airframe. Such work occupies but a fraction of the time taken to complete the airframe inspection. Again by comparison, it shows a marked contrast to the reciprocating engine, which may take up to 60 man-hours.

A typical minor inspection for the centrifugal compressor gas turbine will include :—

(a) Impeller-blade inspection for signs of cracks, etc. (visual).

(b) Removal and partial inspection of the combustion assembly for distortion or flame tube buckling, also for any signs of carbon formation, due to fuel spray impingement or flame chilling.

(c) Air casing inspection (for distortion and fracture) (visual).

(d) Turbine nozzle guide vane inspection (visual). Jet pipe removed for the examination for cracks, blade distortion or local overheating.

(e) Turbine blade inspection (with jet pipe removed) for signs of fatigue cracks, buckling or loose blades.

(f) Turbine blade tip clearance check. It is normal to check the tip clearances at 45 deg. intervals around the periphery of the shroud ring to determine the minimum blade clearance. This action gives a mechanical check on the growth of the turbine disc and blades or distortion of the shroud ring. (Turbine blades usually carry a safety lip at the tip which is designed to give way in the event of a turbine " rub " Such troubles, however, are now very rare.) Conversely, excessive tip clearances are detrimental to the turbine efficiency since the gas leak rate is increased.

(g) Exhaust cone inspection for buckling and cracks.

(h) Oil scavenge filter inspection.

(i) L.P. and H.P. fuel filter inspection.

(j) General visual inspection of the engine.

Major Overhauls

These will necessitate the removal of the engine from the airframe and the carrying out of a complete strip for both visual and dimensional checking. In the past it has sometimes been found necessary to renew the flame tubes and refit new burners. Little deterioration is experienced with the main rotor assembly.

Ground Handling

Practically all ground equipment required for the normal servicing and maintenance of jet aircraft is standard. Typical items peculiar to jet engines (apart from the relevant tool kits and engine slings) may be considered to consist of high-capacity, close-mesh fuel filters from the Bowser supply to the aircraft fuel tanks, air intake and propelling nozzle covers to protect the compressor and turbine when not operating, and portable pyrometry test gear for thermo-couple testing.

Certain essential precautions are enforced in the interests of safety during all ground running of jet engines installed in aircraft, particularly during proof runs when the nacelle cowlings are not fitted. Apart from the discomfort of noise, it is unwise to approach the vicinity of the compressor intake when the turbine is operating under power, due to the high suction effect in the proximity of the air intake. Possible consequences may be serious to the individual and disastrous to the engine.

In this respect, loose items of clothing or articles are a great source of potential trouble. One-piece boiler suits are considered the ideal clothing for ground personnel engaged on this work. It is also highly recommended that all ground personnel associated with continual ground running of jet engines wear ear defenders for the protection of the ear drums from the high-frequency vibrations which are emitted during power running.

When carrying out ground runs it is most important that the compressor intake or intake duct is facing into wind. This is essential for three reasons : first to ensure that the exhaust gases do not recirculate to the air intake, which would have the detrimental effect of raising the jet pipe temperature (particularly emphasised at idling r.p.m.), the latter being dependent on the square of the intake temperature change ; secondly, cooling of the engine is assisted ; and thirdly, on shutting-down, the ram effect from the ambient air has the helpful result of purging the engine.

Observation should also be made to ensure that the exhaust gas stream has a clear path after emission. No area or objects subject to heat effect or deterioration should be in the path of the jet stream.

In preparing a jet engine for storage, the normal protective action is taken by inhibition spraying of the engine. It is unnecessary to carry out any special precautions other than the normal blanking, etc. Corrosive reaction is not present, since leaded fuels are not used. If practicable, it is advisable periodically to rotate the rotor to preserve the oil film on the moving components, though this is not considered absolutely essential.

Operational Faults and Rectifications

Due to the inherent simplicity of the simple gas turbine, it has been stated that little trouble is normally experienced concerning the servicing and operation compared with a modern reciprocating power plant. What troubles are experienced can be traced and analysed without much difficulty The troubles encountered may be separated into four main categories :—

(a) Failure to start.
(b) Rough running.
(c) Erratic operation.
(d) Incorrect jet pipe temperature indication.

Failure to Start

When a gas turbine fails to start there is little object in continuing the attempt. Actually it may prove disastrous by possibly producing an excessively hot start, or alternatively aggravating existing mechanical failure. The cause will invariably be traced to one of the following troubles :—

(1) *No Ignition.*—Elimination of the ignitor plugs, booster coils, electrical starter circuit and accumulator state will define this cause.

(2) *Insufficient Fuel Pressure to the Burners.*—Low fuel pressures may be due to one or more of the following causes : (a) A faulty fuel pump ; (b) excessive fuel leaks ; (c) an excess A.C.U. relief (if fitted) ; (d) failure of the pump valve or fuel accumulator to operate ; (e) insufficient r.p.m. to produce requisite fuel pressure and

mass flow ; (*f*) slow-running adjustment of the throttle by-pass set at too low a value ; (*g*) air in the fuel system.

Items (*b*) (*d*) and (*e*) will be indicated visibly, while (*a*) (*c*) (*f*) and (*g*) can be examined independently.

(3) *Insufficient r.p.m.*—This usually indicates a low voltage of the accumulator. It may also be caused by the starter motor not receiving full electrical power due to the energising solenoid resistance not breaking contact. Alternatively, the partial seizure of the rotor or an auxiliary drive may be the cause. (The r.p.m. indicator should first of all be checked for correct reading before suspecting any of the above faults unless they are obviously apparent.)

(4) *Mechanical Failure.*—It is seldom that the rotor (combining the compressor rotor or impeller and turbine) gives rise to any mechanical failure. It will be appreciated that this is more apt to happen when running under " power " conditions. This failure, however, is a very rare occurrence. Secondary mechanical failures include the fracture of auxiliary drives and gear trains affecting components such as H.P. fuel pump, starter motor, oil pressure and scavenge pumps and any auxiliary components.

Rough Running

As a gas turbine produces its power by rotation of the major components there is very little vibration compared with the reciprocating I.C. engine where high opposed inertia forces are present. There are in certain engines, however, the characteristic critical periods operating through certain ranges of r.p.m. which it is advisable to avoid in view of the resonance set up, which eventually may lead to an impeller or turbine blade failure in the form of fatigue. What little vibration does exist in a gas turbine is of very high frequency, around the order of r.p.m. cycles per second. If there are any signs of unusual roughness, this may possibly be due to the impeller and turbine rotor combination being out of dynamic balance, probably due to a partial failure of an impeller or turbine blade. Both these instances are of a serious character and necessitate a complete strip of the engine. Defective rotor bearings or auxiliary drive failures may also promote rough running.

Erratic Operation

Erratic running will be attributed in practically every instance to the fuel system, and in such cases it is customary to change either the throttle valve or the A.C.U. (if fitted). When the fuel system is incorporated with an " all-speed " governor, this unit will be suspect. In certain cases, erratic running may be due to one or more burners in the combustion system being choked, thus causing bad distribution ; this fault is usually indicated by viewing up the propelling nozzle from a distance while the engine is running and observing any local hot-spot areas which may be apparent around the annulus of the turbine blades.

Failure of the flame tubes of the combustion system will also produce erratic running plus a loss of power, usually indicated by a high burner pressure and a high jet temperature. A loss of power may be due to one or more of the following causes :—

(*a*) Insufficient burner pressure (indicated by a low jet pipe temperature).

(*b*) A faulty combustion system due to excessive carboning or failure of one or more flame tubes due to heat deterioration.

(*c*) Choked burners (indicated by high burner pressure and a drop in maximum r.p.m.).

(*d*) Excessive clearance of the impeller to the impeller casing, allowing a large pressure loss.

(*e*) An aerodynamic breakdown of the turbine nozzle guide vanes or turbine blades.

(*f*) Gas leaks at the turbine shroud exhaust cone joints or jet pipe.

(*g*) Distortion of the propelling nozzle.

(*h*) Partially seized bearings.

Fig. 124.   Accessibility of the Goblin turbine-jet unit is an outstanding feature of the D.H. Vampire fighter.

High Jet Pipe Temperature

May be due to one or more of the following causes :

(a) Faulty Pyrometry.—In the event of the instrumentation being at fault this can be checked by introducing a master thermocouple, which has a known calibration, into the jet pipe.

(b) Engine Overspeeding.—This will be indicated on the r.p.m. counter and also by a high burner pressure.

(c) Partially Blocked Compressor Intake.—This causes a high fuel/air ratio.

(i) Running the engine with the aircraft heading out of wind, so causing the hot exhaust gases from the propelling nozzle to recirculate and re-enter the air intake.

(ii) Turbine Cooling Air.—At fault, causing excessive blade temperatures.

(d) Faulty combustion, such as buckled or partially collapsed flame tubes or a heavy gas leak, causing a high F/A ratio.

(e) A falling-off in compressor performance.

High jet-pipe temperatures must be investigated without delay.   On this depends the life and safety of the engine.   Short bursts of high jet-pipe temperature may be permitted on certain engines for a matter of seconds, particularly when starting, but this condition should never be allowed to continue to any saturation point.   When an engine has been subjected to overheating, particular attention should be given to the turbine blading for any indication of temperature fretting or distortion.   These faults are only a general appreciation.   Each particular type will necessarily have its own peculiarities.

CHAPTER XI

CURRENT TYPES OF TURBINE-PROPELLED AIRCRAFT

DUE note having been taken of pioneer aircraft powered with gas turbines it will now be useful to review the characteristics and performances of modern types. In view of the high speeds attainable with the turbine power plant it is not surprising that with two exceptions these aircraft were designed primarily as fighters. Heavy bombers and large civil air liners, as well as mail planes and freighters, are imminent or on the way.

Regrettably, it is not yet possible to mention any Russian machines using gas turbines, though Soviet designers are known to have been studying this class of power plant since before the war and are now able to draw on the wide experience of German technicians. Japan too was busily developing jet-propelled aircraft based upon German types when hostilities ceased.

The advanced state of development achieved in five years is an impressive tribute to the inherent simplicity of the gas turbine and the surprising ease with which the unit in its various forms can be incorporated in new designs of aircraft. Among the new types reviewed are examples of aircraft with turbine-airscrew as well as turbine-jet units. The desirability of " mixing " power units in this manner on a single aircraft was discussed in previous editions of this book. Other examples are in the development stage.

GREAT BRITAIN

De Havilland Vampire

This remarkably successful fighter has a single Goblin II turbine-jet of 3,000 lb. thrust and with full operational equipment, including four 20 mm. cannon, attains a top speed of 540 m.p.h. This figure has been handsomely exceeded during development flying, but it can be taken as the Vampire's normal " guaranteed " maximum at 20,000 feet—neither the outcome of any special modification, nor the result of designing an aircraft for a high maximum speed at the expense of other considerations. The installation of a De Havilland Ghost of 5,000 lb. thrust further improves performance.

The Vampire's wing loading—32 lb./sq. ft. at normal operational weight —is very low for the class, and is, in fact, some 10 to 12 lb. less than that of the Mosquito and Hornet. The effects of this moderate loading, coupled with very good control response at all speeds, can be seen in the Vampire's astonishing qualities of manoeuvre and comparatively low landing approach speed.

From the operational viewpoint the layout of this single-jet fighter has considerable advantages. The rear position of the unit gives the pilot an excellent view, even when approaching to land slowly under power. The absence of an airscrew makes the nose wheel a practical proposition, while the " pusher " layout enables the armament to be mounted in the fuselage ; the guns do not, therefore, need to be harmonised for a particular point of impact. Finally, the use of the turbine jet power unit means that no time need be wasted in warming-up prior to take-off.

It might have been imagined that a " pusher " design would have involved the designers in difficult problems concerning centre-of-gravity location ; in fact, such a layout could hardly have been practicable with a normal piston engine and airscrew. However, the low weight of the unit, coupled with the fact that heavy items, such as the cannon, can be carried well forward of the c.g., has made the design not only practicable but even congenial.   The total " fuselage " structure is claimed to be lighter than any more conventional layout of a shape and size necessary to provide a jet outlet.   Locating and shaping the necessarily large air intakes was not easy, but with the layout adopted something like 90–95 per cent. of available ram effect has been utilised without encountering any specially difficult airflow repercussions.   The fact that the Goblin compressor is of the " single-sided " type considerably simplified the positioning of the intakes.

Although, with its boomed tail, the Vampire may appear strikingly unconventional (and it is certainly ingenious in conception) the detail construction is quite straightforward.   The entire aircraft is, so to speak, built around a simple nacelle unit with its power plant and wing attachments and

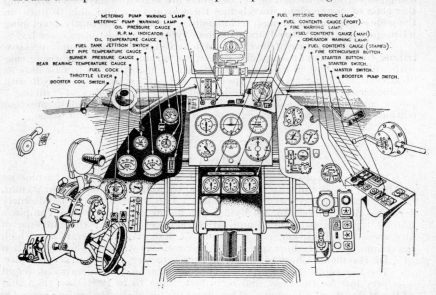

Fig. 125.   The cockpit layout of the D.H. Vampire fighter, showing the simplicity of instrumentation attainable in a single-jet aircraft.

its intake duct system.   The nacelle itself is constructed, on familiar Mosquito lines, of balsa wood sandwiched between plywood sheet, and is made in two half-shells with joints along the top and bottom centre-lines.   The wing is sharply tapered in plan and thickness and has an N.P.L. section designed to give the least possible drag at high speeds while retaining good low-speed characteristics.

There is nothing unusual about either the controls or the tab arrangement.   The split flaps are in four portions and can be set at an angle up to 80 deg.   Further outboard are the air brakes which can be applied at any speed up to 500 m.p.h.

Fuel in the Mk. I Vampire is carried in three tanks—one in the nacelle and one in each wing.   These last can be either of the 50 or 100-gallon size and are continuously pressurised.   The Mk II version has extra tankage outboard of the undercarriage wells.

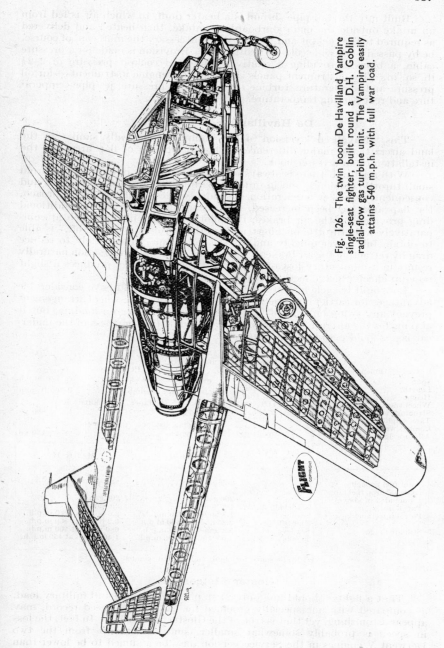

Fig. 126. The twin boom De Havilland Vampire single-seat fighter, built round a D.H. Goblin radial-flow gas turbine unit. The Vampire easily attains 540 m.p.h. with full war load.

Built into the tail pipe shroud is a heater muff, to which air is fed from an intake outside the main starboard air intake, then heated and delivered as required to the cockpit and guns. When necessary the muff can, of course, be by-passed to provide cold-air ventilation. Provision is made for a pressure cabin, a blower providing a relatively increased cockpit pressure of 2–2½ lb./sq. in. The instrument panels carry only six engine instruments—for oil pressure and temperature, turbine r.p.m., burner pressure, jet pipe temperature and rear bearing temperature.

De Havilland Sea Vampire

This " Navalised " version of the Vampire is basically similar to the land aircraft, the major differences being an increase of flap area and the installation of an arrester hook.

With a jet unit there is always some slight delay in power build-up from small throttle openings, and in order to permit high turbine revolutions and consequently quicker acceleration if suddenly needed during the approach, the flap area has been increased. By using full flap, with the additional drag provided by the air brakes, the pilot can make his approach at comparatively wide throttle openings, and, in the event of a " wave-off," is able to obtain full power quickly and, at the same time, immediately to reduce drag by retracting the air brakes. The result of air-brake retraction naturally results in a momentary loss of lift, but, at the same time, produces a slight nose-up effect which effectively cancels out the loss.

Low-built tricycle aircraft such as the Vampire should have considerable advantages for carrier operation. Not only does the nose-wheel arrangement prevent any swing on take-off and ballooning tendencies on landing, but it also makes the aircraft easier to manhandle, while the shortness of the under-carriage should permit simpler stowage.

D.H. 100 VAMPIRE
GOBLIN II TURBINE JET.

Dimensions and Weights :		Performance :	
Span	44ft.	Maximum speed (20,000ft.) ...	540 m.p.h.
Length	30ft. 9in.	Initial rate of climb ...	4,200 ft./min.
Height	8ft. 10in.	Take-off distance to 50ft. at	
Wheel track	11ft. 3in.	10,298 lb.	850 yd.
Structure weight	2,517 lb.		
Tare weight	6,372 lb.	Landing distance from 50ft. at	
Combat weight	8,578 lb.	8,578 lb.	1,150 yd.
All-up weight	10,298 lb.		

	FUEL AND RANGE		MARK I	MARK II
Total fuel capacity ...	—		402 gal.	554 gal.
External drop fuel tank (included in above)	—		200 gal.	200 gal.
Patrol duration ...	Sea level	...	1.8 hours	2.6 hours.
Patrol duration* ...	Sea level	...	1.8 hours at 270 m.p.h.	2.6 hours at 270 m.p.h.
	30,000ft.	...	2.25 hours at 400 m.p.h.	3.2 hours at 400 m.p.h.
Still air range ...	Sea level	...	500 miles at 400 m.p.h.	680 miles at 400 m.p.h.
	30,000ft.	...	1,050 miles at 450 m.p.h.	1,400 miles at 450 m.p.h.

* With allowance for climb and 15 min. combat.

Gloster Meteor IV

That a fighter should lose only 21 m.p.h. by carrying full military load, as compared with one specially groomed for the world's speed record, may appear astonishing, yet that is true of the Gloster Meteor IV. In fact, the loss in speed is probably somewhat smaller, since the thrust from the two Derwent V engines in the Service version may be assumed to be lower than that available in the 606 m.p.h. record machine, the power units of which, though capable of 4,000lb. thrust, were throttled back to deliver 3,600 thrust lb. during the record flights.

In the Service Meteor IV the two Derwent V units deliver a static thrust at sea level of 3,500lb. each.   The total thrust from the two at full power gives the machine the impressive speed of 585 m.p.h. at sea level and 560 m.p.h. at 30,000ft.   At the former speed, with the power units giving 7,000lb. thrust, the equivalent thrust horse-power is no less than 10,920 h.p. To obtain the same thrust from piston engines driving airscrews would require,

Fig. 127. The Gloster Meteor IV single-seat fighter with two Rolls-Royce Derwent V radial-flow gas turbine units. In Service trim the Meteor IV attains 585 m.p.h. at low altitudes and climbs to 30,000ft. in five minutes.

allowing an airscrew efficiency of 80 per cent., no less than 13,650 b.h.p. The tremendous thrust has a great effect on climb as well as on speed, as is obvious from the fact that a height of 30,000ft. is reached in five minutes. Coupled with this remarkable rate of climb is a service ceiling of 50,000ft. at a weight of 13,000lb.   By the time some of the fuel has been consumed, and the weight has been reduced to 12,600lb., the service ceiling has gone up to 52,000ft., which is well into the stratosphere.

By way of comparison, and to show how great is the effect of increased thrust, it will be of interest to quote a few figures for the older Gloster Meteor III.   Its loaded weight was 12,200lb. and the power units gave a static sea-level thrust of 1,950lb. each, producing a maximum sea-level speed of 460 m.p.h.   The maximum rate of climb at sea level was 4,000ft./min., the time to 30,000ft. being 11.5 minutes, and the service ceiling just over 40,000ft.   The take-off run to clear a 50ft. obstacle was 1,000 yards.

At an economical cruising speed of 350 m.p.h. at 30,000ft. and with 275 gallons of fuel, the range of the Meteor IV is 500 miles, which corresponds to 0.55 gal./ml. or 1.8 miles per gallon—a very reasonable figure when allied to the speed.   This means that the hourly fuel consumption is just over 190 gallons for the two units.   The aircraft is designed for an ultimate tankage of 330 gallons (giving a cruising range of 585 miles), in addition to a ventral drop tank of 180 gallons.   Making allowance for the climb to 30,000ft., the extreme range should be about 800 miles.

Structurally the Meteor IV is of orthodox design and of normal stressed-skin construction.   A prominent feature is the high setting of the tailplane ; this is necessary to get it clear of the jet streams, but has the disadvantage of splitting the rudder into an upper and a lower part.   The wing is of normal two-spar construction and is divided into a centre-section and two outer portions, the latter being attached just outboard of the turbine-jet units.

Another interesting feature is the mounting of the two power units. They are located between centre-section ribs, and are carried on trunnion-type side mountings, one of which is free to float sideways to allow for expansion. At the rear, the power unit is steadied by a " diamond " bracing which also allows expansion.

The main self-sealing fuel tank, of 330 gallons capacity, is carried in the fuselage behind the pilot and is divided into halves. Each compartment of the tank normally feeds one engine, but there is an interconnecting balance cock which is normally closed. Fuel is fed to the burners by electric and engine-driven pumps.

The armament of four belt-fed 20 mm. cannon is grouped in the forward part of the fuselage with the four ammunition boxes behind the pilot. Provision is made for a pressure cabin.

GLOSTER METEOR IV
TWO ROLLS-ROYCE DERWENT V TURBINE JETS

Dimensions		Performance	
Wing span	43ft.	Take-off over 50ft. (max. weight) ...	720 yards.
Length	41ft.	Landing over 50ft. (light weight) ...	740 yards.
Wing area	374 sq. ft.	Take-off speed (maximum weight)	115 m.p.h.
Height	13ft.	Landing speed (light weight) ...	95 m.p.h.
		Climb to 30,000ft.	5 mins.
Weights and Loadings		Service ceiling (maximum weight)	50,000ft.
Tare weight	9,880 lb.	Service ceiling (mean weight)	52,000ft.
Maximum weight	13,900 lb.	Economical cruise at 30,000ft. ...	350 m.p.h.
Mean weight...	12,580 lb.	Range with 275 gal.	500 miles.
Wing loading at maximum weight 37.2 lb./sq.ft.		Range with 330 gal.	585 miles.
		Range with 455 gal.	820 miles.

All ranges quoted are at an operational height of 30,000ft., and allowance has been made for the fuel used in reaching that height.

U.S.A.

Fig. 128. The American Bell XP-83 single-seat fighter with two General Electric I-40 radial-flow units. This aircraft is exceptionally large for a fighter and weighs over 27,000 lb.

Bell XP-83

An experimental long-range fighter with two General Electric 1–40 units, this all-metal mid-wing monoplane has a span of 53ft., and weighs about twelve tons. The turbine-jet units are mounted under the wing, snug against the fuselage. A tricycle undercarriage is used and the high-set tailplane has a dihedral angle in order to clear the jet effluxes.

Consolidated–Vultee XP–81

This new long-range fighter with twin power plants is of exceptional interest because the tractor airscrew is driven by a gas turbine while a separate gas-turbine jet unit is installed in the rear of the fuselage.   The speed should be greatly in excess of 500 m.p.h., in view of an announcement that the combination of power units can produce virtually as much power as all four engines of a B–29 Superfortress (8,800 h.p.)   The XP–81 is a comparatively large aircraft for a fighter, having a span of 55ft. 6in., a wing area of 425 sq. ft. and a flying weight of 19,500–22,000lb.   For cruising over long ranges the machine uses the turbine-driven airscrew alone, and in the main the rear jet is employed only when a very high speed is required.

Fig. 129.   The Consolidated-Vultee XP-81 has, in addition to a General Electric TG-100 turbine airscrew unit, an I-40 jet unit in the rear of the fuselage.

The pilot is seated above and slightly aft of the forward power unit— a General Electric TG-100 of the axial-flow compressor type.   The rear unit is a General Electric I-40, similar to that used in the Lockheed Shooting Star, with radial-flow compressor.   Apart from driving the airscrew the front unit gives a certain degree of jet propulsion, the turbine exhaust gases being ejected through a pipe projecting through the underside of the fuselage approximately amidships.

Before the TG-100 unit was installed, the XP-81 was tested in flight with a Rolls-Royce Merlin engine mounted in the nose.   In that form, therefore, it resembled the Ryan Fireball (described later).   The TG-100 unit is much more powerful than the Merlin, but of lower specific weight, and so the weights of the two units may have been sufficiently alike to bring the c.g. into the correct position with either.   The weight of the I-40 unit so far aft has obviously made it necessary to push the front unit farther forward than is usual in relation to the wing, hence the long nose of the XP-81.   The fin and rudder do not appear to be above normal size to counteract the forward " fin effect " of the long nose and the large four-bladed airscrew.

The wing is of orthodox plan form but its aerofoil section is one of the new N.A.C.A. laminar-flow types, and in order to get the surface as smooth as possible, the skin is of heavy gauge so that no dimpling occurs at the rivets, the heads of which are milled.   In this way, it is claimed, no painting or other treatment is necessary to fill in depressions.   Thermal de-icing is used for the wing and tail leading-edges, and is provided by the heat from the TG-100 exhaust.

Structurally the fuselage is of orthodox type, with semi-monocoque construction and flush-riveted skin plating.   A bubble-type canopy cover the pilot's cockpit and is arranged to slide back, either to the extreme of its travel or to intermediate stops. A device will be fitted for catapulting the pilot from his cockpit in case of emergency. The pilot's cabin is pressurised by the air from the TG-100 compressor, and refrigeration is also provided, so that conditions can be kept comfortable regardless of altitude or climate. An automatic pilot is installed, in view of the long ranges for which the machine might be used.

The large air scoops formed on the sides of the fuselage supply the I-40 jet unit in the tail; the TG-100 obtains its air through an annular scoop around the airscrew reduction gear. The normal supply of fuel for the two power units is carried in tanks just aft of the pilot's compartment. For long-range operation provision has been made to carry external drop-tanks.

Design of the XP-81 began in September, 1943. The first test flight with the Merlin installed in the nose was made on February 11th, 1945, and the first flight with the TG-100 unit on December 21st, 1945.

Lockheed P–80A (Shooting Star)

Apart from the Bell Airacomet trainer the P80 is the first jet-propelled fighter to be adopted by the U.S. Army Air Forces. The Shooting Star is a single-jet monoplane of very clean aerodynamic form. Although it has a much higher performance than the twin-engine Lightning and mounts approximately the same armament, the production manhours are about half those of the Lightning, due largely to the simplicity of the single-jet installation. The Shooting Star was originally designed for a British

Fig. 130. "Nostril" intakes are a feature of the Lockheed P-80A Shooting Star fighter, now a standard type in service with the U.S. Army Air Forces. The power unit is a General Electric I-40.

de Havilland H.I. turbine jet unit supplied in July, 1943. The prototype was designed, built and flown in just over twenty weeks.

The General Electric I-40 radial-flow turbine jet unit is now installed in the central portion of the fuselage, with "nostril" intakes on each side, projecting forward of the leading-edges of the wing. The subtle shaping of the intake ducts indicates that the form and location of these items must have been very critical. The rear section of the fuselage, which includes the jet nozzle, is readily removable and the complete power plant can be changed in twenty minutes. Self-sealing fuel tanks are installed in the wing and a jettisonable tank can be carried on each wing tip. This unusual

Fig. 131. The cockpit of the Lockheed P-80A Shooting Star. Canopy pressure is automatically reduced when the gun firing switch is operated, to prevent injury to the pilot from decompression should the cockpit be pierced by enemy fire.

location is accounted for by the necessity for not interrupting the air flow over the wing. It also gives additional ground clearance.

It has a pressurised cabin for pilots wearing G-suits and a particularly interesting feature is the provision for automatically reducing the cockpit pressure when the gun-firing switch is operated. This is intended to prevent injury to the pilot from sudden decompression should the bubble type canopy be pierced by enemy fire.

Six 0.5in. machine guns are installed in the nose, but can be replaced by photographic equipment for reconnaissance duties. The low cantilever wing is of laminar-flow section with knifelike leading-edge and the ailerons are fitted with hydraulic boosters to improve control. Manoeuvrability is assisted by electrically operated flaps.

The span of the Shooting Star is 38ft. 10in., length 34ft. 6in., height 11ft. 4in., and wing area 337 sq. ft. Empty and maximum weights are 8,000 and 14,000 lb. respectively and the claimed top speed is over 550 m.p.h. The ceiling is over 40,000ft.

McDonnell–FD.I–Phantom

The first " straight " jet-propelled fighter to be acquired by the U.S. Navy this design uses two Westinghouse axial-flow units mounted in the deep wing roots. The span is 40ft. (16ft. folded) and the gross weight under 10,000 lb. A speed of " over 500 " m.p.h. is claimed and the range exceeds 1,000 miles.

Republic XP–84

Although data on this design are restricted, general features are apparent in the accompanying photographs. The general resemblance to the pioneer Gloster E.28/39 is immediately evident, although the design is more refined to permit a higher performance to be obtained from the single axial-flow

Fig. 132. A modern single-jet fighter of exceptional aerodynamic cleanness, the Republic XP-84 has a General Electric turbine-jet with axial-flow compressor.

General Electric turbine-jet unit. Aerodynamically the XP-84 is perhaps the cleanest aircraft ever built. The wing appears to be exceptionally thin, even according to modern standards.

Ryan FR–I Fireball

In this new American deck-landing fighter there is a conventional radial engine (1,350 h.p. Wright Cyclone) in the nose driving a tractor airscrew and a turbine-jet unit (General Electric I.16) in the rear of the fuselage. But for the jet discharge nozzle in the tail of the fuselage it is impossible to distinguish the Fireball as a jet-propelled type ; the intakes for the jet unit are in the leading-edge and might easily be misjudged as oil radiators.

Fig. 133. For maximum speed the Ryan FR-1 deck-landing fighter has a General Electric I-16 turbine jet unit in addition to the Wright Cyclone radial piston engine.

The U.S. Navy and the Ryan Company combined to produce in the FR-1, a carrier-based fighter with first-class performance and combat characteristics together with economical cruising for duration and range. Stability and good vision for landing and simple handling on the deck were further requirements. The Fireball can fly and land on either engine singly and, of course, gives its best performance using both in unison.

For cruising at all normal altitudes, the nine-cylinder air-cooled Cyclone engine is used alone. This particular type of engine was chosen for economy and reliability, and its compactness and close cowling, together with the distribution of engine weights, allows the pilot to be placed forward of the leading-edge. In this way better forward visibility is obtained than if the entire power output was taken in the more normal American manner from a single large radial engine.

Flying on the front engine alone, the maximum speed of the Fireball is about 320 m.p.h. and at a speed of 207 m.p.h. the greatest range is 1,500 miles. The maximum speed using the jet unit alone is about 300 m.p.h., depending on altitude and speed at which the jet takes over. With both power units the top speed should be about 425 m.p.h.

Two fuel tanks of 125 and 51 gallons capacity, are carried in the fuselage, and an external, jettisonable tank holding 100 gallons can be mounted under the starboard wing. These three tanks feed either or both units. The very low percentage of the total power required for cruising gives the Fireball its unusually long range. The use of a common high-octane fuel for the turbine as well as the piston engine is a noteworthy departure which simplifies replenishments in service use.

GERMANY
Arado AR 234B

During the last phase of the war the Germans operated considerable numbers of this type of twin-engine bomber and reconnaissance aircraft. Potentially it could carry one 2,200 lb. bomb under the fuselage and one 1,100 lb. bomb under each gas-turbine nacelle; in service only the fuselage

F

bomb was carried. To illustrate how undesirable it is to hang external loads
on a high-speed jet aircraft it may be mentioned that the full external bomb
load reduced the maximum speed by 60 m.p.h.

The Ar. 234B is a shoulder-wing cantilever monoplane with a tricycle
undercarriage retracting into the fuselage. Two Junkers Jumo 004 axial-
flow gas turbine units are mounted in underslung nacelles on the wing. The
fuel tanks, with a capacity of 836 gallons, are in the fuselage and drop-tanks
can be carried as alternatives to the outboard bombs. Rockets for assisting
take-off can be attached under the wings outboard of the nacelles.

ARADO AR 234B
TWO JUNKERS JUMO 004 TURBINE-JET UNITS

Dimensions					Weights	
Span	...	...	...	... 47ft. 4in.	Normal flying weight	18,500 lb.
Length	...	...	...	... 41ft. 7in.	Maximum permissible weight (with-out A.T.O.)	19,500 lb.
Height	...	...	...	... 13ft. 8½in.	Maximum permissible weight (with	
Wing area	...	...	...	... 298 sq. ft.	A.T.O.)	22,000 lb.

Performance

Maximum speed	470 m.p.h. at 19,700ft.
Service ceiling	37,700ft.
Take-off run (unassisted with 3,300 lb. in bombs)	1,950 yd.
Take-off (assisted with 3,300 lb. in bombs)	940 yd.

Arado AR 234C

This is a development of the Ar 234B fitted with four BMW 003 turbine-
jet units paired under the wing. A maximum speed of 546 m.p.h. is reached

Fig. 134. The Arado Ar 234C was a promising four jet-bomber under development in Germany. The power units are BMW 003.

at 20,000ft. The rate of climb at sea level is 3,600 ft./min. and the service
ceiling is 37,700 ft. At full thrust, without drop tanks, the endurance is
40 minutes, but using 60 per cent. thrust endurance is increased to 1 hour
25 minutes.

Heinkel HE 162

The so-called Volksjaeger (" People's Fighter ") was designed for quick
production and utilising as little as possible of structural materials in short
supply. The design is chiefly interesting in that the turbine-jet unit is mounted
above the fuselage.

The wooden wing is built in one piece and is attached to the fuselage by four bolts. Semi-monocoque construction is used for the fuselage, which is of flush-riveted duralumin except for the plywood nose. The cone which carries the tail unit may be moved in flight to adjust tailplane incidence. The tailplane has a marked dihedral angle and the twin fins and rudders are mounted at right-angles to it. The narrow-track tricycle undercarriage retracts into the fuselage.

Fig. 135. A single BMW 003 unit is mounted above the fuselage of the Heinkel He 162 Volksjaeger fighter, operated in smaller numbers by Germans towards the end of the war. The pilot has a catapult seat.

The single BMW 003 gas turbine unit is mounted centrally on top of the fuselage on three attachment fittings and is fed from fuel tanks in the fuselage and wings.

The armament is two 20 mm. or two 30 mm. guns mounted low in the sides of the fuselage.

HEINKEL HE 162
ONE BMW 003 TURBINE-JET

Dimensions					Weights		
Span	...	...	...	23ft. 7¾in.	Normal all-up weight	...	...	5,480 lb.
Length	...	...	...	29ft. 8½in.	All-up weight with maximum fuel...	5,940 lb.
Wing area	...	...	...	120 sq. ft.			

Performance

	SEA LEVEL	19,700FT.	36,000FT.	38,400FT.
Maximum speed (m.p.h.) ...	490	522	485	—
Rate of climb at mean wt. ...	4,200 ft./min.	2,460 ft./min.	690 ft./min.	—
Time for climb at mean weight ...	—	6.6 min.	20 min.	—
Full throttle range, normal fuel...	136 miles ...	267 miles ...	410 miles ...	434 miles
Full throttle range, maximum fuel	242 miles ...	—	620 miles ...	—
Full throttle endurance normal fuel	20 min. ...	33 min. ...	67 min. ...	—
Full throttle endurance, max. fuel	30 min. ...	—	85 min. ...	—
Ceiling at mean weight ...	39,400ft. ...	—	—	—
Take-off run, normal fuel ...	710 yards ; with A.T.O. units—350 yards			
Take-off run, maximum fuel ...	875 yards ; with A.T.O. units—415 yards			
Landing speed	102 m.p.h. ...	—	—	—

Messerschmitt ME 262A

The Me 262A-1 is a fighter with four 30 mm. guns and the A-2 a bomber with two guns. Many variants were developed, including two-seater night fighters.

The Me 262A is of all-metal construction with a swept-back single-spar

Fig. 136. The first military aircraft with gas turbine units to be put into operation was the Messerschmitt Me 262 powered with Junker 004 gas turbine units. The top speed of the fighter version was 525 m.p.h. at 23,000ft.

cantilever wing having automatic slots along the entire leading-edge. The fuselage is composed of four main sections and carries four fuel tanks, two of 198 gal. capacity, one of 38 gal. and one of 132 gal. The undercarriage is of tricycle design and the pilot's cockpit is in the centre of the fuselage. Armament is grouped in the nose and bombs or drop-tanks are carried externally beneath the fuselage.

The twin Jumo 004B axial-flow gas-turbine units are mounted in nacelles slung beneath the wing.

MESSERSCHMITT ME 262A
Two Jumo 004 Turbine-Jet Units

Dimensions		Weights	
Span	41ft.	Flying weight (522 gal. of fuel and	
Length	34.9ft.	full fighter load)	15,500 lb.
Height	12.7ft.	Flying weight (528 gal. of fuel,	
Wing area	234 sq. ft.	two guns and 2,200 lb. of bombs)	15,400 lb.

Performance			
Maximum speed 525 m.p.h. at 23,000ft.		Take-off run (unassisted)	1,090 yd.
Service ceiling (11,450 lb.) ... 39,400ft.		Take-off run (2 A.T.O. rockets each	
Climb to 26,300ft. ... ... 11 min.		of 1,100 lb. thrust)	655 yd.

Fig. 137. The prototype of the Junkers Ju 287 jet-propelled bomber which had a swept-forward wing. The aircraft shown has four Jumo 004, but various power unit combinations were later to be tried.

Junkers Ju 287

Two prototypes of this unusually interesting jet-propelled bomber were built during the war. The design is notable for its swept-forward wing, adopted primarily in order that the bomb bay should not be obstructed by the spar.

Although it was ultimately intended to fit either six BMW 003, four Heinkel Hirth 001 or two BMW 018 jet units, the first aircraft had four Jumo 004s, mounted two beneath the wing and two attached to the sides of the fuselage. The operational crew was to comprise a pilot, bomb aimer-navigator, and wireless-operator-gunner.

JUNKERS Ju 287
SIX BMW 003 TURBINE-JET UNITS

Dimensions		Weights	
Span ... ... 66ft.		Normal all-up weight ... ... 47,500 lb.	
Length ... ... 60ft.		Maximum bomb load ... ... 9,900 lb	
Wing area ... ... 628 sq. ft.			

Performance

Maximum speed at 16,400ft.	... 537 m.p.h.
Maximum speed at sea level	... 509 m.p.h.
Range with 6,600 lb. of bombs	... 1,175 miles.

British Civil Types

It will have been remarked that the foregoing notes refer exclusively to military machines. Lately, however, several turbine-powered commercial machines have been announced, both in Great Britain and the U.S.A., the largest being the Bristol Brabazon I, or Type 167, with a span of 230ft.

For initial flight trials the Brabazon I will be fitted with eight Bristol Centaurus radial piston engines of about 2,500 h.p. each, arranged in pairs, each pair driving 6-blade contra-rotating propellers. In the second prototype, Bristol Proteus gas turbines will be substituted but the coupled arrangement will be retained. The Brabazon I with Centaurus engines will weigh about 250,000 lb and attain a maximum speed of over 300 m.p.h. at 25,000ft. For Atlantic service, 72 passengers will be accommodated.

Fig. 138. A model of the tail-first Miles mail-carrier developed from the Libellula. The version shown has three turbine jets.

A second British airliner, intended for two or four gas turbines, but which, in the first place, will have two Bristol Centaurus piston engines is the Airspeed AS-57 or Ambassador (Brabazon IIa). With Centaurus engines, this high-wing monoplane will cruise at speeds up to 285 m.p.h. The span is 115ft. and all-up weight 45,000 lb. According to range, 24 to 40 passengers will be carried. Still another project announced is the Armstrong-Whitworth all wing liner with six turbine-jet units, referred to in Chapter XV.

Bristol Theseus turbines are to be installed in the Hermes III, the Handley Page airliner with accommodation for sixty-four passengers. Wing span is 113 ft. and fuselage length 95ft. 6in. The de Havilland Dove feeder service airliner is to be fitted with small turbine-jet units. Saunders-Roe also announce a large flying boat having six gas turbines driving contra-rotating airscrews.

The exceptional promise of the turbine-jet as a power plant for high-speed mail-carriers has already been noted. Foreshadowing development on these lines Miles Aircraft has announced a design, already submitted to the Postmaster General, for a jet-propelled mail-carrier developed from the Libellula, an unorthodox tail-first or canard type, powered either by three Power Jets W.2/700s or two Rolls-Royce Derwent Vs. The estimated maximum cruising speed is 500 m.p.h. for a range of 2,000 miles and the payload, 4,000 lb. A photograph of a model appears as Fig. 138.

American transports eventually to be powered with gas turbines include the Republic Rainbow (this achieves a maximum speed of 450 m.p.h., with four 3,250 h.p. piston engines), the Douglas D.C.8 and a development of the Martin 202.

Fig. 139. The Douglas XB-43 bomber has "nostril" intakes to twin jet units. The undercarriage retracts into the fuselage; a feature that is likely to become more common on high-speed jet propelled aircraft due to the relatively thin wing.

CHAPTER XII

JETS VERSUS AIRSCREWS

DUCTED FANS : CONTRA-ROTATING AND CO-AXIAL AIRSCREWS

THE extraordinary interest aroused by jet propulsion has tended to convey the impression that in its application to aircraft the gas turbine is associated solely with propulsion by direct reaction. Although this aspect of its employment is patently of major importance, it is the view of the writer that the cardinal achievement is the development of a small, light, continuously operating prime mover alternative to the piston engine. Propulsion may be either by jet reaction or airscrew drive.

With inherent characteristics the four-cycle reciprocating engine can never attain the smoothness of operation of a perfectly balanced rotating mechanism, as is possible with a turbine generating continuous power; neither would it seem possible for the reciprocating engine to be operated at speeds even approaching those practicable in a turbine. The lubrication of so many surfaces in rubbing contact and exposed to combustion gases may be mentioned as a further disadvantage, though it is not suggested that the turbine is without its peculiar lubrication problems, particularly that of feeding oil to shafts rotating at extremely high speeds and under high-temperature conditions.

To produce a high-velocity jet of gas to propel an aircraft the essential components of the turbine-jet power plant are an air compressor, a combustion system and a turbine. The same components may be proportioned and arranged to deliver mechanical energy to an airscrew shaft for either tractor or pusher installations while utilising the exhaust from the turbine as an auxiliary propulsive jet. Comment will later be made on the potentialities of ducted fans which, although not identical with propellers, are essentially similar in purpose and construction.

In the turbine-jet power plant the turbine itself is a subsidiary component, the sole function of which is to drive the largest possible compressor to deliver a mass of air at high velocity. If mechanical power is required, however, the role of the components is reversed, i.e. the compressor becomes in effect an auxiliary component, merely supplying a sufficient quantity of air for combustion of the fuel to produce gas to drive the largest possible turbine.

It must be remembered that the useful power delivered by a

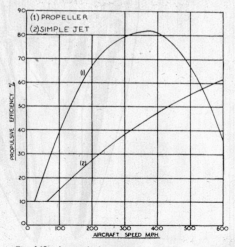

Fig. 140. A graph demonstrating the propulsive efficiencies of conventional airscrew and simple jet unit at various aircraft speeds.

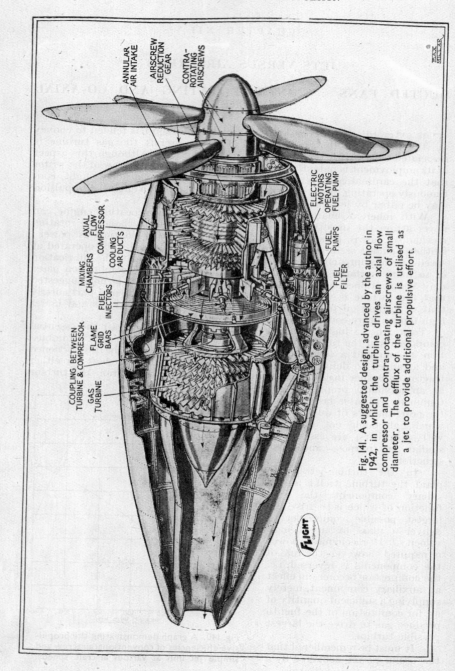

ANNULAR
AIR INTAKE

AIRSCREW
REDUCTION
GEAR

CONTRA-
ROTATING
AIRSCREWS

ELECTRIC
MOTORS
OPERATING
FUEL PUMP

AXIAL
FLOW
COMPRESSOR

FUEL
PUMPS

MIXING
CHAMBERS

COOLING
AIR DUCTS

FUEL
FILTER

FUEL
INJECTORS

COUPLING BETWEEN
TURBINE & COMPRESSOR

FLAME
GRID
BARS

GAS
TURBINE

MAX MILLAR

FLIGHT
COPYRIGHT

Fig. 141. A suggested design, advanced by the author in
1942, in which the turbine drives an axial flow
compressor and contra-rotating airscrews of small
diameter. The efflux of the turbine is utilised as
a jet to provide additional propulsive effort.

turbine- compressor unit is much less than the power developed internally. As much as 75 per cent. of the power of the turbine may be absorbed in driving the air-compressor. Thus to deliver 60 lb. of air a second the compressor of the D. H. Goblin requires nearly 6,000 h.p.

Design Considerations

The functions of a turbine-compressor unit can be varied within certain limits and are determined by the duty and conditions of operation for which it is intended. Governing factors in the case of aircraft include the duty (military or civil), range, speed, payload and operating height ; for the ultimate criterion is not the specific efficiency of the power plant but the overall efficiency of the complete aircraft.

The influence of the gas turbine on aircraft design is separately treated, but it may be stressed here that due to its relatively small dimensions, smooth contour devoid of excrescences and light weight resulting from its high operating speed, the turbine may be conveniently submerged in the wing or fuselage of an aircraft with an extremely beneficial effect on aerodynamic design. Aircraft can be smaller, lighter and of much cleaner out-line. This improvement will apply in a different degree whether jet propulsion or airscrew propulsion is employed, but the advantage is more marked in the case of pure jet propulsion. This factor is of such importance that, despite the lower thermal efficiency of the gas turbine as compared to an orthodox reciprocating engine, it is possible for a jet-propelled aircraft to have a greatly superior performance.

At low aircraft speeds and altitudes a jet unit has relatively low thermal and propulsive efficiencies. It follows that as regards take-off and initial rate of climb a jet-propelled aircraft is inferior in performance to a comparable aircraft employing airscrew propulsion. To overcome this handicap at take-off, thrust-augmenters have been proposed. These take the form of ducted fans or small diameter airscrews to increase the mass of air projected rearwardly.

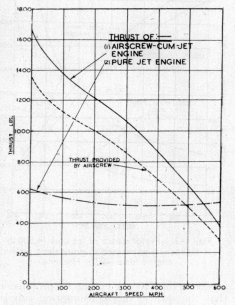

Fig. 142. Comparison of pure jet and airscrew-jet units. The gas horse power of both units under static conditions is 1,000.

Once a jet propelled aircraft is airborne it can climb at high speed ; but note that there is a difference between *speed* of climb, *rate* of climb and *angle* of climb. The efficiency of the turbine plant rises rapidly as the air flow through the compressor and turbine is accelerated commensurate with the forward speed of the aircraft. It has already been stressed that low temperature air entering the compressor at altitude has a beneficial effect. Moreover, just as the thrust horse power rises with speed, the consumption of fuel tends to fall, because the necessary mass of air for efficient combustion is now passing through.

Since the rate of fuel consumption of a turbine-jet is particularly high at full throttle and low altitudes, there must be a severe limitation on the range of an aircraft unless load is reduced. These facts suggest that in the immediate future pure jet propulsion will be confined to ultra-high speed, short-range aircraft or special high-speed transport types operating at great altitudes. One may deduce from such considerations that the gas turbine power plant challenges—for the present, at least—the reciprocating engine rather than the airscrew.

The combination of airscrew and gas turbine suggests very interesting possibilities but until aircraft operators can definitely specify their requirements in respect of speed, altitude, carrying capacity, degree of comfort, range, etc., it is not possible to plan an optimum solution. In other words gas turbines will need to be more specialised as there are so many possible variations in design and application.

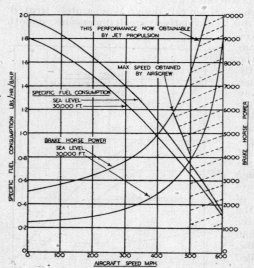

Fig. 143. Performance of jet unit (4,500 lb. static thrust) expressed in equivalent piston engine form.—(Dr. Hooker.)

Speed and Altitude

Here it is appropriate to quote from a 1943 observation in a previous edition of this work : " If large passenger transports with pressurised cabins flying at 500 m.p.h. at very great altitudes are the aim, then jet propulsion will almost certainly be employed. On the other hand, if opinion is confirmed that transports of the future will cruise at about 250 m.p.h. at the lower altitudes, then turbine-driven airscrews may well be chosen for propulsion. It must, of course, be presumed that the rate of fuel consumption can be improved as development work proceeds, and that metallurgists can assist by the production of better heat-resisting steels for the turbine blades." Amendment of the foregoing paragraph is hardly warranted to-day though it may be added that transport aircraft with turbine-driven airscrews should be flying in a year or two.

An incidental advantage of the airscrew is its adaptability for use as a brake, not only for landing, but for dive-bombing, manœuvring a flying boat on the water, and checking " float " on a deck-landing aircraft.

Selection between the plain jet and turbine-airscrew will demand careful deliberation by aircraft designers. This is particularly true in the case of flying boats for which the plain jet offers elimination of potential troubles arising from spray striking the airscrews on take-off and landing but gives relatively poor take-off characteristics, whereas the turbine-airscrew offsets its drawbacks by facilitating braking, manœuvring and take-off.

It has been said that the overall noise level in an aircraft with turbine-jet units is 30 decibels below that in a machine with equivalent piston engines and airscrews.

An objection to the use of airscrews with turbines is that a rather complicated and weighty reduction gear becomes necessary due to the high rotational speed of the turbine—over 10,000 r.p.m. for example. It is earnestly to be hoped that purely mechanical considerations of this sort will not delay unduly the clearing of the new gas-turbine/airscrew combinations for commercial operation.

Contra- or counter-rotating airscrews, tractors or pushers, with as many as five blades to each unit, should to some extent lessen the designer's burden by providing adequate blade area with a reduced diameter and permitting operation at higher rotational speeds without exceeding the permissible linear speed [of the blade tips. They possess the further advantages of

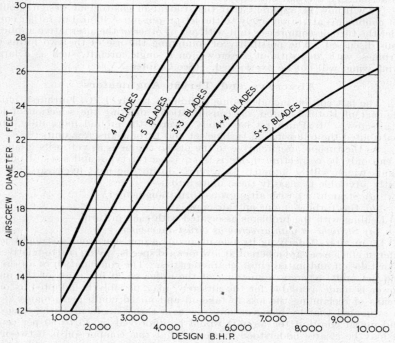

Fig. 144. Curves illustrating airscrew diameter for a design condition of 400 m.p.h. at 40,000ft.

permitting a shorter and lighter undercarriage, and of smoothing out the slipstream and consequently improving the air flow over the control surfaces. If pusher type airscrews become the vogue, interference with air flow by the effects of the slipstream will be eliminated.

Airscrews for gas turbines will duplicate in essential design those for equivalent piston engines, but reduced vibration will permit the weight of the duralumin airscrew to be decreased by using thinner blades and smaller root sections than hitherto.

The weight of airscrews to absorb very high powers will continue to be a very serious design consideration ; for example, a ten-blade counter-rotating airscrew for a piston engine delivering 4,000 h.p. at 40,000ft. at 550 m.p.h. will weigh 1,500 lb. with duralumin blades and 1,170 lb. with wood blades. For an equivalent turbine installation the duralumin-bladed airscrew will scale somewhat less for reasons already stated. Precise data on possible weight saving in the turbine-driven airscrew are still lacking.

After several years of development we are only slowly emerging from the chrysalis stage with small turbine-compressor units. Although 500 h.p. turbine units are in the development stage, it is a fact that the larger the size employed the fewer the problems to be surmounted ; furthermore, as the diameter of the turbine is reduced, the speed of rotation must be increased. Multi-stage compressors and turbines, particularly if variable-pitch blading becomes a practical proposition, may conceivably improve the present unsatisfactory thermal efficiency.

It will now be apparent that the student of gas-turbine design should not confine his attention solely to the jet-propulsion system, but rather consider the turbine-compressor unit with one or other of the alternative applications discussed. The possibility of combining the use of the two forms of turbines, with and without airscrews, on a single aircraft, such as a large flying-wing, will not be overlooked. (See Chapter XV).

Airscrews and Thrust Augmenters

The last edition included some comments by Mr. L. G. Fairhurst, chief engineer of Rotol Limited, on considerations affecting the selection of jet or airscrew. Mr. Fairhurst has lately covered the ground more fully, and contributed the following on turbine-jet and turbine-airscrew units :

As the turbine unit relative to the piston engine is as yet in its infancy, it can only be conjecture if one is to envisage the types and sizes of power plants which will be adopted for aircraft during the next five years. It is firstly advisable to classify these units into :—

(a) Straight-jet with airscrew as thrust augmenter.

(b) Gas turbine engine and airscrew.

Dealing with the problems associated with each in turn :—

(a) *Straight jet with airscrew as thrust augmenter.*

In an aircraft deriving its sole means of propulsion from a straight jet, inferior efficiencies are inherent at low forward speeds, giving rise to relatively poor take-off and initial climb characteristics. The combination of airscrew and jet unit, wherein something of the order of 20 per cent. of the unit power is made available for the airscrew, may possibly be adopted as one means of reclaiming the loss in take-off and initial climb performance. It is estimated that by using an airscrew as a thrust-augmenter, the take-off and initial climb of the aircraft would be improved by 45 to 50 per cent. It may be clearly understood, however, that this comparison is between a straight jet installation where the turbine is designed without consideration of an airscrew, and an installation where the turbine is so designed to provide a certain percentage of the total power of the unit for the airscrew.

With such an airscrew the problem of control arises, and to which of the operating conditions (i.e., forward speed, thrust, or engine r.p.m.) the airscrew is to be responsive will considerably tax the ingenuity of both engine and airscrew designers. In a normal constant-speed airscrew on a piston engine the airscrew is designed to absorb the full engine power, is responsive to changes in engine r.p.m. through the medium of an engine-driven governor, and has a pitch range adequate to handle the full range of power and r.p.m. of the engine. In the jet unit installation in question, as the airscrew would be designed merely to handle a small portion of the total unit power, control of the airscrew by a governor responsive to unit r.p.m. may give unsatisfactory constant-speeding characteristics on the take-off and initial climb.   In a normal piston engine installation under conditions of take-off and climb, the airscrew starts in a temporarily fixed-pitch condition.   As the aircraft slowly gathers speed the airscrew in this condition absorbs less power, and if it remained in fixed pitch overspeeding would result.   The fact that the airscrew is under governor control responsive to r.p.m. prevents this condition arising by automatically coarsening the pitch to suit the forward speed.   In the jet unit installation in question, the reduction in power in the airscrew as the aircraft gathers speed is only a

Fig. 145.   A Gloster Meteor fitted experimentally with Rolls-Royce Trent turbine-airscrew units.

very small percentage of the total unit power, and it is, therefore, questionable whether the rotational speed of the whole airscrew/turbine/compressor system would increase sufficiently to permit the governor to apply the requisite correction.

The best system may be to provide a separate turbine to drive the propeller, to which the propeller could be made responsive without having any reference to the main turbine.   This would ensure satisfactory constant-speeding on take-off and climb, and the neutralisation of the airscrew at top speed could be carried out by feathering.

(b) *Gas turbine engine with airscrew.*

The combination of gas turbine and airscrew will, with little doubt, be the stage immediately following the piston-engined aircraft, and will be used in aircraft such as multi-engined bombers and commercial airliners of the freight- and passenger-carrying class up to a maximum speed of 400 m.p.h.   The propulsion unit will consist of the usual compressor, combustion chamber and turbine, the latter driving the airscrew through a reduction gear.   Approximately 80 per cent. of the unit power will be allotted to the airscrew, the remaining 20 per cent. issuing in the exhaust gases as kinetic energy.

In considering a range of turbine-airscrew units the powers of 1,000 h.p. to 10,000 h.p. may be expected during the next five years.   Operating altitudes of 10,000 and 40,000 ft. have been considered, as these are the most likely extremes to be met covering the non-pressurised and pressurised aircraft.

In considering the application of airscrews to such units, no difficulty at all is likely to be experienced in catering for powers up to 10,000 h.p. at 10,000 ft. Indeed, the largest diameter necessary is 18 ft. for the optimum case, which could be reduced to 16 ft. without seriously affecting the efficiency. It is obvious, however, that a more difficult problem confronts the designer at 40,000 ft., especially at the lower speeds. Here optimum diameters of 30 ft. are required which, even if reduced to say 27 ft., will still present a serious problem to the aircraft designer in providing sufficient space. It is not foreseen, however, that any insuperable difficulties will arise from the airscrew side in designing and building airscrews of these sizes.

An interesting point is the very large saving in diameter which can be effected by increase in the number of blades. At 5,000 h.p. at 40,000 ft., for instance, a diameter saving of the order of 10 ft. can be achieved by changing from an eight-bladed (4+4) to a ten-bladed (5+5) counter-rotating airscrew.

Ducted Fans

Mr. Fairhurst is of the opinion that no treatise on the possible future development of airscrews would be complete without examining broadly the question of ducted fans. These systems, although not identical with airscrews as we know them, are sufficiently similar in purpose and construction to justify consideration under the general heading of airscrews.

The ducted fan system of propulsion, as discussed by Mr. Fairhurst consists of a fairly large diameter ducted fan or axial compressor of relatively low compression ratio at the intake to the nacelle. Only a small portion of its delivery air is taken by the turbine, the remainder being by-passed directly to the jet.

This system appears to him to have two main advantages, viz :—(a) A slightly higher overall efficiency than both airscrew and jet systems over a relatively small intermediate speed range ; (b) It embraces the possibility of burning fuel freely in the air by-passed from the turbine and thus increasing fairly considerably the power available for short periods, but at an enormous cost in consumption.

The main disadvantage is the size of fan and of possible ducts required to deal with the exceptionally large volume of air required. This would appear to complicate the design of suitable aircraft applications by virtue of the large bulk to be disposed, which might well increase the drag sufficiently to nullify any efficiency increase over the jet or airscrew system when considering the performance of the aircraft as a whole. There would appear to be no great problems to be overcome from the designer's point of view, indeed sufficient work has been carried out on similar axial-flow fan installations in the past for various applications to give one confidence in approaching these designs of the future.

There is little doubt that a considerable amount of work will have to be carried out in the future both on design and actual practical test before the relative value of this system of propulsion is definitely established, but it is Mr. Fairhurst's feeling that the disadvantages will be found to outweigh the advantages and that the ducted fan as such will disappear, leaving the clear-cut problem of airscrews versus jet.*

Airscrews with Two—speed Drive

At speeds of 500 m.p.h. upwards the tip speed of an airscrew may be greater than that of sound. Such conditions in the supersonic region

*A different conception of the ducted fan is described under " Metropolitan Vickers " on p. 99.

introduce the need for a two-speed gear drive to the airscrew in order to reduce the tip Mach number at top speed by use of a relatively low gear ratio, and still have available a second ratio of a high value for take-off and climb. The need for the two-speed gear on heavy classes of aircraft, such as bombers and commercial types, is not by any means as pronounced as in the fighter class, since in the former ample airscrew diameter is usually afforded and the top speeds are such that the Mach numbers never approach the figures for the fighters. Certainly the two-speed gear considerably

Fig. 146. The American General Electric TG-100 turbine-airscrew unit on a test rig.

extends the use of the airscrew as a means of aircraft propulsion by permitting its use at higher speeds without jeopardising the take-off and climb performance.

The maximum number of blades so far used in a single hub is five, and this would appear to be the limit on both aerodynamic and mechanical grounds. The aerodynamic limitation is mainly due to the heavy swing at take-off which occurs in the 2,500 h.p. high-speed fighter. An aircraft operating from a fleet carrier suffers more than any other type on account of the restricted landing platform, together with the allied difficulties due to roll, etc. This is accounted for by the temptation to absorb high powers by increasing the number of blades in a single hub which, although it reduces the loading per blade to within reasonable limits still does not overcome the high disc loading present. A further aerodynamic limitation occurs in a turbine-airscrew installation with an air entry duct annular to the airscrew. The presence of five blade roots rotating in one direction in front of the duct may cause a reduction in efficiency due to the presence of swirl and turbulence behind the blade roots.

The mechanical limitation consists of the difficulties arising in keeping down to a minimum the height of the hub socket so as to keep it wholly inside the spinner, and also to provide an efficient blade airfoil shape at the spinner periphery. This difficulty is particularly pronounced on turbine airscrews where the spinner diameter in front of the air duct is considerably smaller than the piston engine spinner, demanding an airscrew hub with the absolute minimum height of blade socket.

The aerodynamic attributes of counter-rotating airscrews are generally well known, and intensive flight-testing carried out over the past two to three years has confirmed the various claims. Also, this endurance testing has given ample opportunity of progressively improving the actuating mechanism and to-day the airscrew can be said to be mechanically sound.

The number of blades so far used has been a maximum of six $(3 + 3)$ but no difficulties are foreseen, either aerodynamic or structural, in increasing the number to eight $(4 + 4)$ or ten $(5 + 5)$.

It has been shown by wind tunnel tests that the most efficient counter-rotating combination is that in which equal torques are absorbed by both front and rear halves. In order to achieve this it is necessary to operate the rear half at a slightly finer pitch setting than the front, due to the different inflow to the rear half occurring from the presence of the front component.

Up to the present the counter-rotating airscrew has shown little or no improvement in performance at top speed, although a very definite improvement in performance has been evident under highly loaded conditions of take-off and climb. As forward speeds increase, however, i.e., of the order of 450 m.p.h. upwards, it is necessary to limit the rotational tip speed more and more in order to keep the tip Mach number within reasonable limits and we can hope to see a useful advantage of the counter-rotating airscrew at top speed, due to its ability to reclaim the rotational energy losses associated with heavily-loaded airscrews.

The entire elimination of swing with the counter-rotating airscrew makes it not only attractive for ease of aircraft handling but an absolute essential for aircraft of the deck-landing type. Mr. Fairhurst maintains that no specification for a deck-landing airscrew-driven aircraft should ever again be issued to the industry without an insistence on the use of counter-rotating airscrews.

The application of the counter-rotating airscrew to the turbine engine will no doubt become universal in units employing airscrew propulsion. Firstly it enables a reduction in diameter to be obtained by multi-blading and hence assists undercarriage design and, secondly, should be a considerable improvement over the single-hub type, because the reduction in swirl and turbulence is considerable and improves the conditions of airflow around the air entry duct into the unit.

Co-axial Airscrews

The term " co-axial " airscrew differentiates the type from the counter-rotating type wherein the whole engine power is absorbed by both halves, and the type in which each half of the airscrew is driven by an independent power unit. The two halves still rotate in opposite directions. One outstanding reason for adopting the co-axial type is to improve the safety of the aircraft, since in the event of the failure of one engine unit it will still be possible to continue flight with the second unit, driving as it does its own half of the airscrew. In this case the particular half-airscrew allied to the " dud " engine will be feathered. A further advantage of this arrangement, associated with buried engines, is that two power units can be used, arranged in such a manner as to present only one airscrew unit at the leading- or trailing-edge of the wing. This is the general scheme being followed by the Bristol Aeroplane Co. for the large Brabazon II which is to have eight turbines and four airscrews. Apart from the complication of the double reduction gear, the main problems which arise with an airscrew of this type consist firstly of the effect on efficiency of the operating half when it has a stationary feathered airscrew either in front or behind and secondly the sensitivity of the blade angle required for feathering one half in the presence of the other half rotating in front or behind.

Among the conclusions reached by Mr. Fairhurst in a paper before the Royal Aeronautical Society, after an exhaustive study of factors affecting airscrew development are the following :—

(1) *The limit of the efficient use of an airscrew* as a means of aircraft propulsion will firstly occur on fighter aircraft with a 4,000 h.p. piston engine developing its power at 40,000 ft. at a forward speed of 550 m.p.h.

(2) *Beyond 550 m.p.h.*, and considering mainly forward speed as the criterion, the straight jet will replace the engine-airscrew combination.

(3) As a possible thrust augmenter for straight jet installation the airscrew will still remain a serious competitor to other forms of thrust augmentation.

(4) *The gas turbine-airscrew* combination will become increasingly favourable over the next five years for multi-engined bombers and multi-engined commercial aircraft. Powers up to 10,000 h.p. at 40,000ft., with a forward speed of 400 m.p.h., can be catered for with an airscrew.

(5) *Airscrews over the next five years* will be extended to counter-rotating six- (3 + 3), eight- (4 + 4) and ten- (5 + 5) bladed types.

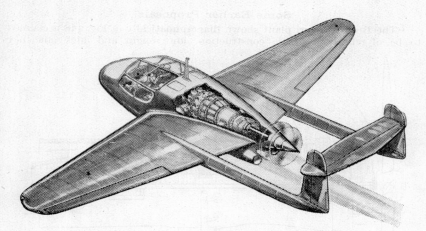

Fig. 147. Proposal for a four-seat private aircraft advanced by the author when visiting the U.S.A. in 1944. It has a turbine with small diameter, five blade, contra-rotating airscrews and residual jets.

CHAPTER XIII

TURBINE-AIRSCREW PROJECTS

TURBINE-AIRSCREW units constitute the most important phase of recent gas turbine development. At take-off, during climb and in operation at medium speeds and altitudes (say 300–400 m.p.h. and 20,000–25,000ft.) they offer advantages in performance and fuel economy in comparison with turbine-jet units. Even with the addition of the necessary high ratio reduction gear, the turbine is still considerably lighter than an equivalent reciprocating engine and, moreover, is less costly to produce. Until pressurization of cabins becomes the current practice and more is known of compressibility factors, therefore, the simple jet engine will suffer a handicap for commercial use. Except for military and special purpose aircraft, it is only at high altitude and high speed that the jet unit excels in consumption and range. In the view of many aircraft engineers, the turbine-airscrew unit will predominate in this second phase of the development. However, this phase is considered to be merely temporary, and the long-term programme will be concerned with pure jet propulsion and ducted fans.

For particulars of British turbine-airscrew units under development the reader is referred to Chapter VII, which includes brief notes on Armstrong-Siddeley, Bristol and Rolls-Royce types. In Chapter VIII the American G.E.C. unit TG–100 is referred to. Interest is added to the present trend towards turbine-driven airscrew units by earlier projects described in patent specifications and outlined below. So far as is known, none emerged from the design stage.

Some Earlier Proposals

The Brown-Boveri plant shown diagrammatically in Fig. 148 is claimed to be of relatively simple construction, low weight and high efficiency

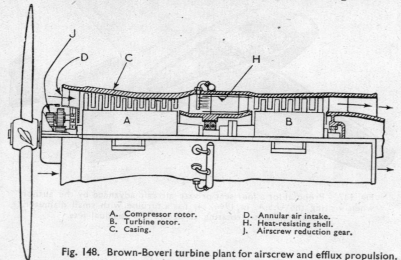

A. Compressor rotor.
B. Turbine rotor.
C. Casing.

D. Annular air intake.
H. Heat-resisting shell.
J. Airscrew reduction gear.

Fig. 148. Brown-Boveri turbine plant for airscrew and efflux propulsion.

Outstanding features conducing to this end are (1) the arrangement by which the gas flow between compressor and turbine undergoes no substantial deflection or change in velocity; (2) the diminution of the axial velocity of the air in the compressor to that required for satisfactory combustion; (3) the provision of small passages serving as mixing chambers in the annular space between the compressor and turbine, and (4) the increase of the axial velocity of the gas as it flows through the turbine.

Compressor rotor A and turbine rotor B are on directly connected coaxial shafts, and the stator blades of both components are mounted in a tubular casing C forming the main duct. Air enters at the annular inlet D and is compressed in the usual manner in the forward (con‧vergent) section of the compressor. Thereafter the duct diameter is parallel and the angle of the rotor blades is decreased. Only 20 to 30 per cent. of the air delivered by the compressor is required for the combustion of fuel; the remainder is employed to lower the tempera‑ture of the combustion gases.

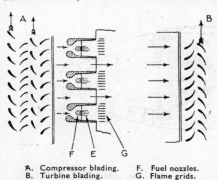

A. Compressor blading.
B. Turbine blading.
E. Mixing chambers.
F. Fuel nozzles.
G. Flame grids.

Fig. 149. Developed section of Brown-Boveri annular combustion space with mixing chambers and flame grids.

This small quantity of air is passed into a plurality of separate mixing chambers E in the annular space, as shown in the plane de‑velopment diagram Fig 149. In these the air is further reduced in velocity and mixed with the fuel injected through nozzles F. Flame forms at or beyond the grid bars G, which furnish a number of friction surfaces along which the boundary layers of the mixture move at a lower velocity than the ignition velocity. Small flames are formed locally which preheat and ignite the main mass of the mixture and thus maintain stable conditions. The flaming mixture is reduced in temperature by the excess air which flows through the passages between the mixing chambers. To protect the walls of the annular space a shell H of heat-resisting sheet metal may be fitted. Cooling air passes between the shell and the walls.

Although this plant is primarily intended to drive an airscrew mechanically through reduction gear J the turbine effluent is employed to give a supplementary propulsive effort by jet reaction. The turbine, therefore, differs from the usual type, which is of increasing (divergent) diameter to reduce the gas velocity and exploit the gas expansion in order to minimise exhaust losses. To be effective for propulsion the gas outlet velocity should be about 1.5 times the flying speed of the aircraft. Accordingly, the turbine is substantially of parallel diameter and the rotor blade angle is progressively increased towards the outlet to raise the gas velocity at the discharge nozzle.

A Swedish Project

Another combined airscrew and efflux propulsion unit, projected by the famous Swedish concern Aktiebolaget Ljungströms Angturbin, is shown diagrammatically in Fig. 150. The air is compressed in a multi-stage centrifugal blower, and to reduce overall length the annular mixing chamber envelops the turbine. Particular importance is attached to rapidly increasing the propulsive effort for take-off and in emergency and special control arrangements, resembling those employed in this firm's jet propulsion unit shown in Fig. 40, are provided for this purpose.

Housed in a streamlined casing, the four-stage centrifugal compressor A draws in air through inlets B and delivers to a space C surrounding the annular mixing chamber D. At a bulkhead E the air stream is reversed and enters the mixing chamber past a plurality of shrouded fuel nozzles F. Combustion occurs in the vicinity of the nozzle shrouds and the temperature

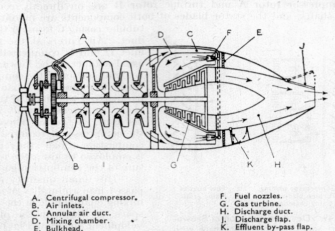

A. Centrifugal compressor.	F. Fuel nozzles.
B. Air inlets.	G. Gas turbine.
C. Annular air duct.	H. Discharge duct.
D. Mixing chamber.	J. Discharge flap.
E. Bulkhead.	K. Effluent by-pass flap.

Fig. 150.   Ljungströms Angturbin screw and efflux propulsion unit with multi-stage centrifugal compressor.

of the combustion gases is lowered by the excess air. At the forward end of the mixing chamber the flow is again reversed to enter the gas turbine G. From the annular outlet of the turbine the relatively low velocity effluent flows along a convergent duct H which raises the velocity at the nozzle.

Normal regulation of aircraft speed is effected by adjustment of supply of fuel at nozzles F. For rapid acceleration, however, a sudden and substantial increase of fuel would raise the gas temperature unduly as the compressor cannot be instantaneously accelerated to deliver a corresponding supply of air. To facilitate this speed-up, the power input to the compressor is temporarily increased by reducing the power applied for propulsion of the aircraft, either by the airscrew or the efflux reaction or both. Subsequently the proportionate division of energy between compressor and propulsion is restored to normal at the higher level, and it is claimed that this operation is considerably quicker than the method of gradually increasing the fuel supply to the desired amount.

For this purpose a flap J in the discharge duct may be raised to increase the area of the discharge orifice. Alternatively or additionally, a flap K adjacent to the turbine outlet may be lifted to by-pass a portion of the effluent. By either or both means the propulsive effort is lowered, the back pressure on the turbine is reduced giving an increased heat and pressure drop in the turbine, which thus produces more mechanical energy which is entirely absorbed by the compressor. Another method of achieving the desired results, either instead of or in addition to decreasing back pressure, is to increase the slip of the airscrew by temporarily fining the pitch.

A Futurist Design

Constituting an interesting " peep into the future " is the multi-screw plant projected by L. E. Baynes and the Alan Muntz Co. for large transport aircraft. The general layout of the plant in a large flying boat having a pressure-sealed hull for high-altitude operation is given in plan and elevation

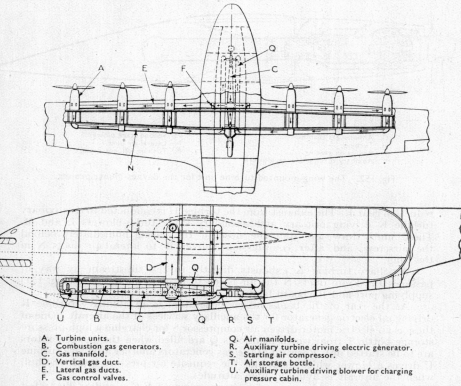

A. Turbine units.
B. Combustion gas generators.
C. Gas manifold.
D. Vertical gas duct.
E. Lateral gas ducts.
F. Gas control valves.

Q. Air manifolds.
R. Auxiliary turbine driving electric generator.
S. Starting air compressor.
T. Air storage bottle.
U. Auxiliary turbine driving blower for charging
    pressure cabin.

Fig. 151. Baynes-Muntz layout of a multi-screw turbine plant for a large, high-altitude flying boat.

in Fig. 151. Six wing-mounted turbine units A driving airscrews are supplied with combustion gases from a battery of generators B located in the pressure hull where they can be given attention or adjustment during flight.

The generators are arranged in two banks, one on each side of the centre line of the hull, and deliver gas to a common manifold C from which a vertical duct D carries it to the wing level. Here it passes to lateral ducts E serving port and starboard turbines, the distribution being controlled by butterfly valves F which enable speeds to be adjusted and permit directional control when taxying on the water.

Details of the generators are not specified, but they may be of the Pescara type, in which the driving gases consist of the combustion products from the engine cylinders of free-piston compressors. The generators may be cooled by liquid circulated along the wing leading-edge to prevent icing.

The arrangement of the turbine units driving the airscrews is illustrated in Fig. 152. From duct E driving gases enter the annular space G and pass forward to the inlet of the turbine H, which drives the airscrew through a

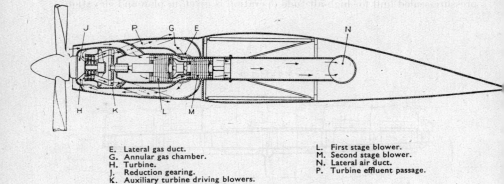

E. Lateral gas duct.
G. Annular gas chamber.
H. Turbine.
J. Reduction gearing.
K. Auxiliary turbine driving blowers.

L. First stage blower.
M. Second stage blower.
N. Lateral air duct.
P. Turbine effluent passage.

Fig. 152. The wing-mounted turbine unit for the Baynes-Muntz project.

reduction gear J. The exhaust from the turbine H is conducted to an auxiliary turbine K driving primary and secondary stage turbo-blowers L and M. These units draw air from the nose of the casing immediately behind the airscrew, and after compression deliver it to lateral air ducts N in the wing.

Auxiliary turbine K exhausts directly to the slipstream by way of passages P. From ducts N the air is fed to pairs of manifolds Q (Fig. 151) supplying port and starboard banks of gas generators.

At the rear of the banks of gas generators is an auxiliary turbine R driving an electric generator for the ancillary services of the aircraft. One of these is an electric motor-driven air compressor S for charging a high-pressure storage bottle T from which manifolds Q are filled when the gas generators are to be started up. Forward of the gas generators another auxiliary turbine U drives a blower which maintains the requisite air pressure inside the hull when the aircraft is flying at high altitudes.

A more recent scheme is of German origin (A.E.G.), and is illustrated diagrammatically in Fig. 153. Air enters the compressor A at the front of the fuselage (the airscrews are pushers) and is delivered by way of a heat exchanger B to the main combustion chamber C, thence to the high-pressure turbine D which drives the airscrew through the reduction gear H. The gases are then passed via a re-heat combustion chamber E to the low-pressure turbine F (this drives the compressor) through the heat-exchanger B to the residual jet pipe G.

The estimated fuel consumption was 0.3 lb./b.h.p./hr. and the weight 3.5 lb./h.p. at 33,000ft. A special heat-exchanger utilising porous ceramic material was to be employed.

Jets for Helicopters

An unusual application of a turbine-jet unit for a helicopter is proposed by G. & J. Weir, Ltd., of Glasgow, and C. G. Pullin. Instead of the jet being discharged rearwards, it is conducted to the hub of the lifting and

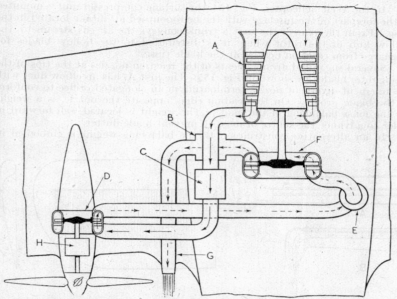

Fig. 153. The German A.E.G. scheme in which the pusher airscrews are driven by high-pressure turbines. The principle of operation is described in the text.

sustaining rotor, and passes along the hollow blades to reaction nozzles at the blade tips. Thus the gas stream reacts to drive the rotor and does not *directly* propel the aircraft.

Proposals have previously been made for discharging engine exhaust gas from the tips of airscrew blades to supplement the normal mechanical drive, to drive an air compressor by an engine and employ a mixture of air and exhaust gas to rotate the airscrew and to drive a helicopter rotor by air from an engine-driven compressor. In the last project engine exhaust is utilised to warm the air to maintain the blades at a temperature sufficient to prevent icing. Such schemes may be regarded as modern versions of Hero's æolipile, Barker's water mill of the seventeenth century, the Avery rotary engine of the early nineteenth century, and the pure reaction turbine which enjoyed a limited vogue before de Laval and Parsons each developed their turbines.

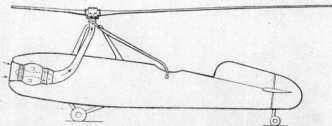

Fig. 154. The Weir helicopter with rotor driven by jet reaction at the blade tips.

In the Weir helicopter, Fig. 154, the turbine-compressor unit is mounted in the forepart of the fuselage with the bell-mouthed air intake located in the nose. From the rear of the unit a trunk conveys the air/gas stream to the hollow hub of the rotor where it is distributed to the hollow blades for discharge from reaction nozzles at the blade tips.

Several suggested arrangements of the reaction nozzles at the tips of the lifting rotor blades are shown in Fig. 155. The first A, has an elbow duct with a convergent-divergent nozzle terminating in an elongated orifice to conform to the blade profile. On the leading edge, opposite the nozzle, is a weight for the mass balancing of the blade. The weight is located well forward in order to advance the centre of mass to prevent blade flutter.

In an alternative construction B, the balancing weight is embodied in

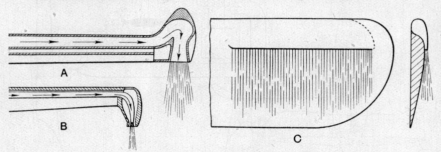

Fig. 155. Three types of blade tip reaction nozzles.

the leading edge, and the nozzle is of the ejector type comprising a chamber with an air inlet at the front edge and a venturi nozzle at the rear. Into the throat of this nozzle the working fluid is discharged by an ejector nozzle, and thus the mass flow is augmented by entrained air.

For the third proposal, C, the nozzle constitutes a continuation of the hollow blade spar forming the working fluid duct and discharges through a slot-like orifice over the upper or low pressure surface of the blade at about the region of maximum thickness. The thrust is applied close to the mass axis of the blade, and the jet is discharged where the external air stream has its maximum local velocity and tendency to separate from the blade profile.

CHAPTER XIV

AERODYNAMIC PROBLEMS : BOUNDARY LAYER
CONTROL : COMPRESSIBILITY EFFECTS

THE very simple principle of the turbine makes it a most desirable power unit for many forms of propulsion. In addition to this inherent quality it has already been emphasised that there is immense contributory benefit to be derived from the employment of a type of power unit for aircraft which is of relatively small dimensions, and permits a design of excellent aerodynamic form, devoid of excrescences which create parasitic drag and air flow turbulence. The turbine-compressor is such a unit ; it is compact, self-contained and of convenient cylindrical shape.

In the consideration of an aircraft equipped with a turbine, the necessity for providing an air intake for the compressor can be turned to advantage by arranging the intake inlet to exert an influence on the boundary layer air flow. The following observations, amplifying earlier notes on the subject, are the result of collaboration with C. B. Bailey-Watson of *Flight*.

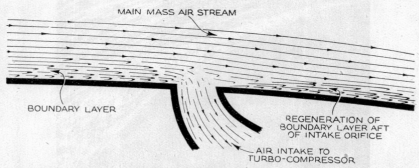

Fig. 156. Diagrammatic illustration of boundary layer formation and relation to major air stream, showing abstraction into the turbo-compressor of air from the boundary region in order to delay the separation point.

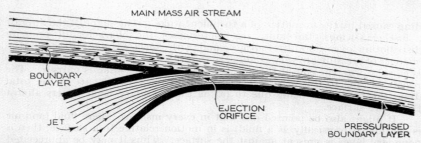

Fig. 157. This shows the efflux from the turbo-compressor being ejected tangentially to the aircraft skin curvature in order to accelerate the boundary layer air and so prevent separation.

169

The boundary layer is that region adjacent to the skin of the aircraft where particles of air are in a transitional stage of acceleration up to the speed of the air flow past the aircraft. This is illustrated diagrammatically in Figs. 156 and 157. The layer of air immediately next to the skin tends to adhere to it, the layer above that is less able to resist the general air flow, and so on successively until the outer layer of the boundary region is moving at the same speed as that portion of the main air mass flowing past the aircraft. It must be pointed out, however, that the phenomenon is by no means quite so simple of explanation as this ; there are numerous factors which influence boundary layer characteristics, and the composition of the layer itself is also subject to variation. The description above is, at best, very general, and anything further than this is both beyond the scope of, and out of place in, a book of this nature. Readers who desire to investigate this aspect of aerodynamics for themselves are referred to Warner—*Airplane Design (Performance)* ; and Dodge and Thompson—*Fluid Mechanics* (from which Figs. 158, 159 and 160 are taken).

The resistance to motion through the air for any aircraft can be considered as being made up to two quantities, (a) the effect of viscous shearing stresses in the air, the resultant being known as skin-friction, and (b) the

Fig. 158.   Boundary layer flow near the separation point on a circular cylinder.
Direction of air flow, left to right.

drag caused by the formation of a turbulent wake. The shape of the aircraft —fuselage, wings, tail unit, etc.—determines the character of pressure distribution over its entire surface, and with *finely streamlined shapes* the changes of pressure are very gradual, so that separation of flow into turbulence is close to the rear end of the body, and the resulting wake is narrow. The resistance due to (b), in such cases, is only a very small part of the total drag, the remainder being due to (a) as the boundary layer covers almost the entire surface.

It might also be pointed out that in every instance where fluid (and air is considered physically as a fluid) is in motion relative to a surface, then a boundary layer is present against the surface. Thus it may be appreciated that the high-velocity flow of great volumes of air through a compressor and turbine also involves very careful consideration of boundary layer characteristics within the unit—to the blades, throats, nozzles and, in fact, all internal surfaces subject to relative fluid flow. However, the complication incurred in evolving a control system for boundary layer within the turbine is of such magnitude that it is very unlikely anything can be done in this direction—the only means of affecting boundary layer in these circumstances

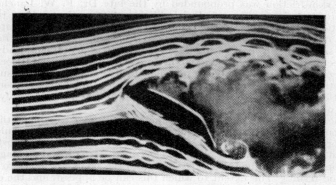

Fig. 159.   Flow of air around a flapped airfoil at a large angle of attack.

is by meticulous design of the components in order to delay the stagnation point as long as possible.

Effect on Mass Flow

Disregarding the physical properties of the air, the depth and growth of the boundary layer is influenced in relation to the curvature of the shape, this curvature being mathematically constructed according to the fineness ratio, i.e., the ratio of length to maximum cross-sectional diameter. However, the break down into turbulence near the separation point in a boundary layer, as shown in Fig. 158, profoundly affects the character of the major

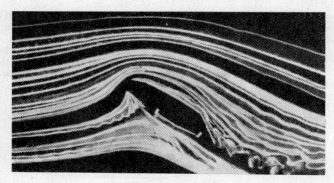

Fig. 160.   The same airfoil as in Fig. 159 but with boundary layer control by suction applied, showing the suppression of breakdown into turbulence.

air stream flow, and does, in fact, induce a break down from laminar flow into general turbulence in the wake, so that the two quantities (a) and (b) which compose total drag are inter-related.

Boundary layer control, with a view to reducing drag and thereby improving overall performance, has been the subject of a great deal of research and experiment for over 40 years, ever since Prandtl introduced, in 1904, what has become known as his boundary layer theory. As a side issue to this it is of interest to record that the first explanatory theory covering the field of skin-friction was propounded by the late Dr. F. W. Lanchester in the Aerodynamics section of *Aerial Flight*. As speeds tend to rise, the application of boundary layer control assumes paramount importance in view of the tremendous part it can play in ensuring a smooth air flow over control surfaces—this being aside from the very great aerodynamic advantage to be accrued from a major reduction in drag and an increase in lift coefficients by its employment. However, it was not until the advent of the successful jet-reaction propelled aircraft that boundary layer control could be considered a practicable possibility, this type of propulsion being admirably suited to the objective.

The control of boundary layer characteristics aims at reducing the depth increment of the layer and thus delaying the separation into turbulence by either or both of two methods ; (i) (developed by Prandtl) by abstracting air from the boundary layer through slots in the wings and fuselage ; and (ii) (proposed by Baumann) by ejecting on to the boundary layer to achieve the same result. The extent to which this can be applied, and the effect, is very clearly shown by Figs. 159 and 160, the control in this case being achieved by the suction method.

With a jet-propelled aircraft the necessity of providing an air intake for the turbine unit, and an orifice for the ejection of the jet, present an excellent opportunity for exercising these methods of boundary layer control with the tremendous advantages they bring. In one of his early patent specifications Air Commodore Whittle, who evidently was well aware of the possibilities, allowed for the first of these applications, for he suggests having an annular forward-facing intake at a distance of two-thirds to three-quarters of the total length back from the leading end, or in the zone where a considerable depth of boundary layer is found to be present. He also makes provision for abstracting air into the turbo-unit from a series of orifices in the wings.

One of the primary reasons for not having utilised these advantages in orthodox aircraft is the great volume of air to be inhaled and/or ejected. Dr. Warner gives this as being 1.2 cu. ft./sec./sq. ft. of area at a speed of 100 m.p.h., the resulting maximum coefficient of lift being 3.0—an extremely high value. Obviously, in an orthodox aircraft the auxiliary power plant

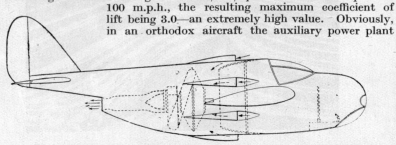

Fig. 161. Air Cdre. F. Whittle patented this layout in 1938. The forward-facing air-intake scoops can be clearly seen together with the tail orifice for the jet.

required for this purpose would need to be disproportionately large, but with an aircraft powered by a gas turbine unit the main power plant does the job and the whole aircraft gains thereby. What is also of great interest is that this extremely convenient avenue toward boundary layer control is equally open similarly to the low and moderate speed aircraft as well as to the high speed machines.

The primary criterion in effecting boundary layer control is the moving of huge quantities of air. With gas turbines, this can be achieved, and the great reduction in drag, with allied increase in lift coefficient, in addition to enhanced control-surface operating conditions, must be of the greatest benefit to all aircraft so powered. This applies irrespective of the lower efficiency of the turbine-compressor unit, as compared with the orthodox engine/airscrew combination as already explained.

Fig. 161 is a reproduction of a drawing in the patent specification taken out by Air Commodore Whittle in 1938. As may be seen, the air intake is in the form of radially disposed, forward-facing scoops, which would provide a definite ram effect, but Whittle covers himself in the specification text by stating that in the drawing the extent to which they project into the relative air flow is exaggerated in proportion. That this is, in fact, the case, is confirmed by the investigations carried out by Schrenk, for Warner quotes Schrenk as having found in 1928 that the best method of effecting control of the boundary layer —by the suction method—is by means of simple, wide, flush slots in the surface.

Utilising Waste Exhaust

For the reason stated earlier, the application of such a system to an orthodox type of aircraft would be more limited in its scope. Nevertheless, some advantage could be obtained. This was appreciated in a project sponsored by the Bristol Aeroplane Co., Ltd., A. H. R. Fedden and F. M. Owner, in 1936, shown diagrammatically in Fig. 162. This is of interest as

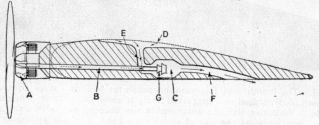

A. Exhaust collector ring.	D. Perforated skin.
B. Exhaust tail pipe.	E. Air conduit.
C. Gas/air mixing chamber.	F. Discharge conduit.
	G. Ejector nozzle.

Fig. 162. Bristol exhaust-actuated boundary layer control.

it employs the energy of the exhaust gases from a normal engine, which would otherwise be lost, to suck in the air from the boundary layer over part of the upper surface of an aerofoil. No demand is made on the power output of the engine and no auxiliary source of power is required.

A radial engine driving an airscrew is mounted forward of the leading edge of the wing of what is apparently a very large aircraft. The exhaust gases are collected in a ring A, located at the leading edge of the engine cowling, and delivered by a tail pipe B to a mixing chamber C. The upper surface of the wing, along a band D lying at about the middle of the chord and running lengthwise the wing, is formed with a series of perforations. These are preferably small, closely pitched holes, say, one sixty-fourth of an inch diameter and spaced one-quarter of an inch apart.

An inlet conduit E leads from the perforated strip to the chamber C, from which a conduit F leads to an outlet orifice in the lower surface of the wing near the trailing edge. From the tail pipe the exhaust gases discharge through a Mélot type multiple ejector-nozzle, or " thrust augmenter " G.

Together, nozzle G and chamber C constitute a fluid ejector which draws air through the perforated strip D, along the conduit E to the chamber and expels it rearwardly, together with the exhaust gases, through conduit F. The path from the perforations to the outlet is designed to give a smooth flow and diverges gradually to the chamber and then converges to the outlet. In this manner the kinetic energy of the air in the conduit E is converted to pressure energy. In chamber C the air is entrained by the exhaust gases

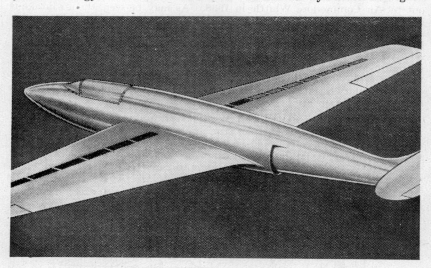

Fig. 163. The Prandtl and Baumann proposals for boundary layer control. They are shown incorporated in a suggested finely streamlined aircraft propelled by jet reaction. Velocities hitherto unattainable may become well within the bounds of possibility by the use of aircraft designed on these principles.

and in flowing to the outlet the pressure energy is reconverted to kinetic energy and a forward thrust is thereby obtained to assist the propulsion of the aircraft.

Fig. 163 shows an imaginative arrangement of a jet-propelled aircraft in which the boundary layer air flow is abstracted from the fuselage—it would also be taken likewise from the wings—and the efflux or jet is delivered on to the boundary layer region near the tail. In this type of design advantage is taken of both the Prandtl and Baumann proposals.

The Compressibility Problem

The foregoing remarks are concerned only with air flow conditions at subsonic speeds. However, as present day fighter aircraft of both airscrew and jet-reaction propulsion type are capable of approaching sonic speeds in various circumstances, a brief appraisal of the effects and their possible correction through boundary layer control is worthy of attention.

Because physical conditions are such that flow form undergoes a radical change as sonic speeds are approached and surpassed, the problems are

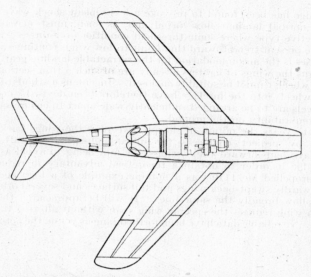

Fig. 164. The thin wing section of the Me 1101 single
jet fighter project necessitated provision for the retracted
undercarriage within the fuselage.

intensified. At the sonic threshold shock waves form about the body, the
intensity and magnitude of the waves depending upon the Mach value,
i.e., the ratio of relative velocity to the speed of sound at the conditions
obtaining. It should be pointed out, however, that the criterion is almost
invariably a *local* Mach value—for example, the ratio of speed of air flow
over, say, the wing leading edge, to the speed of sound at the height at which
the machine is flying—and not the *overall* Mach value. It is entirely possible
that the aircraft might be flying at Mach = 0.4 (40 per cent. of sonic speed)
and yet at the same time the speed of air flow over the wing leading edge
might easily be 0.65 sonic velocity.

Should the local Mach value exceed the critical for any limiting condition,
that is to say, if the wing root, for example, has a critical Mach value lower
than that of any other part of the machine, then when that lowest critical
condition is exceeded, trouble in some unpleasant form is very likely to occur
due to the onset of shock waves which bring about a disruption in the air flow.
With the incidence of shock waves the flow form of the air about the body
changes in such fashion as to bring about a separation in the flow which,
as we have seen, results in an increase in the wake. Further, in these
circumstances the wing wake will have increased to such an extent that it
almost inevitably must envelop the tail surfaces and this will result in
buffeting or, in extreme cases, in the partial or even complete breakdown
of elevator and rudder response.

Faced with entirely new problems, the aim of the designer of really
high speed aircraft is to evolve a form of such character that the effects of
immutable physical laws are to a certain extent nullified. The intensive
research given to the creation of high efficiency laminar flow airfoils is an
example of progress towards the desired goal. A great deal has still to be
learned about the subject ; nevertheless, the very thin wing with knife-like

leading edge has been found to provoke a less violent shock wave formation than the normal laminar flow airfoil and, as such, must necessarily be a more effective type where sonic threshold conditions obtain.

If the present trend toward thin laminar flow wings continues, a problem which arises is the accommodation for the retractable landing gear. In some late designs the wings of fighters already are of such a thin section that the retracted wheels cannot be suitably enclosed. Ingenious methods of retracting legs and wheels into the fuselage have therefore been devised—no easy task if the wheels are to be arranged sufficiently wide apart to ensure safe landing and manoeuvrability on the ground.

Of late years the notion of sharply sweeping the wings back has been favoured by project engineers for ultra high-speed aircraft. Certain designs have had forward-swept wings, the aim being to avoid a horizontal leading edge in order to obtain a theoretical advantage in reducing drag. The jet propelled Me 1110 was a notable example of a high speed fighter with rearwardly swept-back wings and tail surfaces and several other futurist designs follow broadly the same lines. It will be appreciated that a " V " formation wing reduces the specific wing span without altering the effective wing area. No reliable data have been forthcoming as yet on the actual benefits

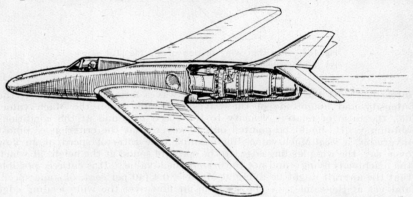

Fig. 165. Another Messerschmitt, the 1110 fighter project, had rearward swept wing and tail surfaces and a single jet unit mounted in the rear of the fuselage.

derivable and the subject remains one for study and argument among technicians as sonic speeds become attainable and problems of compressibility threaten to constitute a barrier to further progress. A disadvantage of the " arrow-head " wing design is that the maximum lift coefficient is adversely affected.

Thickness/Chord Ratio

In an excellent paper presented to the Albany (New York) Society of Engineers, C. E. Pappas asserted that, in order to possess good characteristics, the thickness/chord ratio of a high-speed profile should not exceed 12 per cent.; a fairly thin section.

Although various high-speed modern aircraft have been successfully flown at overall Mach numbers as high as 0.8 (and thus at local Mach numbers probably approaching unity) it has been generally established that the actual critical effect of compressibility begins at Mach numbers exceeding 0.65 at moderate values of lift of the airfoil. Streamline shape breaks down completely, and the drag coefficient increases rapidly with increase of Mach number; for example, between M = 0.60 and M = 0.75 it has been shown that the drag of a 12 per cent. t/c symmetrical profile increases tenfold and the lift breaks down.

In the light of this, it seems quite extraordinary that modern fighters—with fairly orthodox airfoils—should have been able to fly at Mach values in excess of 0.8. The explanation of this apparent anomaly would appear to be that the aircraft concerned have occasioned the most confused flow forms of air about themselves when so flying yet, at the same time, have not been so susceptible to flow deformation as to break-up. That they have, however, exhibited marked disinclination to control response verging on the unmanageable has been reported, and it is an established fact that one of the most serious difficulties in the way of attaining very high speed flight is that of providing adequate control. It may here be interpolated that propulsion units of requisite power output are available and, for the first time, the engine manufacturer is ahead of the aircraft designer.

When the intensity of the shock wave increases (intensity is the ratio of pressure ahead of the wave to pressure behind the wave) rotation of the

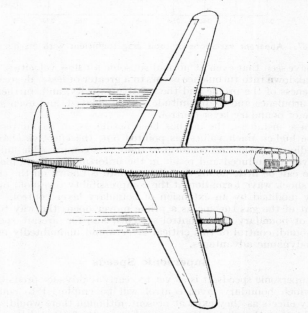

Fig. 166. A forward swept wing was a feature of the Junkers 287 bomber which, in this version, had twin 3-jet units.

field sets in and a turbulent flow region exists behind the wave, and the intensity of turbulence increases with the intensity of the shock wave. Eventually separation sets in, especially at the higher angles of attack and, as indicated in Fig. 167, at this point the drag increases precipitously and lift decreases rapidly. With the introduction of separation, wing circulation is decreased with the resultant loss in maximum lift coefficient. The turbulent field behind the shock wave will cause the tail surfaces to buffet and, consequently, the location of the tailplane is of paramount importance since it is very difficult to position this surface so that it will be out of the wing wake, particularly so since the wake increases appreciably when rotation of the field is created by the shock wave.   In the light of these remarks, the Gloster Meteor which attained 606 m.p.h. is a pointed example.

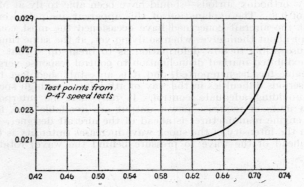

Fig. 167. Apparent variations of total drag coefficient with Mach number.

We have seen that even at normal subsonic air flow velocities, separation and a breakdown into turbulence occurs to a greater or lesser degree according to the fineness of the profile and the relative velocity, and, further, that the onset of turbulence and its magnitude can be delayed, and even suppressed, by the use of boundary layer control.

In these instances, the air has been acting as an incompressible fluid, but at the higher Mach values, as pointed out, the effective characteristics of the medium change, and conform to those of a compressible fluid whereby shock waves are induced and result in the unfortunate effects mentioned.

There can be little doubt that, when more is known on the subject, the effects of shock wave formation at the compressibility threshold may well be materially modified by an extension of boundary layer control.   Certainly, the advent of the gas turbine as a prime mover opens the way towards the adoption of boundary layer control systems, and for aircraft speeds below those of sound, control of this critical layer would undoubtedly bring about great aerodynamic advantages.

Supersonic Speeds

For supersonic speeds, it is as yet too early to advance predictions of the way in which boundary layer control will be employed to counter compressibility effects as they exist at present, although there would seem to be little doubt that the abstraction, or suction method (Prandtl) would prove to be more effective in this direction than the ejection system (Baumann).

The most efficient forms of orifices for both the suction and pressure systems have been found to be similar to those shown respectively in Figs. 156 and 157, where the suction orifice—air intake—is flush with the skin contour and at right angles to it, whilst the pressure orifice—jet—is arranged with its leading edge feathered to a sharp point profile in order to expel the air tangentially to the skin curvature.

No matter whether a single or multi-engine design is in contemplation the boundary layer can be beneficially controlled in the manner described

When propellers are used in conjunction with turbines, they will most probably be of the pusher type in order to gain whatever advantage is obtainable by deriving the engine intake air from the boundary layer region.

Studious reflection on the shape of aircraft to come, bearing in mind the conditions briefly surveyed, leads to the belief that, in contradistinction to the high speed aircraft of the present time, the development of future ultra high-speed machines is likely to bring forth entirely new types. For example, the wing may be the foremost member, and the fuselage a trailing appendage with the tail surfaces mounted as high as possible. Such a design would overcome the possibility of shock waves about a protruding nose interfering with the wing, as the latter component would be passing through relatively undisturbed air.

In any such study, one is naturally led to consider tailless types and all-wing designs (discussed in the following chapter) which, so long as aircraft rely on static airfoil surfaces for their support in flight, can be looked upon as approaching the ultimate in type design. Considering the all-wing aircraft in relation to the present state of knowledge of aerodynamics one is forced to the conclusion that to speculate upon their possible characteristics for supersonic flight is somewhat premature—the tailless and all-wing types have yet to be fully developed for flight at more modest subsonic speeds.

For the next few years to come it must be appreciated that the greatest aeronautical efforts must be directed towards achieving an economically tenable increase in both the lifting power and the cruising speed of commercial airliners. An increase of 100 m.p.h. or 150 m.p.h. in cruising speed, coupled with an increase in the aircraft's lifting power is no inconsiderable task when the criterion is economically acceptable operating costs. That effective boundary layer control would have a material effect on the attainment of this goal cannot seriously be denied. With the development of turbines of low specific fuel consumption it is likely that we shall, in the comparatively near future, see boundary layer control in normal employment. Advantage will be taken of submerging the power units within the wings. It is apparent that no possible means of increasing operative efficiency can be ignored in the competitive years ahead, and gas turbines, either with airscrews or as pure jets, offer opportunity for a considerable step up in speed. Successful solution of the problems involved could be regarded as a major advance in the science of aeronautics. In a general sense, power unit development is to-day ahead of progress with aircraft structures suitable for very high speeds and high altitudes. The solution of the problem of pressurized cabins is a prerequisite.

CHAPTER XV

TAILLESS AIRCRAFT AND THE FLYING WING : FUTURE TRENDS AND POSSIBILITIES DISCUSSED

IN the summary of advantages of turbine-compressor combinations for jet propulsion in Chapter I, it was mentioned that their convenient shape enabled such units to be completely enclosed in the fuselage or wholly submerged in the wings. The desire to eliminate the conventional fuselage and tail surfaces has been current among designers for many years. New aircraft of such a character have been introduced from time to time since 1910 when Junkers patented the *Tragflächen*, later known as the *Nurflugel*, from which arises the designation " all wing " or " flying wing."

Less was known in those days, however, about stability which is by far the most critical factor in tailless design. Col. J. W. Dunne was one of the pioneers who realised the advantages and disadvantages of the tailless type—which should not be confused with the modern conception of a flying

Fig. 168. The Westland-Hill series of Pterodactyl designs was a notable British contribution to the development of tailless aircraft. Illustrated is a fighter with Rolls-Royce Goshawk engine.

wing, that is, a deep-section all-wing aircraft providing accommodation internally for passengers, crew and cargo as well as for the motive units. Dunne foresaw that to ensure longitudinal stability it was necessary to sweep back the wings sharply in order to get the control surfaces (combination ailerons and elevators) well aft of the centre of gravity and so give them a reasonable " lever arm." His experiments were made in the period 1910–1912, and his aircraft were markedly vee-formed in plan.

About 1921 Lippisch experimented with models of tailless aircraft and was assisted in his work by Hermann Köhl. From 1928 they jointly produced five tailless monoplanes named the Delta, the last two having dihedral wings, the tips of which were turned sharply downward to improve stability. Lippisch designs employed a thin fabric-covered wing with a central engine and control cabin. Bristol or Fafnir engines of 30 h.p. were used with tractor airscrews. In support of his original layout Lippisch, against the normally accepted theoretical conceptions, claimed it was possible to achieve the necessary dynamic stability without any major difficulty.

Early British Types

During the years between the wars, Capt. Geoffrey Hill revived interest in the tailless type with his " Pterodactyls," which were demonstrated at British flying displays. On these the sweep back was rather less pronounced than in the Dunne aircraft, although still fairly considerable.

Flying wings, by virtue of their reduced " wetted area " and freedom from protuberances, promise greatly increased efficiency, particularly when they are sufficiently large to enable submerged power units to be employed. With the rapid increase in the size of aircraft being built or projected (100 tons all - up weight and wing spans of 200ft. are now common talk) the obvious trend is to enclose the power units completely in the wing and so effect a reduction in drag. To this end horizontally - opposed, horizontal H- and acute X-type engines have been specially developed for submerged installation.

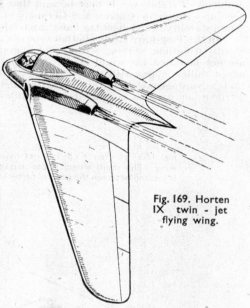

Fig. 169. Horten IX twin - jet flying wing.

It was foreshadowed in earlier editions of this work that the advent of the gas turbine must necessarily bring such projects nearer fruition and create something of a revolution in aircraft design. Instead of concentrating thought on the possibility of adapting conventional types of aircraft to propulsion by turbine-jet or turbine-airscrew units, the perfection of prime movers of the type under discussion will bring about a complete transformation. That is, new aircraft will in future be designed around the power units rather than adapting and modifying orthodox types of aircraft to receive them. This trend is, indeed, already becoming established and is apparent in the design of the de Havilland Vampire and of the Lockheed Shooting Star, without recourse to study of the extremely advanced and, in some cases, almost incongruously novel designs projected in Germany immediately prior to her defeat. Some projects are illustrated.

It may be claimed that ultra high-speed aircraft design is a highly specialised branch of aeronautical science and the design of large civil aircraft may be widely divergent to meet different operating conditions. This is true, with the proviso that what applies to military aircraft to-day may well become applicable to civil types in the near future. Accordingly, we are justified in looking ahead and considering likely trends in large scale airliners of the future and the possible influence of the gas turbine power unit on their design.

Such a forward survey necessarily includes the attractive proposition of the flying wing, for although the idea is as old as the industry itself, only in comparatively recent years have advances in aerodynamic and structural knowledge brought the essentially deep section wing to the stage of practicable realisation. Consequently, the problem of housing the power units internally in addition to providing accommodation for passengers and crew is no longer merely a dream of designers. Whether the type will finally emerge successfully in large sizes will depend upon the progress made in solving basic problems of stability. It may be said that so much development work has been undertaken in America and Germany as well as in this country, that all-round stability is no longer the handicap to all-wing types that it former.'y was.

In this long-term study another type of exceptional aerodynamic qualities merits attention. Flying wings, which involve deep sections throughout, are not favoured the world over. There is, indeed, a decided tendency to adopt tailless types with thin section, " knife edge " airfoils on account of their advantageous characteristics at the high speeds now attainable. With a true flying wing, as compared with a tailless design, it is a criticism of some

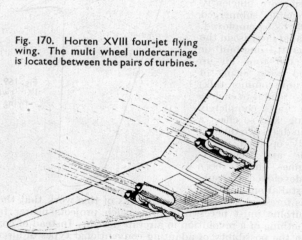

Fig. 170. Horten XVIII four-jet flying wing. The multi wheel undercarriage is located between the pairs of turbines.

importance that the location of the passenger compartment in the wing section tends to restrict the field of vision afforded to the occupants. Upward and downward views are certainly not as pleasing or reassuring as the wide vistas obtainable from the sides of a fuselage. However, promenade space could and probably would be arranged in the leading edge of the wing in the large transport types. The tailless design, it is urged, would avoid that criticism by permitting a large capacity fuselage in combination with thin section wings designed for operation at conditions of high Mach number.*

* Mach number is a decimal figure indicating local air speed relative to the speed of sound at the prevailing atmospheric conditions. Sonic speed is expressed as Mach number 1.0.

This consideration, among others, is diverting the attention of forward-thinking designers from true flying wings to modified tailless forms of aircraft, which may well have thin wings swept sharply backward or, possibly, forward. Prior to the advent of the gas turbine when speeds of military aircraft were about 300 m.p.h., and of the 200 m.p.h. order for civil aircraft,

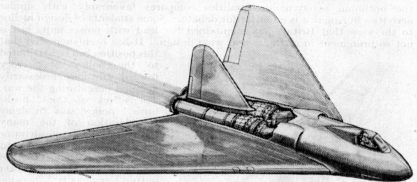

Fig. 171. Design for a twin-jet tailless fighter.

a mere 20 m.p.h. or so increase per year was a decided gain. The troubles which come with compressibility were not unduly pronounced, although they were recognised as needing study for the future as speeds steadily mounted. The arrival of the gas turbine, making possible a jump in operational speeds to nearly 600 m.p.h. and a consequent approach to the threshhold of sonic speed, not only vested the problem of boundary layer control with added importance but, as the volume of air passing through a

Fig. 172. Conception of single-jet tailless fighter with forward-swept wings.

turbine system is so immense, opened the way to a practicable method of achieving such control. The importance of this subject cannot be overstressed for a tremendous enhancement of performance would result. It is a subject for special study by research engineers.

In general, it may be observed, the overall design position is that power units are now ahead of aircraft structures. Aerodynamicists could have been expected to maintain their relatively advanced position had reciprocating engines merely continued to achieve their regular year-by-year increment in power output.   The proved gas turbine of high power and small dimensions, however, completely altered the picture.   Compressibility factors suddenly became urgent problems demanding early solution.

Whether in Britain progress towards airframe and wing designs possessing the optimum aerodynamic qualities compares favourably with similar activities in America is a matter for debate.   Some students of design incline to the view that Britain has maintained her lead with power units but is not so prominent in airframe and wing design.   It has been suggested that this position can be attributed to the policy of secrecy toward turbines necessarily adopted here during the war. The effect of the " hush-hush " policy was to delay consideration of the many problems confronting airframe designers until lightweight turbine propulsion units of enormously increased power output suddenly became available for operation.

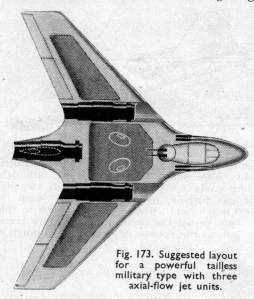

Fig. 173. Suggested layout for a powerful tailless military type with three axial-flow jet units.

In fact, it can be accepted that the extraordinarily rapid advance of the new rotating prime mover literally caught many aircraft engineers napping.

Much of the possible benefit derivable from the application of a compact turbine-jet unit in lieu of a piston engine of larger size and greater weight but comparable thrust horsepower is lost if full advantage is not taken of the inherent cleanliness of the turbine aerodynamically, and the shorter and lighter undercarriages made possible by the absence of airscrews.

Of late years aircraft constructors have mainly devoted their attention to two- or four-engine types. One wonders whether the advent of the small and compact turbine may not re-divert attention to three-engined aircraft. Attractive layouts are possible in this connection, and an example of a futurist type with swept-back wings projecting well behind the nose of the fuselage is submitted in Fig. 173. Three turbines are employed, one in each of the wing roots and the third in the tail. All-round visibility would be a feature of this powerful multi-purpose design.

It may be stated with some justification that for years the liaison between aircraft project engineers and power unit specialists has not been as close as it could and should have been. The war corrected to some degree the policy of watertight compartments and development by separate groups working in a detached way. With turbine applications the closest possible liaison between structural engineers and the power unit specialist is a *sine qua non*. The ever-present need for co-operation becomes doubly important if we are to achieve the maximum benefit in the shortest time from the

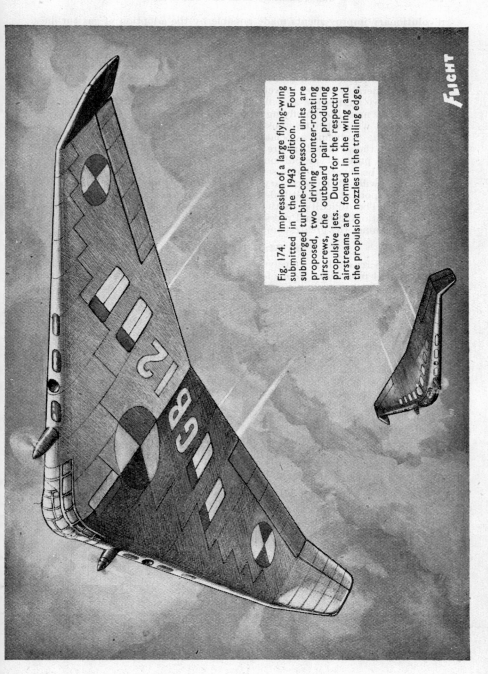

Fig. 174. Impression of a large flying-wing submitted in the 1943 edition. Four submerged turbine-compressor units are proposed, two driving counter-rotating airscrews, the outboard pair producing propulsive jets. Ducts for the respective airstreams are formed in the wing and the propulsion nozzles in the trailing edge.

revolutionary improvements made possible by the adoption of gas turbines. With first-class team work, the advanced designs of the next five years will be spectacular in appearance as well as performance.

It has been estimated that a flying wing has from $33\frac{1}{3}$ per cent. to 50 per cent. less total drag than a normal type, which implies that comparably less thrust power is needed to attain the same speed. Since a jet propulsion unit is considerably lighter in weight than an equivalent reciprocating engine with its many auxiliaries, a double advantage is suggested from a technical diagnosis, by marrying the flying wing to the gas turbine. It seems a logical development with attractive possibilities.

Until the problems associated with large capacity pressure cabins for operation in the stratosphere are solved, and there are many, the full benefit of flight by pure jet propulsion will not be attainable. A great deal of research has been carried on in several countries, but much hard thinking and experiment will still be necessary before a large airliner can be operated for public transport at high altitudes where the turbine-jet functions at higher efficiency. The difficulties with small pressurised cabins are not so great ; it is in maintaining normal pressures in capacious passenger cabins that the problem assumes the greatest importance.

Fast Mail Plane Services

For this reason it is conceivable that ultra-fast jet-propelled mail planes with a small pressurised cabin for the crew may be the first to be used on long-distance transocean services to Canada, America and Australia. Flying high and extremely fast under the most economical conditions, speedy air mail services to all parts of the globe would be possible if H.M. Postmaster-General encourages such projects. The technical equipment could be relatively quickly available if manufacturers are given the necessary support.

Reverting to passenger transports, a tricycle or tractor type undercarriage is a desirable feature of the specification in order to provide a natural level for a large multi-engined aircraft and ease of passengers in moving about when the aircraft is on the ground and also to aid manoeuvrability on the airfield. As already stressed, a very low build is possible since little ground clearance is required with the comparatively small-diameter counter-rotating airscrews likely to be employed, and less still if propulsive jets are used exclusively. Inside the aircraft a small independent auxiliary engine or turbine driving a generator would be desirable to take care of the many electrically-operated components and mechanisms such as starters, airscrews, undercarriage, flaps, lighting and radio.

" Mixed " Power Units

By way of illustration of the possible form our future airliners may take, the author, in 1943, roughly sketched for execution by R. E. Poulton an impression of a large flying-wing transport embodying control surfaces of the Lippisch or Northrop type (page 185), which was extensively reproduced in U.S.A. It is of very wide span and powered by four submerged turbine units. The inboard pair drive counter-rotating airscrews, whilst the outboard units are of the jet propulsion type. A feature of this bare layout is that ducts for the respective air intakes are arranged in or near the point of the wing section of greatest depth in order to effect boundary layer control, and the propulsion nozzles are arranged in the trailing-edge.

Since the weight of the airscrews is considerable, it is suggested that they would be employed on the inner pair in order to concentrate weight near the central axis and permit lighter construction. In this arrangement the efflux of the turbines could be utilised as auxiliary propulsive jets. By suitable ducting, as much of the heat as necessary could be diverted along the leading-edge of the wing and control surfaces to prevent ice formation when operating under adverse atmospheric conditions.

Variants of this scheme might with advantage form a subject of investigation. For example, as another of the drawings indicates, the four or more turbine units could be of the jet propulsion type without airscrews, or alternatively two of them might drive tractor airscrews or pusher type propellers. Again all four turbines could have pusher type contra-rotating propellers.

A further modification would be to use a "mixed" system on a four-unit or six-unit design. That is, the inboard pair might be orthodox two- or four-stroke reciprocating engines and the outboard units turbine-jet propulsion plants. The advantages suggested by such an arrangement are that reciprocating engines with contra-rotating airscrews would enable a quicker take-off and rate of climb, aid manoeuvrability of the aircraft on the ground, and prove more efficient at the present normal operating altitudes. At the higher altitudes, as the efficiency of the reciprocating engines tended to fall away,

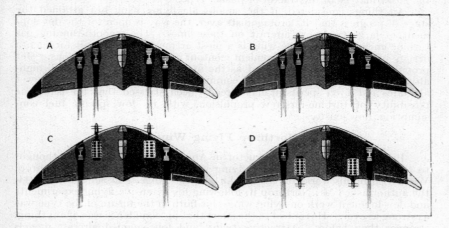

Fig. 175.   Four suggested arrangements of power units on flying-wing aircraft.

A. Four continuous combustion turbine and axial compressor type jet propulsion units.
B. Two turbine-driven counter-rotating airscrews and two jet propulsion units.
C. Two reciprocating engines driving counter-rotating airscrews and two jet propulsion units.
D. Two reciprocating engines driving counter-rotating pusher airscrews and two jet propulsion units.

the jet propulsion units would compensate for the loss, and could also possibly be used as the sole means of propulsion for economical cruising. Under certain conditions of high-altitude flight, particularly when operating over long ranges, it might be an advantage if the reciprocating engines could be stopped to conserve fuel, propeller blades fully feathered, and the aircraft carry on solely by jet reaction. Again, for military uses, a turbine-compressor unit might with advantage be used on existing heavy bombers to enable quicker take-off under full load conditions, and also to give increased speed when desirable in certain emergencies. In this connection the idea of utilising the greatly improved efficiency of rockets in combination with turbine-jet planes will not be overlooked. Already rocket-assisted take off has been regularly used on military and naval aircraft with marked success.

Scope for Designers

The idea of associating conventional petrol reciprocating engines driving airscrews with the combustion gas turbine and compressor plant producing a propulsive jet was first propounded by the writer in *Flight* of November 26th, 1942, in a note emphasising the urgent need for a Government policy on post-war air transport.   Some time prior to that date, and following a talk with a non-technical artist, a futurist drawing was produced of a mammoth long-range air liner embodying every travel comfort for world-wide transport.   The drawing showed eight reciprocating engines driving contra-rotating airscrews, the power units being submerged in the wings, and independent or subsidiary means of jet propulsion by a gas turbine-compressor combination located in the tail of the fuselage.

In the likely event of the flying wing being combined with a plurality of gas turbine motive units, many alternative methods of employing them individually or collectively offer considerable scope for the ingenuity of designer and project engineer.   It is obvious that should a part of the power plant be in the form of reciprocating engines or turbines with airscrews, the latter may be of the tractor or pusher type.

All things considered, if the small-scale flying wing has attained the stage of progress that its protagonists aver, the way is open for the development of large transport aircraft on these lines.   The smooth-running gas turbine enclosed within the wing is a most attractive power unit for such a design by reason of its convenient contour and other considerations.   Jet propulsion is now being accepted as the most suitable for high-speed, high-altitude flight, but in the case of commercial transport operating at lower altitudes and lower speeds, it has already been stressed that the economic possibility of turbine-airscrew propulsion, with its low specific fuel consumption, now exists.

Northrop Flying Wings

Probably no aircraft constructor in America has devoted more thought to the design and production of flying wings than Mr. Jack K. Northrop. When visiting his works on the outskirts of Los Angeles in September, 1944, the author asked Mr. Northrop if, following his extensive flying experiments and development work on flying wings, his faith in the future of the type was as strong as ever.   He replied to the effect that his confidence was, if anything, stronger than before.   Attractive twin- and four-engined aircraft models decorated his office and although the Northrop works were, at that time, busily occupied on the twin-engined, twin-boom Black Widow night-fighter, one may confidently expect further advanced flying wing designs from this enterprising Californian factory.

A small scale flying model of the Northrop flying wing which, first powered with two 65 h.p. four-cylinder Lycoming engines and later with two 120 h.p. six-cylinder Franklin engines, has been subjected to extensive testing in America over some considerable period.   This machine has a 38ft. span and is 17ft. long.   After the initial tests in 1940 it was reported that adequate controllability and stability about all three axes had been achieved, obtained through the shape of the wing rather than through the use of external fins, rudders, stabiliser or other auxiliary services.   The wings are swept acutely backward and although the tips were originally dropped downward in a negative dihedral form following the example of Lippisch designs, these were subsequently changed in favour of normal tips.   The horizontal-type reciprocating engines are housed entirely within the wing section and drive pusher airscrews.

Although fitted with four Pratt & Whitney piston engines driving pusher type contra-rotating airscrews, the Northrop XB35 experimental bomber announced as this edition goes to press, is of particular interest as such a type is especially suited to gas turbine propulsion. Particulars of this cantilever, all-metal, flying wing which has no tail surfaces and uses " elevon " controls as both elevators and ailerons are appended :

Design weight empty	..	89,000 lb.	Tip chord ..	..	9ft. 4in.
Design weight loaded	..	162,000 lb.	Overall height	..	20ft. 1in.
Span ..	..	172ft.	Overall length	..	53ft. 1in.
Root chord	..	37ft. 6in.	Propeller clearance	..	9ft. 8in.

The new XB35 was due to undergo flight tests in the summer of 1946. It is understood that turbine units, both jet and airscrew types, will be employed on later models. A suitable power unit is being developed by the Northrop-Hendy Co.

Fig. 176. The Northrop XB-35 flying-wing bomber with four piston engines. An aircraft of this type and size is eminently suited for gas-turbine power plants.

Speaking of California reminds one that in no other district of America is interest in turbine-jet propulsion so pronounced as on the Pacific Coast. Mr. Hall Hibbard, Chief Engineer, and Mr. Clarence L. Johnson, Designer of the Lockheed Shooting Star, have tremendous enthusiasm for the types for which they are responsible. Mr. Hibbard expressed the view that in a relatively short time we shall see turbine-jet aircraft speeds passing through the compressibility range and exceeding the speed of sound (approximately 725–775 m.p.h. at sea level). Similar confidence was evident to a greater or lesser degree among aircraft engineers with whom the author discussed the power unit position when the guest of the American Society of Automotive Engineers at their Aeronautical Convention, Los Angeles, in 1944.

Fig. 177 shows three models by the Hawker-Siddeley group for tailless and flying-wing aircraft. The types represented will obviously have important civil and military applications. To speed development and permit study of design and handling problems associated with aircraft of this class, Sir W. G. Armstrong-Whitworth Aircraft Ltd. have built a two-seat flying-wing glider with a laminar-flow wing and a novel control system, the horizontal moving surfaces of which occupy approximately 50 per cent. of the wing chord. The span is 53ft.

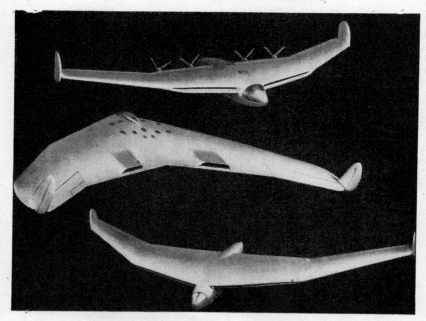

Fig. 177. Three Hawker-Siddeley models for tailless and "flying wing" aircraft. Top, a tailless design with submerged power plants driving pusher airscrews ; centre, a flying wing with jet outlets above the trailing-edge ; and, below, a jet-propelled tailless aircraft resembling the airscrew-driven design.

Transocean Turbine–jet Liner

Based upon successful tests with this flying-wing glider, Armstrong Whitworth have recently announced their interest in a transocean all-wing night flying passenger and freight liner of 160-foot span to the designs of Mr. John Lloyd. Six Rolls-Royce Nene turbine-jet units are proposed with fuel tanks of 10,000 gallons capacity. A payload of 29,700 lbs. is provided at a speed exceeding 400 m.p.h. Wing area is 4,400 sq. ft., mean chord 27ft. 6in. and wing loading 41 lb. sq. foot. The pressurised cabin will provide accommodation for 24 to 28 sleeping passengers.

Design, Initiative and Policy

In his 1940 Wilbur Wright Memorial lecture to the Royal Aeronautical Society, Dr. H. Roxbee Cox took as his subject the " Future of British Civil Aviation." On the problem of the " all-wing aircraft " he said :

"Aircraft design is improved by the desire for greater safety, convenience, economy and prestige, and is a compromise between these four. Our future success will depend on our technical initiative. Some of the big jumps are appearing—pressure cabins, laminar boundary layers, pusher airscrews, diesel and direct injection engines, all-wing aircraft.

"I have previously discussed the general problem of large aircraft, explaining the necessity for spreading the masses across the span. This led naturally to the all-wing design, which is highly efficient structurally, but is efficient as a load container only in very large sizes. This is because the ratio of surface to volume is large and because head room is restricted.

Fig. 178. The Armstrong Whitworth 52-G all-wing glider in the air.

" In Fig. 179 the ordinates of the full lines give wing stowage space, and the difference between dotted and full lines gives fuselage stowage space. Taking 50 lb. sq. ft. as a wing loading likely to be realised soon, we see that for small aircraft there is no room for passengers in the wing. At 100,000 lb. the wing begins to have a little accommodation in it, and for a 15 per cent. stowed load at 280,000 lb. the wing can accommodate as much as the fuselage. At 380,000 lb. there is no need for a fuselage. Fig. 180 emphasises that true all-wing aircraft will be big. From Fig. 182 we see the gain in performance obtained by utilising the wing for stowage. The first steps towards the

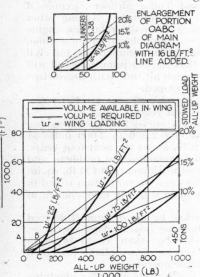

Fig. 179. Wing stowage space.

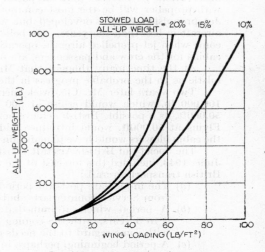

Fig. 180. Advantage in large sizes.

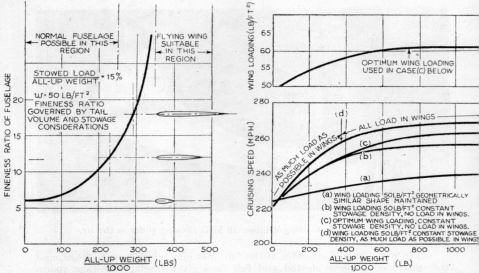

Fig. 181. Transition from normal to flying   Fig. 182. Performance improvement with wing
          wing type.   stowage.

all-wing design were taken in a most notable German aeroplane, the Junkers G.38, which, with its wing loading of 16 lb. sq. ft., and with a stowed load of about 13 per cent. of the all-up weight, fits well into Fig. 179."

No less talented a designer than Mr. Roy Chadwick, chief designer of the four-engined Avro Lancaster bomber and Tudor airliners, expressed his views in November, 1943, on post-war civil aircraft.   Among other observations he forecast that the petrol-burning internal-combustion engine with propeller will be the most common type of propulsion for some time. Jet propulsion will be developed but will not be in common use for civil aircraft in less than ten years.   He believed that the big jump in speed will come when jet-propelled aircraft, operating at high altitude with pressurised cabins for the crew and passengers, are fully developed.

At the time many thought that Mr. Chadwick's views were too pessimistic as to the probable progress in the next ten years.

Two years later Mr. Chadwick mentioned a pure-jet airliner weighing 100,000 lb. which would cruise at 500 m.p.h. for 2,500 to 3,000 miles at 50,000ft. as a possible British achievement within about the next four years. Flying at 50,000ft. would introduce additional pressurisation problems and the cabin blowers would have to maintain a pressure differential of 11 lb. sq. in.

The Society of British Aircraft Constructors in a memorandum issued in June, 1943, included this forecast of the three main stages in development of British transport aircraft :

(a) The immediate post-war period, marked by use of aircraft derived from Service counterparts, but embodying present-day experience.

(b) A period which, if immediate action be taken, could begin in 4 to 5 years, with the coming into service of aeroplanes projected with some regard to the needs of airline operators.

(c) A period beginning, perhaps, in ten years, using aircraft embodying jet propulsion, boundary layer control, flying-wing design.

Fig. 183.

At high altitudes higher flying speeds are possible with less expenditure of power. At about 33,000ft. an aircraft gains 40 per cent. in speed and 50 per cent. in range for the same overall consumption of fuel as a similar aircraft flying at low altitude.

The chart herewith shows the heights above the earth's surface attained by balloons, heavier-than-air craft and the V-2 rocket weapon.

The layer nearest the earth, known as the troposphere, extends for 6 to 10 miles. Beyond that is the stratosphere continuing to a total distance of about 30 miles. Between the two is a layer called the tropopause in which the transition from one layer to the other takes place.

In the troposphere temperature decreases at a uniform rate of 2 deg. C. per 1,000ft. as the distance from the earth's surface is increased. Temperature is constant at — 55 deg. C. in the stratosphere and difficulties due to atmospheric conditions are virtually non-existent.

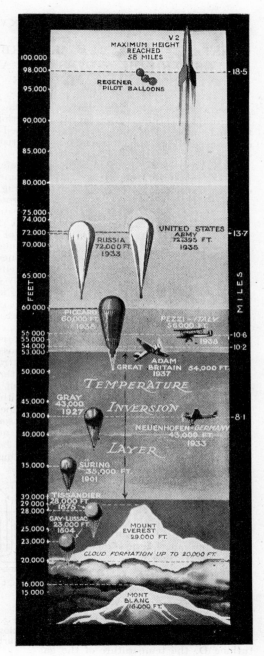

CHAPTER XVI

CONSTANT-PRESSURE GAS TURBINES OPERATING ON A CLOSED CYCLE : GASEOUS AND LIQUID WORKING MEDIUMS

CONSTANT-PRESSURE gas turbine plants may be divided into two groups according to whether they function on an " open " or " closed " thermal cycle. The three systems described in this article are all of the closed-cycle type and represent Swiss, British and American ideas on the subject.

Earlier reviews of turbine units have referred exclusively to open-cycle plants. They were true *combustion* gas turbines, and to avoid the possibility of confusion arising, a diagram is given in Fig. 184. The rotary compressor A draws air from the atmosphere and delivers it under pressure to a combustion chamber B into which fuel is sprayed continuously through injector C. The combustion gases are expanded through the turbine D, producing mechanical energy which drives the compressor and delivers useful power at the output shaft E. To improve the thermal efficiency, heat remaining in the gases leaving the turbine is utilised in a contra-flow heat exchanger or regenerator F to raise the temperature of the air coming from the compressor.

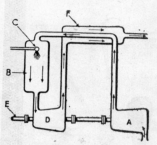

Fig. 184. Diagram of open-cycle, constant-pressure combustion gas turbine plant with regenerator.

By comparison, it would seem that closed-cycle plants possess features that render them particularly attractive for aircraft installation. It is claimed that a thermal efficiency at least equal to that of an up-to-date steam plant can be obtained without excessively high pressures or temperatures, and consequently metallurgical problems are greatly simplified. The working medium may be air or some other gas, or a liquid, and may be non-inflammable, non-toxic, and non-corrosive to metals. Any suitable fuel, solid, liquid or gaseous, may be employed, and the products of combustion have no access to any moving parts. Thus frictional losses and wear are reduced while safety in operation is enhanced.

Regenerative Closed Cycle

A Swiss firm, Escher Wyss Engineering Works, Ltd., of Zürich, have for some time had a large industrial plant of this description in operation driving an electric generator. How such a system functions may be seen in the diagram, Fig. 185. The working gas (air is used in the Escher Wyss plant) is compressed isothermally in a rotary compressor A, having several stages and intercoolers. On its way to the turbine D, the temperature of the gas

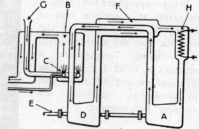

Fig. 185. Diagram of Escher Wyss closed-cycle, constant-pressure gas turbine plant with oil or gas fired furnace.

194

is raised by passage through a regenerator F, and before reaching the turbine inlet it is superheated in a furnace B. In this unit is an oil burner C supplied with combustion air entering at G, and pre-heated by the products of combustion which are discharged to atmosphere. The working medium is expanded through the turbine to drive the compressor and deliver power at shaft E in the usual manner. After leaving the turbine the medium passes through the regenerator, where it gives up heat to the compressed air on its way to the furnace, and then through a cooler H, which further reduces it to the desired temperature at the compressor inlet. Thus the working medium is compressed, warmed, heated, expanded and cooled ready for re-compression in a completely closed circuit.

Working under ideal conditions with no loss, it can be shown that for specified maximum and minimum temperatures of the medium, the thermal efficiency depends solely on the ratio of the maximum and minimum pressures and not on the absolute magnitude of the pressures. The lower the pressure ratio the higher the efficiency. In practice, of course, heat is lost at the compressor stage coolers, at the final gas cooler H, at the furnace flue, by friction and radiation. Nevertheless, the principle holds good approximately for a system in which losses occur. Whilst a steam plant requires high pressures and high temperatures to achieve efficiency, in the closed-circuit gas turbine plant it is not necessary to raise pressures to improve efficiency. Thus it offers the possibility of substantial advantages in weight, first cost, and maintenance of both the main units and also the valves and control equipment.

The separation of the gas circuit from the combustion process enables the flow passages to be of reduced cross section, as there is no liability of impedance or restriction by accumulation of solid matter from the products of combustion. Size and weight are also favourably influenced owing to the entire circuit operating under pressure, as the rate of heat transfer is nearly proportional to the pressure. These considerations apply with particular effect to the regenerator, which can conveniently be of smaller dimensions than an equivalent unit for a freely discharging, open-cycle system.

Working Pressures

With an initial pressure of 10 atm. abs. at the compressor intake, instead of the 1 atm. abs. as is usual with the open-cycle system, and with equal temperatures and speeds, the diameters of both turbine and compressor can be reduced by 66 per cent. Even with such a reduction, the Reynolds number for the rotor blades would be three times as great as for the equivalent open-cycle rotor.

Also of importance is the facility for control by regulating the density of the working medium in the closed-cycle without altering either the temperature or the speed. If, in the smaller units referred to, the pressure at the compressor inlet is lowered from 10 atm. abs. to 1 atm. abs., the output would be reduced by 90 per cent. Actually the medium in the closed cycle can be reduced to a negative pressure in order to reduce the power required for initial rotation when starting up the plant.

The English Electric Company also have a project for closed-circuit turbine plants using a gas as the working medium. Specifically they exclude vapours, for example, steam or mercury vapour, and also air. As there is no loss of the medium from the closed circuit, it is possible to employ relatively rare gases. The general layout of the plant is essentially similar to that of the Escher Wyss system and is indicated diagrammatically in Fig. 186.

The working medium is compressed in an axial flow compressor A and is passed through a tube in the furnace C and thence to the inlet side of turbine B. The heater may be oil fired, although pulverised fuel, or indeed any type of fuel may be used. The gas leaving the turbine on the return half of the circuit still retains a considerable amount of heat and is therefore passed through a regenerator D in order to preheat the cool gas on its way from the compressor to the furnace. If, after leaving the regenerator, the return gas is still at a higher temperature than desirable, it may be passed through a cooler, not shown in the diagram, before entering the compressor for recirculation. The products of combustion do not, of course, pass into the compressor and turbine system.

The outstanding feature of the English Electric system is the use of a monatomic gas as the working medium. A monatomic gas may be briefly defined as one in which the molecule, the smallest division retaining all the characteristics of the gas, contains only one atom. The molecules of diatomic and triatomic gases, carbon monoxide and carbon dioxide, for instance, have respectively two and three atoms. For a monatomic gas the ratio of the specific heat at constant pressure to the specific heat at constant volume is approximately 1.66 as compared with 1.4 for a diatomic gas and 1.3 for a triatomic gas. The higher the value of this ratio the lower will be the pressure ratio required for a compressor and turbine designed to give maximum efficiency at chosen values of maximum and minimum limits of temperature in the system.

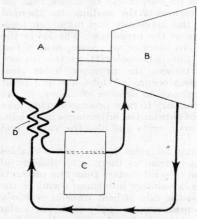

Fig. 186. Diagram of English Electric closed-cycle turbine plant employing a monatomic gas as the working medium.

Furthermore, within given temperature limits and with a given pressure ratio, the greater the density of the gas the smaller will be the adiabatic heat drop in the turbine. As a consequence, providing that rotor diameters, speeds of rotation and ratios of blade speed to gas speed remain the same, the number of stages required in the turbine and in the compressor will be fewer. Additionally, the greater the density of the gas the smaller will be the dimensions of the flow passages. A monatomic gas is not liable to dissociation at high temperatures, and if a relatively inert gas is used, the corrosive action on the turbine and compressor blades will be less than that of air.

By using a monatomic gas, such as argon, all these advantages can be realised. This inert gas has a density approximately 1.38 times that of air at the same temperature and pressure. The rare gases krypton and xenon could also be used to further advantage, as their densities are respectively 2.87 times and 4.53 times that of air. Some proportion of neon, another monatomic gas, could be included in the working medium, although its low density, only 0.696 that of air, is a disadvantage.

The question of relative density is of considerable importance. As an alternative to the comparatively rare gases mentioned, the English Electric Co. propose the use of carbon dioxide for the working medium, as it has a density of 1.52 times that of air at the same temperature and pressure. This despite the fact that it is a triatomic gas and consequently less suitable for the purpose than a monatomic gas.

From the U.S.A. comes a proposal by B. B. Holmes to employ a liquid medium in a closed thermal cycle to operate a turbine specifically for driving an airscrew. In the past various fluids such. as alcohol, aniline, benzol, carbon tetrachloride, ether, sulphur dioxide, toluol, water and xylol have been suggested as a working fluid for converting heat into motive power, but all had disadvantages which rendered them impracticable or dangerous in operation and therefore not suitable for commercial use. In the main, the critical temperatures and pressures of such fluids are excessively high and thereby necessitate extremely heavy equipment, or they are highly toxic, corrosive or inflammable and consequently liable to be dangerous to life and property.

The liquids proposed are stable chemical combinations of carbon, chlorine and fluorine, and known as " freons." Four of these compounds, trichloro-monofluoro-methane (F–11), dichloro-difluoro-methane (F–12), dichloro-monofluoro-methane (F–21), and trichloro-trifluoro-ethane (F–113), possess physical and thermodynamic properties which render them suitable for use in a turbine motive unit for aircraft. All are non-toxic, non-combustible and non-corrosive to metal. Each has a low melting point, low critical temperature and low critical pressure.

	SYMBOL	MELTING POINT deg. C.	CRITICAL PRESSURE lb./sq. in. abs.	CRITICAL TEMPERA-TURE deg. C.
F–11 Trichloro-monofluoro-methane	CCl_3F	− 111·1	635	197·7
F–12 Dichloro - difluoro-methane	CCl_2F_2	− 157·7	582	111·7
F–21 Dichloro-monofluoro-methane	$CHCl_2F$	− 135·0	750	178·7
F–113 Trichloro - trifluoro-methane	$C_2Cl_3F_3$	− 35·0	499	213·9

The choice of the liquid for a specific aircraft application will depend upon the prevailing condensing temperature, that is, whether the aircraft travels in sub-zero or higher temperature conditions, and upon the thermal

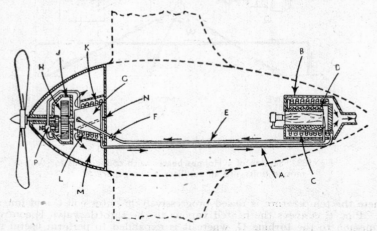

Fig. 187. The Holmes thermodynamic plant shown diagrammatically installed in an aircraft fuselage.

efficiency obtainable from the liquid under the conditions obtaining. Thus an aircraft may be operated in winter or at high altitudes with one liquid, whilst in summer or at low altitudes another might be employed to better advantage.

The liquid is raised to a pressure of between 400 and 1,000 lb./sq. in. ; heat is applied externally to raise the temperature to between 93 deg. C. and 215 deg. C. to vaporise the liquid ; the vapour is superheated to a temperature sufficiently high to ensure dryness throughout the desired expansion range ; the vapour is condensed back to a liquid and the cycle is continuously repeated.

A diagrammatic layout of such a thermal plant in an aircraft is shown in Fig. 187. The liquid under pressure is forced along pipe A to the heater B,

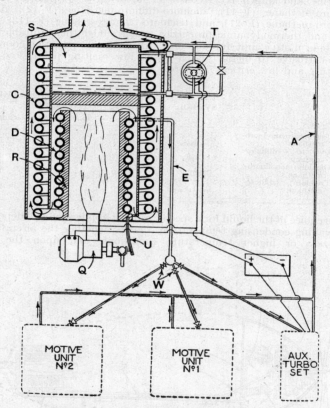

Fig. 188.   Section of a Holmes heater with connections for twin motive units and an auxiliary turbo-generator.

where the temperature is raised progressively in outer coil C and inner coil D.   Pipe E conveys the heated vapour to the throttle valve F controlling admission to the turbine G, where it is expanded to perform useful work. The turbine drives the airscrew through a reduction gear H enclosed in a casing J.   On leaving the turbine, the vapour passes through the annular space K around the turbine which houses a regenerator coil L and enters the condensing chamber M. Here it condenses on the surface of the boundary walls and drains to the lowest point at N. From here the liquid is drawn off by pump P, gear-driven from the airscrew shaft, and forced through the regenerator coil to absorb heat prior to recirculation.

The heater is shown in more detail in Fig. 188 with connections for a twin-screw installation and a small supplementary turbo-generator set for auxiliary power. Outer and inner coils C and D are of seamless Monel metal tubing, and although only single coils are shown, multiple coils arranged in parallel may be employed. Heat is supplied by a fuel oil burner Q of conventional type, comprising an electric motor-driven oil pump and air blower and an oil throttle valve. The inner tube coil is wound on a core R of copper to prevent any part of the tube becoming overheated to a degree likely to endanger the chemical stability of the working medium.

Return pumps P on the turbine units deliver the condensed liquid to a receiver S where it absorbs heat from the escaping flue gases. An electrically driven pump T, equipped with a pressure relief valve and by-pass circuit to maintain a constant pressure, draws the liquid from the receiver and delivers it through the outer coil C and then the inner coil D. The hot combustion gases from the burner travel in a counter-direction to the liquid, being directed by a baffle below the receiver and a cylindrical screen between inner and outer coils. Pump T raises the liquid to a pressure of, say, 800 lb./sq. in., that is, above the critical pressure. Consequently, as it travels through the coils of the heater, it can pass from the liquid to the vapour state without boiling as soon as the critical temperature is reached. To maintain the outgoing vapour at a constant temperature, the valve regulating the supply of oil to the burner is automatically controlled by a thermostatic device comprising a bi-metallic strip U embedded in the copper core of the heater.

Wing-mounted Turbine Unit

A propulsion unit for wing installation is shown in Fig. 189. The turbine G is arranged above the airscrew shaft, which it drives through reduction gears H. Vapour from the common heater mounted in the fuselage reaches

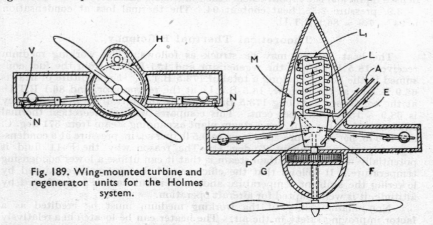

Fig. 189. Wing-mounted turbine and regenerator units for the Holmes system.

the turbine by pipe E through valve F, which is under the control of the operator for regulating the power output. After expansion through the turbine, the vapour enters the central chamber of the regenerator, reverses direction into the annular chamber, and discharges into the condensing chamber M. The outlets from collecting sumps N, provided at the extremities of the lateral extensions of chamber M, are controlled by valves V, which are each opened by a float rising on the condensed liquid. This arrangement ensures that only liquid is drawn off from the condensing chamber when the aircraft is being manœuvred in flight. Pump P, driven from an extension of the airscrew shaft, passes the liquid successively through outer and inner coils, L and L_1, of the regenerator and delivers it by pipe A to the receiving tank of the heater unit.

The operation of the system can best be understood by following the working medium around the complete circle in the specific example put forward by the sponsor of the scheme. Let us assume that F–11 is employed ; that liquid pressure in the heater is 800 lb./sq. in. ; that heater temperature is slightly in excess of 371 deg. C. ; that the aircraft is travelling at a high altitude, and that the ambient temperature will ensure a condensing temperature of − 17.7 deg. C. References to temperature are given in deg. C., to pressure in lb./sq. in. absolute, and to heat content in British Thermal Units.

One pound of the F–11 liquid in the condenser, having a volume of 0.0192 cu. ft., has temperature − 17.7, pressure 2.55, and heat content 7.9. Sump pump P raises the pressure of the liquid and delivers it to the regenerator where it absorbs heat and is then passed to the receiving tank of the heater at temperature 32.6, pressure 20, and heat content 26.4. Pump T then increases the pressure to 800 and, as a result of the work expended, the liquid enters the outer coil C of the heater at temperature 37.7, pressure 800, and heat content 28, an addition of 1.6 B.T.U.

In the heater the liquid vaporises as the temperature reaches 197.7, the critical temperature, and it leaves the heater at temperature 376, pressure 800, and heat content 183. After expansion through the turbine G the vapour has a volume of 18.5 cu. ft. and temperature 68.3, pressure 2.55, and heat content 112.5. Thus the thermal energy available for useful power at the shaft is 183 − 112.5 − 1.6 = 68.9 B.T.U.

At the regenerator stage, as noted earlier, heat is given up to the condensed liquid and the vapour reaches the condensing chamber M at temperature − 3.9, pressure 2.55, heat content 94. The thermal loss at condensation is 94 − 7.9 = 86.1 B.T.U.

Theoretical Thermal Efficiency

The heat balance may be struck as follows : The working medium receives 18.5 B.T.U. at the regenerator and 155 B.T.U. from the fuel consumed in the heater, making a total of 173.5 B.T.U. Expenditure of heat is 68.9 B.T.U. at the turbine, 18.5 B.T.U. at the regenerator, and 86.1 B.T.U. at the condenser, totalling 173.5 B.T.U. The theoretical thermal efficiency is 68.9 ÷ 155 = 44.4 per cent. This compares with a theoretical thermal efficiency of 41 per cent. for a steam plant expanding steam from 371 deg. C. and 800 lb. per sq. in. pressure down to 0.5 lb. per sq. in. pressure at a condensing temperature of about 27 deg. C. The reason why the F–11 fluid is potentially more efficient than steam is that it can utilise a lower condensing temperature. It follows that the efficiency of the system is enhanced by lowering the ambient temperature and, as it is substantially unaffected by altitude, it is well adapted for aircraft operation.

Non-inflammability of the working medium must be credited as a factor improving safety in the air. The heater can be located in a relatively safe position in the fuselage, where it can be accessible to the crew and, if necessary, can be effectively protected by armour. Where a centralised heater is employed to supply several motive units, arrangements can be made to isolate a damaged or defective unit without interrupting the operation of the others. Apart from mechanical defects, failure due to rupture by gunfire can occur on the high or low pressure side of the turbine. In the high pressure distribution system, automatic shut-off valves W are provided for each line. These are normally held open by a spring against the throttling effect of the flow through the valve, but in the event of an abnormal pressure drop due to rupture the valve becomes unbalanced and seats, thus cutting out the defective unit.

Should damage occur in the condensing system the effects will vary according to the prevailing condensing pressure. If below atmospheric pressure, air will enter the condensing chamber and efficiency will be decreased, but the unit will not cease to function. On the other hand, if the pressure is above atmosphere a loss of working fluid will occur. Gauges on a control board will show the operator the condition of the condensing system of each motive unit and indicate whether a unit should be shut down or not. Another gauge shows the level of the liquid in the receiving tank of the heater, and will give indication of leakage in the pipe lines, pumps or condensers.

So far as is known the projects described in this chapter have not yet been developed to a practical stage for application to aircraft. At present the open cycle constant pressure gas turbine plant is attracting the most attention, with results which are now public knowledge. Other British, American and Continental concerns are known to be investigating closed cycle systems for industrial applications.

CHAPTER XVII

STEAM TURBINES FOR JET OR AIRSCREW PROPULSION

BEFORE a satisfactory estimation of the possibility of employing steam for the propulsion of aircraft can be made, the inherent requirements must be fully appreciated. Power plants should possess the following characteristics : (1) Low weight per unit power. (2) Compactness. (3) High thermal efficiency. (4) Reliability. (5) Flexibility. (6) Ease of maintenance. (7) Durability. (8) Good performance at high altitudes.

The report on the investigation on steam propulsion for aircraft published by the American National Advisory Committee on Aeronautics concluded that " on the basis of the weight of the power plant alone steam power plants for aircraft are precluded. On the basis of economy alone they are again precluded. On the basis of the resistance of the cooling surface required alone, they are precluded. On the basis of the sum of these three considerations they are absolutely impossible."

While this verdict, pronounced by such eminent experts, appears to wipe out any possibility of steam propulsion, it should not be taken as final. The trend of aircraft design which calls for more powerful propulsion units may bring new opportunities for the employment of steam. Large flying boats, some recently designed and some already under construction, necessitate plants which in power output and size surpass everything hitherto known. The Short Shetland, Britain's largest flying boat has an all-up weight of 58 tons. The American Martin " Mars," the French Potez-SCAN 161 and the Latecoere 631 are in the region of 70 to 100 tons. The Breguet Company is reported to be engaged on projects of flying boats of a weight of 75 to 250 tons. Six gas turbines driving contra-rotating airscrews have been selected to power the 120-ton Saro S.45 flying boat which will measure 220 feet in span and have a pressurised hull. At a cruising speed of 300 m.p.h., or higher, the still-air range will be 5,000 miles. Such large size aircraft may permit the employment of steam propulsion if improvements can be made and existing drawbacks abolished.

In the view of different experts a successful development of steam propulsion will embody the following features : The unit weight of steam plants will have to be considerably reduced. This is possible if the durability of the steam plant is reduced to that of internal combustion aircraft engines. With two-stage turbines it will be possible to make use of the entire available gradient between the working pressure of 100–200 atmospheres and the exhaust back pressure of 0.4 atmospheres. A low specific fuel consumption, already 170 g./h.p./hr. in mercury-vapour plants, is essential.

Such improvements already challenge diesel installations. Whilst the flexibility of steam power plants is as yet far behind that of internal combustion engines, further progress in this direction is possible. Moreover, since they may be mainly destined for larger types of aircraft, it is not necessary to achieve that high flexibility which is required for fighter aircraft.

The necessity of regulation and maintaining a substantial power output at any altitude is evident. A suggestion to supercharge the boiler as a whole and, similar to the practice adopted for supercharged internal combustion engines, expand the combustion gases issuing from the boiler in an exhaust turbine, thus recovering the power required to operate the boiler-supercharging blower, appears to go a long way towards improvement. Air heaters utilising the waste heat can also be coupled in series behind the boiler, and their exhaust further used in reaction nozzles to produce supplementary thrust (Knoernschild).

Finally, there is the problem of space occupied. This is of importance not only from the weight aspect but also because compactness is an essential factor in aircraft design. Here the main problem of a suitable condenser so designed and placed as to produce a minimum of drag is urgent. While American experiments tried to solve it by a " wing radiator " it was suggested (Meredith) that completely enclosed condensers with forced draught are preferable. It was further suggested that in such arrangement and with suitably adapted cooling-air intake and discharge orifices, a portion of the condenser heat could be utilised to produce an auxiliary propulsive thrust.

In April, 1942, it was reported that the Breguet Aircraft Works at Toulouse had designs for a jet-propelled machine to the designs of R. Leduc. This French engineer is well known for his work in connection with the problem of jet propulsion. According to *Inter Avia*, the projected type was basically similar in principle to the Caproni-Campini machine, but with one important exception. Whereas the Italian craft used a standard type of air-cooled radial engine to drive the air compressor unit, Leduc employed a steam turbine for this purpose. Running at 3,000 r.p.m. under a steam pressure of 1,910 lb. per sq. in., the turbine was estimated to develop 1,200 h.p. The speed of the machine was estimated to be in excess of 310 miles an hour.

Experiments, presumably on the test bed, were claimed to have given satisfactory results. No details are yet available, however, of either the boiler or the necessary condenser plant. Condensing raises further problems which are not easy of solution in an aircraft installation. The condenser would most likely be placed in the main air stream so that heat transferred from the steam would be usefully absorbed for the propulsive jet. The development of a jet-propelled aircraft employing such a system will be watched with intense interest by designers throughout the world.

According to present-day standards it would not seem possible for the

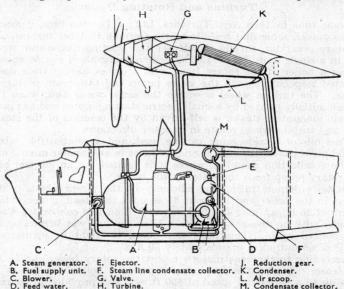

A. Steam generator.
B. Fuel supply unit.
C. Blower.
D. Feed water.
E. Ejector.
F. Steam line condensate collector.
G. Valve.
H. Turbine.
J. Reduction gear.
K. Condenser.
L. Air scoop.
M. Condensate collector.

Fig. 190. The Great Lakes Aircraft Corp. steam plant with wing-mounted turbine and condenser.

rate of fuel consumption to be as low as that of an internal combustion engine.

Leduc's earlier designs, referred to in Chapter III, were of the compressorless type in which a divergent duct was employed to raise the pressure of the " relative wind " admitted when the machine was in motion. Fuel was introduced through a comparatively large number of nozzles disposed across the main stream, as shown in Fig. 30. Combustion of the fuel would therefore be relatively inefficient owing to the low degree of compression attainable, and consumption might be expected to be inordinately high. It was suggested that such compressorless schemes, whilst ingenious, present practical difficulties, and that some form of mechanically driven compressor would seem to be essential. The latest project of M. Leduc appears to confirm this view.

Great Lakes 2,300 h.p. Plant

The Great Lakes Aircraft Corporation of America collaborated with the General Electric Company in the design of steam-propulsion plants intended for installation in large flying boats. The result of this development was a steam power unit of 2,300 h.p. with a La Mont type steam generator, Fig. 190. The main components of the generator were : An air pre-heater, a blower to assist the action of the relative wind, a super-heater, an oil burner, and an exhaust manifold. Wet and superheated steam was carried in alloy steel pipes lining the walls of the generator, arranged axially and forming together a cylindrical casing. Pipes for oil and water were in light alloy.

The boiler was started electrically and produced a maximum of 9.5 tons steam per hour at a temperature of 540 deg. C. and a pressure of 70 atm. The blower for the initial combustion air was driven by means of electric motors fed from a storage battery.

The operational altitude of this power plant was 1.5 km. and the specific fuel consumption was reported to be 270 gr./h.p. showing a thermal efficiency of 23 per cent.

Turbine and Rotating Boiler

Some time in 1938 Aero Turbines, Ltd., a London firm, demonstrated a prime mover, somewhat resembling the German Hüttner turbine, in which the rotary generator, turbine, condenser and starting mechanism were combined in a single unit, Fig. 191. The general principle is simple enough : it includes a boiler of the rotary type, with U-tubes having their open ends connected respectively with the water pump and the steam passage to the turbine. The turbine wheel is within the same casing and, when the unit has been initially rotated by a small electric starting motor and has generated a certain amount of steam, is self-driven by the reaction of the steam jets. Boiler and turbine wheel rotate in opposite directions.

Fuel oils of a wide range can be used, and a combustible mixture of fuel and air is passed through a series of holes in an annular mixing chamber into the combustion chamber, where it is ignited by an electric plug. A small rotary pump feeds the water to the boiler.

In tests demonstrating the efficiency of the power plant, cold water was fed to the boiler and in about 65 seconds the steam gauge indicated a pressure of 25 lb./sq. in. The fuel was turned off and cold water was fed to the boiler with no disastrous results. Then the fuel was turned on and the boiler started again. This particular plant, it might be mentioned, was capable of an output of approximately 30 h.p.

According to the constructor's report the rotary boiler can be used as a condenser. During the development period a boiler was run at various speeds up to a peripheral speed of 830 ft./sec. and provided pressures up to a maximum of 150 atmospheres. The maximum heat transmission capacity at maximum velocity was 553,000 B.Th.U./sq.ft./hr. When the same unit was run as a condenser at the same maximum speed, the maximum heat transmission was found to be 203,000 B.Th.U./sq.ft./hr. In a 2,000 h.p. unit the turbine is run at about 10,000 r.p.m. and the boiler at approximately half that speed. Fuel consumption is 0.35 lb./b.h.p./hr. and the unit weight 2 lb./h.p., according to this report.

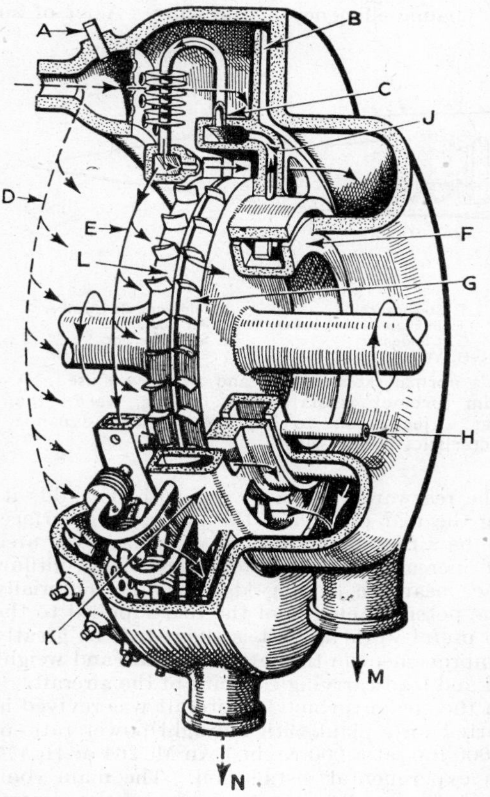

A. Ignition plug.
B. Insulating wall.
C. Atomiser.
D. Path of flame.
E. Path of steam.
F. Centrifugal pump.
G. Reaction disc.
H. Water inlet.
J. Radial water conduits.
K. Annular feed chamber, U-tubes and nozzle ring integral with reaction disc.
L. Turbine rotor.
M. Exhaust steam to condenser.
N. Combustion effluent.

Fig. 191. Part-sectioned drawing of the counter-rotating steam generator and turbine unit developed by Aero Turbines, Ltd.

Auxiliary Turbines

Four different arrangements of power units are disclosed in an American patent in the names of Igor I. Sikorsky, M. E. Gluhareff and R. W. Griswold and assigned to the United Aircraft Corporation. The declared objects are to conserve engine power by the utilisation of waste heat, to improve engine cooling, and to enhance the aerodynamic characteristics of the wing section. Fig. 192 shows a typical layout, while other arrangements include a similar scheme for a V-type, liquid-cooled engine, a method of returning the power generated by the waste heat to the main engine, and the use of the auxiliary power to drive an electric generator for cabin heating.

A normal radial engine A, driving an airscrew, is enclosed in a cowling and the cooling air is drawn in by way of the central forward aperture by the suction of blower B. The air passes between the cylinders to remove excess heat, and is led into a chamber C formed by the leading-edge of the wing. Hence it may be passed along the leading-edge to prevent ice formation.

The blower is driven by means of an exhaust gas turbine D and a steam turbine E operating on a common shaft. The gas turbine is connected directly to the exhaust conduit of the engine, whilst the steam turbine is driven by steam supplied from a boiler F heated by the efflux of the gas turbine. Steam leaving the turbine is passed through a condenser G and the condensed fluid is returned by pump H to a storage tank or directly to the boiler, as shown.

From the leading-edge chamber the blower delivers the air to a mid-wing chamber J, where it is forced through the condenser into an internal duct K. This communicates with a spanwise slot L located to the rear of the upper surface of the wing.

It is claimed that such an arrangement converts practically all the heat of the exhaust gas into mechanical energy which is utilised for cooling the engine and increasing the aerodynamic efficiency of the wing.   A jet of air

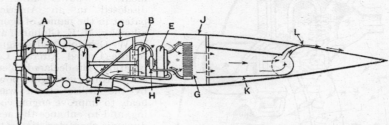

A. Radial engine.	E. Steam turbine.	J. Mid-wing air chamber.
B. Centrifugal blower.	F. Exhaust heated boiler.	K. Air duct.
C. Wing leading-edge air chamber.	G. Condenser.	L. Spanwise slot.
D. Exhaust gas turbine.	H. Water pump.	

Fig. 192.   In this Sikorsky design a normal radial engine and airscrew is used.   A blower driven by gas and steam turbines assists engine cooling, warms the wing leading-edge and furnishes a jet of air to improve the aero-dynamic characteristics of the wing.

forced at high velocity from the rearwardly directed spanwise slot adds its energy to the air flowing along the rear portion of the upper wing surface.

By raising the velocity of the airflow along the upper surface, the area of diminished pressure may be increased, and any tendency of the airflow to break away from the surface near the trailing-edge may be materially delayed.   The proportion of the potential energy of the fuel supplied to the engine which is converted into useful work may, it is suggested, be greatly increased, thus permitting an improvement in the ratio of the size and weight of the power plant to the speed and load-carrying capacity of the aircraft.

Late in the war interest in the steam turbine for aircraft was revived in Germany and designs were started for a plant with a weight/power ratio of 1.5 lb./h.p. to develop about 6,000 h.p. at 6,000 r.p.m.   An Me 264 or He 177 airframe was to be used for an experimental installation.   The main components, which could be distributed according to the layout of the aircraft structure, were four capillary tube boilers measuring 3 ft. diameter and 4 ft. high, boiler feed water pump with auxiliary turbine, main turbine, combustion air draught fan and condenser.   Liquid fuel or a mixture of pulverised coal and petrol could be used.

CHAPTER XVIII

GUIDED MISSILES AND FLYING BOMBS : FURTHER APPLICATIONS OF JET PROPULSION

OUTSTANDING among the technical innovations of the war were various jet-propelled missiles for long-range " area " bombardment and ground-to-air, air-to-ground, and air-to-air employment. The first category embraced the two German reprisal weapons (V-1 flying bomb and V-2 rocket), and certain later American developments, one of which was a reproduction of V-1 (retaining the impulse duct engine so characteristic of that weapon) while another used a small expendable turbine-jet.

Ground-to-air rocket weapons of an elementary type have figured in the A.A. armoury for some years but bear little relationship to the elaborate defensive missiles developed in Germany. Propelled by liquid rockets, usually of Walter or B.M.W. design, these were to be guided or homed on their target. Examples were *Wasserfall* and *Schmetterling*, *Feuerlilie* and *Rheintochter*. *Wasserfall*—called " Baby V-2 "—was over 20 feet long and had radio control.

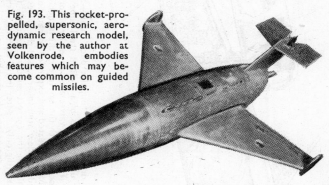

Fig. 193. This rocket-propelled, supersonic, aerodynamic research model, seen by the author at Volkenrode, embodies features which may become common on guided missiles.

Air-to-ground and air-to-ship rocket projectiles were not restricted to the small solid-propellant R/Ps used for some years by British fighters but included heavy weapons like the German Hs 293 and larger missiles of similar type developed in the U.S.A. Liquid-rocket power plants were normal for this class of weapon. The air-to-air variety, likewise utilizing a liquid rocket, is exemplified by the Hs 298 and X.4 designs.

The Fi 103 flying bomb, commonly called V-1, utilized an impulse duct engine, the principle of which is explained in Chapter I and is illustrated in Fig. 194. The flying bomb was 25 ft. long and had a span of 17.7ft. and an area of 51 sq. ft. The all-up weight was 4,740 lb. and at the top speed of about 360 m.p.h. the engine gave a thrust of 600 lb. A ton of high explosive was carried in the nose of the fuselage.

Interesting and ingenious as it was, by comparison with V-2, the flying bomb was crude. Unquestionably one of the great technical achievements of the war, V-2 (officially known as A-4) was 46ft. long and 5ft. 6in. in diameter. Four large stabilizing fins were fitted and the missile, fuelled ready for launching, weighed about 12 tons. The fuels—ethyl alcohol and liquid oxygen—were carried in two tanks amidships and were delivered by

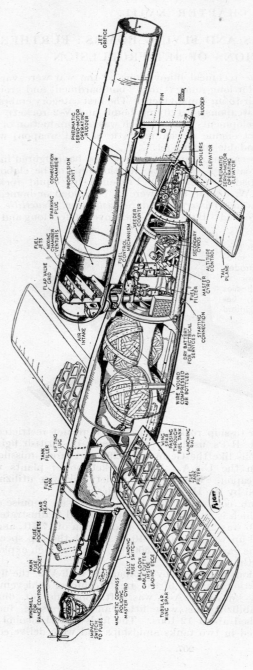

Fig. 194. The Fi 103 ("V-1") flying bomb was driven by an "impulse duct" unit—a variant of the athodyd, descriptively termed "stuttering athodyd." Essentially the power unit consists of a welded steel tube with a block of steel-spring valves and nine rearward-facing fuel nozzles at the front end. The spring valves are opened by air pressure due to the forward speed of the flying bomb (launch is effected by a liquid rocket associated with the carriage of the launching ramp), and the fuel is injected and ignited. The resulting explosion closes the valves so that the heated and expanded combustion gases are ejected from the rear of the tube. Pressure in the combustion chamber is reduced to below atmospheric, and the valves are re-opened by air pressure. This process is repeated about 45 times a second. To maintain the correct mixture strength, fuel feed is regulated according to speed and altitude. After initial starting with butane the unit becomes self-igniting due to the heat of the chamber walls.

turbine-driven centrifugal pumps using steam produced in a generator by concentrated hydrogen peroxide and calcium permanganate. The thrust of 26 tons was used to launch the projectile vertically and a maximum velocity of 3,000 m.p.h. was attained during its ascent to some 58 miles.

The modern war rocket, exemplified by V-2, is undeniably a German achievement, but various countries have proposed even more intricate and accurate supersonic weapons. The development of long-range rockets had reached an advanced stage at the termination of the war. There was a German proposal for the delivery of mails over the Atlantic by a long-range pilotless rocket-propelled craft.

Proposal for a " Combined " Missile

In October, 1943, nearly a year before the V-weapons became a menace, the author submitted to the Dept. of Scientific Research plans for a long-

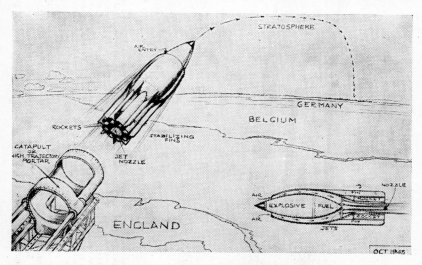

Fig. 195. A proposal submitted by the author to the Director of Scientific Research in October, 1943, for a long-range weapon utilizing both rocket and athodyd principles of propulsion. The original specification is quoted in the text.

range missile, utilizing both rocket and athodyd principles, for the bombardment of Germany from England. His original specification, see Fig. 195 for references, read as follows :

    (1) Launched from huge rocket gun.

    (2) Self-contained rocket propulsion for launch and climb (stage 1) ; Jet propulsion (no engines) for range at determined altitudes (stage 2).

    (3) Plurality of rockets arranged around jet nozzle at tail and fired in grouped series for stage 1.

    (4) Propulsion for stage 2 is by jet reaction. At supersonic speeds air enters annular inlet duct and is compressed in a divergent nozzle (see section). Fuel is introduced through a plurality of burners ignited electrically and the combustion with the oxygen in the compressed air raises temperature and pressure to produce the

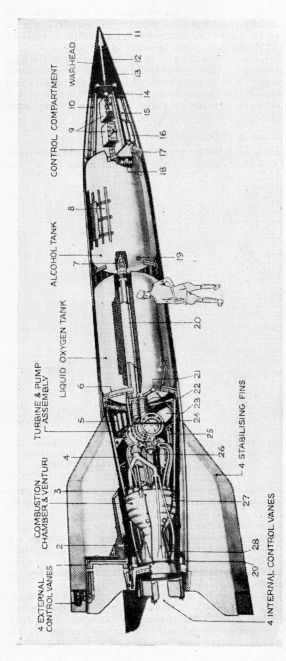

The numbered details indicate :—1. Chain drive to control tabs on external fins from 2, electric motor. 3. Injection nozzles on main combustion chamber. 4. Alcohol delivery piping. 5. Compressed-air bottles. 6. Rear joint ring and lifting point. 7. Servo-controlled alcohol valve. 8. Shell casing support structure. 9. Radio control equipment. 10. Pipe from warhead to alcohol tank. 11. Nose with fusing switch. 12. Conduit for fuse wiring. 13. Exploder tube. 14. Electric fuse for warhead. 15. Plywood support for radio. 16. Nitrogen bottles. 17. Front joint ring and lifting point. 18. Gyros for pitch and azimuth. 19. Alcohol tank filling point. 20. Insulated alcohol feed pipe. 21. Oxygen tank filling point. 22. Expansible bellows connections to alcohol and oxygen pumps. 23. Hydrogen peroxide tank. 24. Tubular support frame for turbine and pumps assembly. 25. Calcium permanganate tank—hydrogen/permanganate steam generator for turbine is located behind this tank. 26. Oxygen distributor unit. 27. Alcohol pipes for subsidiary cooling. 28. Alcohol inlet to double wall of rocket motor. 29. Electro-hydraulic servo motors.

Fig. 196. Ethyl alcohol and liquid oxygen were the main fuels of the German 12-ton long-range rocket projectile of the late war period. Overall dimensions are length 46ft, and diameter 5ft. 6in. The main tanks carry 7,500 lb. alcohol, and 11,000 lb. liquid oxygen for propulsion. Smaller tanks contain hydrogen peroxide and calcium permanganate which on combustion forms superheated steam for the turbine driving the alcohol and oxygen pumps.

propulsive jet (Leduc principle, which is briefly described and illustrated in *Gas Turbines and Jet Propulsion for Aircraft*.) The discharging air/gas stream may be utilized to induce additional air to increase the weight of the propulsive stream (see thrust augmenters Mélot principle in book referred to.) Ducts shown in outer casing inclined rearwardly to prevent formation of boundary layer.

(5) Stabilizing fins on tail. Automatic pilot or wireless control.
(6) Range governed by ratio of fuel to explosive load, say 500 miles.
(7) Proposal is for projectile weighing many tons.
(8) Explosive carried in front section and kept cool. Nose becomes relatively heavy when fuel exhausted.
(9) Similar projectile could also be launched from a suitable aircraft in flight.
(10) The jet propulsion equipment need not necessarily be arranged on the axis. An alternative scheme would be to have a single axial rocket nozzle. In this case multiple thermal jet nozzles could be arranged parallel to the axis and concentric therewith, without ill effect on direction as all would operate at a common pressure.

The note and drawing are reproduced merely to show the trend of thought regarding flying missiles at that time. Immense practical problems were of course involved. During the stress of our prodigious wartime production effort the necessary time and skill for development could not be made available. Since the termination of hostilities, however, some work on rocket and athodyd missiles has been undertaken.

In tests conducted by the U.S. Navy Department in 1946, experimental models of ram-jet missiles weighing about 70 lb. have been successfully demonstrated. On attaining adequate flying speed, after an assisted launch from a ramp, air is rammed into the thermal duct, fuel is injected and burnt and the reaction to the resulting jet accelerates the missile.

The principle is regarded as " a means of propulsion for flight at supersonic velocities up to about 1,500 miles per hour."

CHAPTER XIX

OFFICIAL ADOPTION OF JET - PROPELLED AIRCRAFT : CAREERS OF WHITTLE, CARTER AND WILSON

EVOLUTION OF TURBINE JET PROPULSION

1930.—Frank Whittle took out his first patent applying the gas turbine to jet propulsion.

1933.—Whittle started practical development work on improved jet power units in Great Britain.

1937.—April. First Whittle-designed B.T.H. turbine compressor ran successfully on test bed.

1939.—Air Ministry placed first order for a jet-propelled aircraft with the Gloster Aircraft Co. Ltd. The turbines were built by B.T.H. to the order of Power Jets Ltd.

1941.—May. First successful flight in England of Gloster jet-propelled aircraft. Continuous tests and experiments carried on.

1941.—July. Full information disclosed to General Arnold, U.S. Army Air Force. He asked for the engine to be sent to America, and this was delivered to General Electric Co. in September, 1941.

1941.—Bell Aircraft Co. given an order to build an aircraft suitable to take two Whittle jet units.

1942.—October 1st. Maiden flight of the first experimental aircraft in U.S.A. using G.E.C.-Whittle jet units. U.S.A. allot a number of jet engines to the U.S. Navy for trials and experiment.

1944.—January 7th. Official joint release of news by the Air Ministry and Ministry of Aircraft Production and the U.S. Army Air Forces.

1944.—Summer. Gloster Meteor Jet-propelled fighters in action against V-1 flying bombs. German jet-propelled fighters appeared.

1945.—November 7. Gloster Meteor "Britannia," pilot Grp. Capt. H. J. Wilson, World's Speed Record at Herne Bay. Average 606 m.p.h.

THE official announcement that British jet-propelled aircraft had successfully passed experimental tests was made on 7th January, 1944. It was disclosed in a joint R.A.F.—U.S. Army Air Force statement that both Britain and America had production of these aircraft in hand. Obviously in so radical a break from the orthodox engine/airscrew combination, a great deal of prior development work had to take place, and progress has been very considerable since Air Comdre. Frank Whittle, R.A.F., first started work on gas turbine-jet propulsion units about 1929. His patent of 1930 was the first to propose the application of the gas turbine to jet propulsion.

Whittle's engine first ran successfully in April, 1937. It was built by the B.T.H. Co. to the order of Power Jets, Ltd., to which company the services of Group Captain Whittle were loaned by the R.A.F.

In 1939 the Air Ministry placed the initial orders with the Gloster Aircraft Co., Ltd., for aircraft employing power units of this type, and the machine was designed by W. G. Carter, M.B.E., chief designer to the company. The first successful flight was made in May, 1941, by the late Flight Lieutenant P. E. G. Sayer, R.A.F., chief test pilot of the Gloster Aircraft Co., who was later killed whilst flying an orthodox aircraft.

After the new aircraft had successfully passed its flight trials, full information was given in July, 1941, to General H. H. Arnold, Commanding the U.S.A.A.F., who, like the British Air Ministry, had the foresight to appreciate at once the general possibilities of the new form of propulsion. At his request, the power unit first flown was despatched to the General Electric Company (of New York) in September, 1941, and fitted to an American aircraft—another notable example of " Lease-Lend " in reverse ! As a result of close co-operation between the British and American authorities, a number of jet-reaction units were built in the United States. It is a tribute to the soundness of the British design and the American production methods that the first of the new power units was ready for test in less than six months. At the same time the Bell Aircraft Corporation was given an order to build an aircraft suitable for employing two of the new power units, and the maiden flight in the United States was made within twelve months—October 1st, 1942—Robert M. Stanley, Bell chief test pilot, being at the controls. Since these events, many hundreds of successful flights have been carried out by British and American pilots.

The importance attached to the new method of propulsion may be gauged by the official -measures taken to facilitate development of power units and aircraft. In April 1944, Sir Stafford Cripps, then Minister of Aircraft Production, announced that the Government had acquired Power Jets, Ltd., the pioneer company handling the Whittle projects, to ensure concentration and co-ordination of research and experiment. With official enterprise of this character it may confidently be expected that the splendid British lead in this field will be maintained.

On August 28th, 1941, with the full agreement of Lord Brabazon, who was then Minister of Aircraft Production, the writer commenced the publication of a series of articles in *Flight* reviewing world-wide activities in connection with the jet propulsion of aircraft. These descriptive articles, written in the simplest practical terminology and accompanied by explanatory illustrations, aroused such a wide interest in the subject that it immediately became necessary to re-publish the whole series, with additional matter and comment, in book form.

A cardinal point which, understandably, could not be publicised at that time, was that this country was ahead of all others. For considerations of security, no mention could be made that any work at all was being done towards the actual production of jet-propelled aircraft in British factories. However, there can be no doubt that the readers of *Flight*, and also of the earlier editions of this book, had the advantage of being relatively well-informed on the subject of gas turbines and jet propulsion for aircraft long before the significance of the new developments was generally appreciated.

A British Genius

This new era in the annals of flight has been made a practicable possibility by the genius and unswerving perseverance of one man, Frank Whittle. Born on 1st June, 1907, at Coventry, and educated at Leamington College,

he left in 1923 to become a Royal Air Force apprentice in No. 4 Apprentices Wing, Cranwell. During his apprenticeship, he was trained for the trade of fitter-rigger, and spent all his spare time in making and flying a number of remarkable model aircraft. He also assisted Flight Lieutenant Comper in the design of the Cranwell Light Aircraft. Whittle was awarded a Cadetship on passing out as a Leading Aircraftman—one of six out of about 600. In 1926 he entered the R.A.F. College, Cranwell, as a Flight Cadet and was trained as a pilot in addition to taking practical and scholastic subjects, and, on passing out in 1928, was awarded the Abdy-Gerrard-Fellowes Memorial Prize for aeronautical sciences.

The next 15 months were spent as a Pilot Officer of No. 111 Fighter Squadron, at the end of which he

Air Comdre. Frank Whittle, C.B.E., R.A.F.

qualified as a flying instructor at the Central Flying School, Wittering, later going to No. 2 Flying Training School, Digby. It was whilst here that Whittle, now promoted to Flying Officer, gave, with the late Flying Officer G. E. Campbell, one of the most thrilling exhibitions of crazy-flying seen at the R.A.F. Display, Hendon. For 18 months, 1931-1932, he was engaged in experimental flight testing of float-planes at Felixstowe, and it has been said with authority that Whittle, during this period, did dangerous and valuable experimental flying in relation to catapulting and " ditching " which has never been given the prominence it deserved, being perhaps over-shadowed by his more academic achievements.

After Felixstowe, Whittle went to Henlow on the Officers' Engineering Course, 1932–3, serving 6 months as officer-in-charge test benches, engine repair section. In January, 1934, he was promoted to Flight Lieutenant, and was elected an Associate Fellow of the Royal Aeronautical Society. The R.A.F. had ceased to send officers to Cambridge University, but owing to record results, an exception was made in this case, and Flight Lieutenant Whittle entered Peterhouse in 1934. In 1936 he graduated as a Bachelor of Arts, obtaining First Class Honours in the Mechanical Sciences Tripos, and was made a Senior Scholar of Peterhouse. He spent a further year at Cambridge on post-graduate research work, during which he was associated with Professor Sir Melvill Jones. Work was continued on the Whittle turbine-compressor at both Cambridge and Rugby. He became a Squadron Leader in December, 1937, and was placed on the Special Duty List for work on his engine, becoming a Wing Commander in June, 1940, Group Captain on July 1st, 1943, and Air Comdre. the following year.

During 1943 Air Comdre. Whittle spent three months at the R.A.F. Staff College, and was then re-posted to the Special Duty List for work on the Whittle engine.

Designer of the Gloster Aircraft

The designer of the first aircraft to employ the Whittle jet-reaction power unit, W. G. Carter, M.B.E., was originally chief draughtsman to the old Sopwith Company, and it was he who prepared the production drawings of all the Sopwith war-time aircraft. On the formation of the Hawker Company he eventually became Chief Designer, responsible for the Woodcock, Horsley, Heron, Cygnet and other aircraft.

He was later Chief Designer to the joint Short-White Smith effort with the Crusader, which came to an untimely end during the Schneider Cup races at Venice in 1927, owing to an incorrectly assembled control.

Carter then joined the de Havilland Company, but later left to re-join the Gloster Aircraft Company branch of the Hawker-Siddeley organisation in the capacity of Chief Designer.

W. G. Carter, M.B.E.

From the outset, Carter had great faith in the jet project, and the collaboration between him and Air Comdre. Whittle in the creation of a successful aircraft to utilise the revolutionary means of propulsion, unquestionably added in great measure to the supreme position Great Britain holds in this field of aviation. His work on nine jet-propelled types is being effectively continued.

Carter's crowning achievement is the design and development of the Meteor IV which, on November 7th, 1945, flown by Grp. Capt. H. J. Wilson, averaged 606 m.p.h. in four runs over a course near Herne Bay. The fastest run was at 611 m.p.h. This feat was the more remarkable because the Meteor was not originally designed for flying at very high Mach numbers. Mr. Carter has established a unique reputation as designer of high-speed fighters.

High-Speed Pilots

Grp. Capt. Hugh Joseph Wilson, A.F.C. and two Bars, apart from his association with the world's speed record, has figured prominently in the development of high-speed aircraft. During the Battle of Britain he was charged with research into the performance of the Spitfire, and for this purpose was operationally attached to No. 74 (Trinidad) Squadron. Later, as jet propulsion developed, he became the first R.A.F. pilot to handle jet aircraft and it was he who trained all the pilots of the first Squadron to be equipped with Meteors. By coincidence this Squadron—616 (South Yorkshire Auxiliary) went into action against German flying bombs from Manston Airfield, the base used for the speed record flights.

Grp. Capt. H. J. Wilson, A.F.C., R.A.F.   Mr. Eric S. Greenwood

Grp. Capt. Wilson's three decorations for test flying were all announced during the war. He was born on May 28th, 1908 and began his service career in 1929, when he took a Short Service Commission. While engaged on testing and research flying he piloted 200 different types of aircraft, including captured German machines. He has held the posts of Chief Test Pilot at the Royal Aircraft Establishment, Farnborough, and of commanding officer of the Empire Test Pilots' School at Boscombe and has flown over 4,000 hours. Twice during the war his duties took him to the U.S.A.; he was at Wright Field in 1943.

Two Meteors essayed record figures, the Britannia piloted by Grp. Capt. Wilson, being fractionally faster. The second pilot, Eric Stanley Greenwood, who averaged 603 m.p.h. over the speed record course, served in the R.A.F. from 1928 to 1933. He was test pilot for Sir W. G. Armstrong-Whitworth Aircraft, Ltd., from 1936 to 1941, and for Air Service Training from 1941 to 1944. On joining the Gloster Aircraft Co., Ltd., as Chief Test Pilot in June, 1944, he undertook development flying on the Meteor.

CHAPTER XX

BROADCASTING THE NEWS

NON-TECHNICAL DESCRIPTIONS AND OBSERVATIONS IN RADIO TALKS

WHEN the first official announcement regarding jet-propelled aircraft was made on January 7th, 1944, the Canadian Broadcasting Corporation and the British Broadcasting Corporation invited the author to give talks over the radio from London, on what jet propulsion meant and its implications. The broadcast over the Canadian network was made at 6.15 p.m. on the same day, and a longer talk followed a few days later on the B.B.C. Overseas and Home programmes. In further broadcast talks given by the author on March 28th, 1944, and subsequently during a visit to America, the subject was dealt with on a somewhat wider basis.

The talks were couched in non-technical language, and accordingly abstracts from some of the scripts of these broadcasts are appended in order to assist in clarifying points upon which the student of jet reaction propulsion may be in doubt.

An "Epoch–making Invention"

" That Group Captain Whittle's invention is epoch-making there is no doubt. To state that the basic idea is not new in no way detracts from its importance and value. The principle of employing the reaction of a fluid jet for propulsion was known to Sir Isaac Newton, the famous British astronomer, as far back as 1680. In the last 35 years a great variety of schemes for propelling aircraft by jet reaction have been devised in various countries. Italy produced and publicly flew such a machine in 1940. I had long noted these developments, first with interest and then with enthusiasm, and began to make a close study of the subject.

" Group Captain Whittle has worked in secrecy for years without receiving the public tribute he deserves. During his early efforts Whittle could command but little support or encouragement, and doubtless suffered from the counter pressure of the apostles of orthodoxy. To his great credit, he recognised that a new method of propulsion was necessary and then proceeded to develop a practical solution of the problem . . .

"Don't imagine for a moment that I think the ordinary four-stroke reciprocating engine—of the type you have in your motor-car—will entirely give place to the combustion turbine. The present-day aircraft engine is a marvellously efficient piece of mechanism, and in many applications will not be superseded. The men who overcame the reciprocating engine problems will be the men to tackle the development and production problems of the new rotary units.

Jets and Rockets

" What, precisely, is this propulsion, you may ask. Well, first of all let me tell you what it is *not*. It is not rocket propulsion. It is necessary to be quite clear on this point. Certainly the rocket propels itself by the reaction of a rearwardly ejected stream of hot gases, but these gases are produced from a chemical fuel which embodies all the oxygen required for combustion. Now in turbine-jet propelled aircraft, the combustion of a liquid fuel is effected with oxygen drawn from the air. Indeed, efficient operation is dependent upon a high mass flow of air, which is collected through the nose of the fuselage, or by forward-facing orifices or scoops in front of the engine compartment. Stratosphere flight is now well within the bounds of possibility with, of course, pressurised cabins for the passengers, and the speed of such aircraft can be extremely high. Turbine propulsion units can be arranged to provide a large measure of automatic compensation for variation in barometric pressure and are thus particularly suitable for aircraft operating at high altitudes. But since thermal jet propulsion craft are not independent of atmosphere, and therefore could not fly through inter-stellar space, they must never be confused with fanciful machines for trips to the moon.

The Reaction Principle

" You may wonder why the term ' jet reaction ' is used rather than merely ' jet.' A fundamental law of the science of mechanics is 'Action and reaction are equal in magnitude and opposite in direction.' When you push a wheelbarrow you do not notice the ' equal and opposite ' force being exerted until your feet lose their frictional grip on the ground. Then it becomes immediately evident. The reaction of a jet of water in an ordinary whirling garden spray is quite familiar to all. The high pressure jets of modern fire fighting equipment often cannot be held and controlled by a single fireman. Perhaps the simplest illustration is afforded by the sausage-shaped carnival balloon. If you release the nozzle, the air or gas escapes as a jet and the balloon rushes away from you.

" Let's see how this principle is applied on an aircraft. Imagine a large tubular casing, open at each end and extending the length of the aircraft fuselage. Inside are the two main components, firstly the air compressor or blower, and secondly the combustion gas turbine, both coupled together

Fig. 197. The original Gloster E28/39 fitted with a Whittle turbine-jet made by the B.T.H. Co., of Rugby.

and rotating on a common shaft. Now think of the tube again. Air enters the front end and is expelled from the tail at very high velocity in the following cycle of operations. The rotary air compressor takes in the air, and delivers it at a higher pressure to a part of the tube which serves as a combustion chamber. Liquid fuel is *continuously* sprayed into the combustion chamber and *continuously* mixed and burned with some of the air. From the combustion chamber this burning mixture of air and combustion gases, at relatively high pressure, passes to the turbine entrance. The excess air is added to the gas to lower the temperature sufficiently to prevent damage to the turbine blades. In forcing its way through the turbine the gas/air mixture creates mechanical energy in rotating the turbine wheel and this energy performs the work of driving the air compressor to supply more

air to maintain combustion. The stream of burnt gases from the turbine
issues from the tail nozzle as a high-velocity jet, the reaction of which
propels the aircraft. By ' high velocity ' is meant in excess of the speed
of sound or 740 miles per hour. Of course, the velocity can be varied. . .

Performance of Jet Aircraft

"Do the pilots like jet-propelled machines ? Most decidedly. Highly
experienced and highly critical test pilots say they are easily flown, very
responsive to controls, and the high speed rotary power units are so smooth
and vibrationless in operation that they prefer them to orthodox types. As
to performance, one may not divulge exact figures but, in my opinion, speeds
in the region of 500 to 600 m.p.h. may in due time become commonplace.

"Let me run over some of the advantages of jet propulsion. So-called
' safety ' fuels can be employed without loss of efficiency. Also, there is no
complicated supercharger, with change gears, clutches and boost-control.
Only a simple fuel injection system is required. There are fewer auxiliary
components. Controls and instruments for the pilot are minimised.
Boundary layer air flow may be turned to useful account for the air intake,
and drag thereby reduced. Again, rotary components enable higher operating
speeds to be employed with a reduction of size and weight as compared with
reciprocating engines. Vibration is reduced. And need I remind you that
the airscrew is eliminated, saving further weight, reducing complication and
simplifying control.

"And now you may ask, have jet propulsion units a useful application
in peace time ? Certainly. I venture to predict that the advent of this
successful British gas turbine will revolutionise aircraft design. Turbines
would be most desirable for high speed, high altitude passenger aircraft
and for the huge transport planes now being planned. Gas turbines have
other uses apart from aircraft.

"Thus you will appreciate the Coventry engineer, Frank Whittle, has
turned a page in the history of the conquest of the air and added one more
triumph to the annals of British engineering."

Other Aspects of Jet Propulsion

The text of a third broadcast is appended :

" In January the whole world was interested to hear for the first time
that British jet-propelled aircraft had passed the experimental stage. Since
then many people have seen—and heard ! these new planes flying about this
country. Even technicians unconnected with aeronautical engineering had
not anticipated a new form of power unit which could challenge the highly
successful engines that propel our aircraft, cars and lorries. By years
of development the reciprocating engine—that is to say the ordinary arrangement of cylinder, piston, connecting rod and crankshaft—has become so
perfect that a challenge from an entirely different quarter seemed unthinkable.
It was as fantastic to many people as the possibility of an aircraft flying
without an airscrew. All the publicity that has now been given to jet
propulsion has, in my opinion, given rise to the impression that the new
power unit will be used solely for this purpose. That certainly is its immediate
importance, but actually the gas turbine has a much wider significance.
And it is about the gas turbine that I want to talk.

" The outstanding feature of this remarkable British development is the
practical realisation of a small, light, rotary engine of enormous power.
The dictionary meaning of a turbine is a ' rotary engine driven by water
or steam ' but that definition will need to be modernised to include gas.
A friend recently asked me to describe a gas turbine unit in twenty words.

It simply can't be done, but I offer a simple analogy. You know that in the case of a water wheel driven by a rushing mill stream, power is taken from the shaft it rotates to grind corn. And you will also be familiar with the reverse action, the paddle wheels of a steamer ; which in this case are driven by engine power applied to the axle-shaft. Note that in the first case the wheel is driven, in the other it drives. A compressor and a turbine are much the same save that a tornado of air does the work. In this case the so-called paddles consist of many curved blades disposed around the axle after the manner of a ventilating fan. Imagine then a series of these fans (the compressor) at the front end of a shaft and another series (the turbine) at the opposite end. They are all enclosed in a tubular metal casing. In the middle is a combustion chamber for the continuous burning of fuel and there you have, in effect, the turbo-compressor unit.

How It Works

" The action is as follows :—Air is drawn in by the rapidly rotating compressor fans at the front and forced into the combustion chamber. Into the compressed air in this chamber, paraffin is injected and ignited, and the heat of combustion causes expansion so that the burning gases battle their way through the only exit, the nozzle leading to the second group of fans, that is, the turbine. In so doing the rapidly flowing gases, by impinging on the curved, or should I say cupped, blades, cause the whole mechanism to rotate at great speed. They finally discharge as an efflux, like a high speed jet from a fire hose, sufficient to propel the aircraft by reaction. The reaction is rather akin to the continuous recoil of a gun.

" You will have appreciated that once started it is the rapidly rotating turbine which drives the compressor. As on your car, starting, in the first place, is effected by an ordinary electric starter spinning the compressor to draw in air. An electric glow plug ignites the charge. When under way, efficiency is increased by the aircraft itself collecting a mass of air through the air inlet. Naturally the faster it goes the more air it scoops. This in itself explains why a jet-propelled aircraft excels at high speeds.

Turbines for Shaft Power

" Having, I hope, explained simply the action of a turbine unit and made it clear that the axle shaft revolves very rapidly, it will be apparent that the unit is not only a means of providing a high speed jet of air. Alternatively it is possible to derive from the rotating shaft mechanical power to drive all sorts of mechanism, including the conventional airscrew. The prominence given to the term ' jet propulsion ' has tended to obscure other important possibilities. Jet propulsion for touring cars has recently been discussed, but such a development seems completely remote, as the rapid discharge of hot gas would be calamitous for fully twenty yards behind the vehicle. On the other hand, a similar form of unit adapted to produce shaft horse-power in the way I have explained might conceivably find a place on road vehicles of the future. Perhaps naturally, there have been many discussions among car owners interested in engineering progress, but almost invariably the discussions centre upon jet propulsion rather than the units that produce the jet. Whether turbines will eventually displace the orthodox four-stroke reciprocating engine used in our cars and buses is a very different question. The fact that the turbo-compressor has no piston and no gear wheels, but consists of two components spinning merrily on a single shaft, means that it is almost vibrationless in operation, which is a solid advantage. It is appreciably lighter too and, being less complicated, maintenance work would be considerably reduced. Nevertheless, one fears that so far as touring cars are concerned, the prospects are not promising.

"Contradictory though it may seem I venture the opinion that the world's speed record for cars could be comfortably annexed by a turbine unit. Thus if you should be an aspirant to world-wide fame as the fastest motorist on earth, the new gas turbine offers a quick opportunity when peace returns. Such a racing car need not scale more than half the weight of my friend

Fig. 198. Suggestion of a possible type of turbine jet-propelled car for world's speed records.

John Cobb's 3-ton vehicle which, fitted with two twelve-cylinder super-charged Napier Lion aircraft engines of a total of 2,500 h.p., covered a mile at 369.7 m.p.h. Incidentally the small size and circular shape of the turbine will enable perfect streamlining of the body, a most important consideration when high speed is the aim. The whole problem in a nutshell is thrust versus drag. Since the girth is smaller the drag effect can be reduced and the ratio of thrust to drag improved, with considerable benefit in speed.

Problems With Small Units

"Just why, the listener may ask, is a turbine so distant a possibility for touring cars while its application to racing cars would place the world's record within its grasp? It is simply that the problem with turbines is to reduce the power they develop. That is quite the reverse of the usual state of affairs. To cut down the power to that required for a car entails a turbine unit of amazingly small dimensions with parts as finely finished as a watch and running at tremendously high speed. Imagine all the power you need, and more, from a tiny mechanism packed into a case no bigger than a large vacuum cleaner. At present the smallest practical units are of 400 to 500 h.p. It would be more simple to produce a unit of 2,000 h.p.

"Nevertheless, it seems logical to suppose that eventually this smooth, light, all-rotary power unit must supplant the relatively slow and heavy reciprocating engine for a number of transport purposes. For heavy lorries and buses, needing high power, the chances of adoption are greater than for cars. In other spheres, the gas turbine may be used as a power plant for ships, driving through the marine propeller. On the Swiss Federal railway there is already one example of a main line locomotive driven by a 2,000 h.p. gas turbine.

"And now a few words concerning small gas turbines for aircraft propulsion. Many people jumped to the conclusion that the day of the airscrew was passing. A view I hold is that future development may lead to the adoption of airscrews or propellers driven by the turbine shaft, the jet from the turbine serving merely as an auxiliary means of propulsion. The inference is that the advent of the successful, relatively small size turbine engine may conceivably prove to be even more important than jet propulsion itself.

Turbine—Airscrew Plants

"Turbines thus challenge the supremacy of the orthodox reciprocating engine rather than the airscrew. Let me explain further. It happens that propulsion by jet reaction is particularly suitable for certain, but not all, types of aircraft. It is especially suitable for very high speed and very high altitude. At what are, to-day, normal flying speeds and normal altitudes, the screw propeller method of aircraft propulsion is more efficient. Take-off and climb are better with an airscrew.

"It follows that, in peace-time, the turbo-compressor unit driving an airscrew is likely to be more widely employed on civil aircraft than jet propulsion. As the turbine runs at very high speeds of rotation, it will be necessary to introduce some form of reduction gear to lower this speed to one suitable for an airscrew. With your car, the operating speed of the engine must be reduced through the gear box and the back axle gears to a suitable speed for the road wheels, say from five turns of the engine to one of the road wheels on top gear. With normal aircraft it is necessary to reduce the speed of the airscrew to about 1,200 r.p.m. from, say, 3,000 r.p.m. of the engine. The smaller the airscrew, the faster it can be arranged to run as the tip speed of the blades is the major governing factor. If the tip speed approaches the speed of sound, efficiency is impaired. Consequently, with a turbine of the 10,000 r.p.m. order, it would be necessary to utilise small multi-bladed airscrews to permit high speed of the airscrew and minimum reduction ratio. Now that we have successful ' contra-props,' that is twin propellers rotating in opposite directions, a similar version of a much smaller diameter may conveniently be applied to a turbine. By increasing the number of blades, the diameter, and therefore the tip speed, can be further reduced, and so we get the airscrews nearer to the speed of the turbine, which simplifies the reduction gear problem.

"Talking of propeller speeds, I am reminded that when the late Sir Henry Segrave first proposed to run the single propeller of his record-breaking motor boat, Miss England II, at 12,000 r.p.m., that is some thousands of r.p.m. faster than any previous boat, he told me he was opposed by marine engineers, but he proved that high speed rotation was right for his purpose.

"As a means of converting the latent heat of liquid fuel into mechanical energy, turbines are not yet so efficient as the highly developed reciprocating engine. The modern reciprocating engine has an efficiency of about 33 per cent.. or, in other words, it gives out as useful power about one-third of the potential power which is contained in the fuel it consumes. On a turbo-compressor unit we, as yet, can only obtain an efficiency of 20 to 25 per cent. Therefore, fuel consumption is relatively high for a given power output. Against this it must be appreciated that the turbine operates on cheap low grade fuels, such as paraffin, and does not require expensive petrols.

"Small turbines are still in their infancy. There is much to be done by metallurgists in developing better heat-resisting steels for turbines which, incidentally, operate in a red-hot state. Chemical engineers will find better ways of burning the fuel, aerodynamicists will need to develop better profiles for the turbine blades, and mechanical engineers will devise improved methods of constructing these highly stressed parts rotating at extreme speeds.

"The whole prospect of future turbine development is intriguing. Grp. Capt. Whittle, in collaboration with Power Jets and the B.T.H. Co., has paved the way for a new era in power generation. His achievement is one of immense interest and importance to this country, no matter whether aircraft, road or rail transport, or ships are considered."

Prior to the Record

Prior to the world's record attempt at Herne Bay, a talk on " Jet Propelled Aircraft To-day " was given on Oct. 10th, 1945, of which the following is a summary :—

" How does Britain stand to-day in the development of jet-propelled aircraft, is a question I am often asked. The answer is that enormous strides have been made. Progress is extremely rapid. The best turbine engine one month is handsomely beaten in power output almost the following month. Half a dozen well-known firms vie one with another in evolving units of growing output. Already we are extracting double the power of original designs.

" It is abundantly clear that the gas turbine will soon replace the more complicated reciprocating or piston engine in all high-powered aircraft. Normal aircraft engines are similar in general characteristics to a car engine.

" The first service use of jet-propelled aircraft by the Allies was in August, 1944, when the R.A.F. put the twin-engined Gloster Meteor into action against the German flying bombs, some of which they shot down. The first operation over Germany was by the same aircraft early in 1945. Before these events Germany had introduced single- and twin-engined jet fighters into combat. How do British and German jet fighters compare is actively discussed. Talking in the past tense, enemy jet-propelled aircraft were faster than ours but their engines were not so reliable, they were more complicated, heavier and relatively less efficient than British types.

" Our orthodox fighters shot many of them down. To-day Britain has jet-propelled aircraft far and away speedier and more efficient than anything Germany ever produced. In the near future the actual accomplishment will be officially demonstrated by the R.A.F. as it is reported that an attempt on the world's speed record is in preparation.

" Originally the prototype Meteor had R.-R. Welland turbines, each of which were 43 inches in diameter and gave a thrust of 1,700 lb. for a weight of 850 lb. In April, 1944, Rolls-Royce successfully flight tested a more powerful unit. Known as the Derwent it gave a thrust of 2,000 lb. for each unit, which scaled 920 lb. Still further improvement resulted in series 11 giving 2,200 lb. thrust. The latest Derwent V turbo unit, developing approximately twice the power of the original engine, enables the Meteor to attain amazing speeds—without doubt the fastest ever accomplished by an aircraft of any nationality.

" From April, 1943, when the first R.-R. Whittle type jet-propulsion engine passed its 100 hour type test to the present time, R.-R. have evolved and proved six different designs each better than its predecessor. I mention this in order to stress one great attribute of the turbine, that it is possible to design, manufacture and prove a new design within six months.

" Think what this means to an aircraft manufacturer. He can step up power promptly by substituting a more powerful unit, and he can produce an aircraft of up-to-the-minute design with the knowledge that he will not be delayed by engine deliveries. With orthodox piston engines, it was frequently necessary for an aircraft constructor to wait upon the engine or propeller manufacturer, as the design and production of a multi-cylinder reciprocating engine is necessarily so slow.

" Apart from twin-engined machines another most promising type of jet fighter is the D.H. Vampire, fitted with a single Goblin turbine engine, also of de Havilland production. The only permissible observation of performance is that it handsomely exceeds 500 m.p.h.

"For air transport of the future the turbine engine is going to be very much in the picture. Economy in fuel consumption is being gradually but definitely improved as development proceeds and consumption, measured in distance covered, will not prove a handicap in the future.

"To sum up, British pioneers have made tremendous progress in the development of turbines. When actual speeds of British jet-propelled aircraft can be officially quoted, the sceptics will be confounded ! "

The Record Flight

Appended is the B.B.C. radio comment made in November subsequent to the record of 606.25 m.p.h. (975.6 k.p.h.).

"Within four years of the first turbine jet plane flying in this country a speed of over ten miles per minute has been attained. Even the amazing speed of over 600 m.p.h. which was accomplished by the two Gloster Meteors can be improved upon when we have aircraft able to cope with the aerodynamic problems encountered at a speed approaching that of sound. Not all the power of the Rolls-Royce Derwent engines could be utilised during the record run. When the Meteor airframe was designed it was never imagined that engines powerful enough to propel the machine at over 600 m.p.h. would be available so quickly. It is a great credit to the Gloster engineers that their plane designed for speeds in the region of 500 m.p.h. could be improved and strengthened to withstand the strains and stresses set up at 600 m.p.h. and still remain controllable. During the record run observers noted that both aircraft flew the course as steady as a rock. The pilots, Grp. Capt. Wilson and Mr. Eric Greenwood, set out from Manston airdrome in shirt sleeves as the close fitting cabin becomes so hot in flight due to high speeds. In the 16 minutes they were in the air the two engines of each plane consumed some 260 gallons of paraffin, roughly a thousand gallons an hour. Such a heavy consumption has caused surprise but economy is not important in short record runs. Again, with jet propulsion the turbines are less efficient at sea level. At normal flying altitudes and particularly heights of 30,000 to 50,000 ft. at which turbines fly successfully, fuel consumption will be greatly reduced due mainly to the cooler ambient air and reduced density of the atmosphere.

"The significant thing is that this great British record has set the seal of success upon turbine/jet propulsion. Efficiency and reliability have been achieved and demonstrated to the world. The next important move will be to apply turbine power to civil aircraft and the large projected air liners to give us greater speed. That is a matter engaging the close attention of aircraft manufacturers.

"In the case of a large air liner, four piston engines will weigh say four tons. A saving of two tons may be effected by installing turbine engines. But the weight saving process does not stop there. No heavy propellers are required with jet propulsion. Because of that fact clearance for the propeller blades is not necessary and aircraft may therefore be designed with low, short undercarriages which again contribute to weight saving. Air Comdre. Whittle's enterprise has given to the world a form of rotary power unit which suggests already that orthodox types of aircraft and engines will be revolutionised in performance, appearance and comfort in the course of two or three years. Turbine propelled aircraft will be faster in operation and easier to maintain and service. We have the most powerful aircraft turbine engines in the world, indeed progress has been so rapid that their advantages can only be fully realised when new aircraft structures of advanced type are developed. "

CHAPTER XXI

NOTABLE VIEWS ON TURBINE UNITS FOR AIRCRAFT PROPULSION

THE prospects for turbine units, either pure jet or airscrew types, for the propulsion of future aircraft have in recent years been widely discussed throughout the aircraft industry. The publicly expressed opinions of acknowledged experts are of value when attempting to estimate future development. The following extracts from various papers on the subject, presented by leading figures in the industry, are of interest as showing the trend of opinion.

In a paper entitled " Gas Turbines for Aircraft Propulsion," read before the Derby Branch of the Royal Aeronautical Society, April 1945, Dr. S. G. Hooker, of Rolls-Royce, Ltd., made interesting comparisons between the performance and consumption of gas turbine compressor units and conventional pressure-charged reciprocating engines. He stated : The operational limitations on a piston engine are R.P.M. and boost pressure, whereas the corresponding limitations on a jet engine are R.P.M. and jet pipe temperature—the former because of the very high stresses in the rotating parts, and the latter because of the strength of available materials at the high temperatures which are used.

Let us consider a fighter aircraft fitted with a 1,000 h.p. piston engine. Such a machine, if of the Spitfire size and drag, will have a sea level speed of 300 m.p.h., and consequently, since at this speed 1 b.h.p. equals 1 lb. of thrust, the thrust on the aircraft will be 1,000 lb., and the fuel consumption will be about 0.5 lb. per b.h.p., or per lb. of thrust per hour. A jet-propulsion engine of 1,000 lb. thrust will also drive this aircraft at 300 m.p.h., but at this condition its estimated fuel consumption will be about 1.3 lb. per lb. of thrust per hour, i.e., more than double that of the piston engine.

Now let us consider what we must do in order to give this aircraft a sea level speed of 600 m.p.h. Since the power required varies as the cube of the speed, we shall require 8,000 h.p., even if the airscrew efficiency still stays at 80 per cent. If it falls to 53 per cent., which is more probable, the power required will be 12,000 h.p., and such an engine will weigh at least 12 times the weight of the original 1,000 h.p. engine. On the other hand, the thrust required to double the speed of the machine is only four times as great, so that the jet-propulsion engine will weigh only four times as much as the original 1,000 lb. thrust engine.

Fuel Consumption

Piston engines tend to have a constant specific weight per b.h.p., while for jet engines the weight per unit thrust should remain fairly constant. Comparing fuel consumptions, at 0.5 lb./b.h.p./hr., a 12,000 h.p. engine will use 6,000 lb. of fuel per hour in order to produce 4,000 lb. of thrust, so its fuel consumption will now be 1.5 lb. of fuel per lb. of thrust, whereas the jet-propulsion engine should be approximately 1.4.

In other words, there is now very little difference in the fuel consumption of the two engines, and there is a tremendous advantage in size and weight with the jet-propulsion engine. In fact, whereas the 12,000 h.p. engine will probably weigh at least 20,000 lb. when complete with airscrew and radiators (and would, of course, be prohibitively large for a Spitfire type machine), the jet engine will probably weigh not more than 2,000 lb., and could be accommodated in a machine of approximately Spitfire size. The moral of this is that at speeds in excess of 500 m.p.h. approximately, the simple single-stage jet-propulsion engine is far better than the reciprocating piston engine for aircraft propulsion, and is just as economical. Its overall fuel consumption is large simply because it produces enormous powers.

At 300 m.p.h. the airscrew efficiency is double that of the jet, and this accounts to a large extent for the fact that the fuel consumption of the jet engine is more than double that of the piston engine at this condition. At 550 m.p.h. the jet and the airscrew are equally efficient, and, since the jet is so much more simple and lighter than the airscrews, it follows immediately that jet propulsion must be best at this speed. This is not the whole story, however, because the airscrew is a heavy piece of mechanism, and its weight is associated with a certain drag on the aircraft. This drag must, therefore, be deducted from the useful thrust which the propeller produces. In addition, the airscrew blows a slipstream over the wings or fuselage of the machine, which again produces an adverse drag. Consequently, the practical crossover between the airscrew and the jet occurs at a lower speed, probably in the region of 500 m.p.h.

Lecturing to the Royal Society of Arts on "High Speed Flight" in February 1946, Dr. Hooker emphasised that for turbine-jets to have an application to civil aircraft they must fly as high as possible, and cabin pressurisation will be necessary. Due to the forward speed of the aeroplane, the air taken into the machine is heated up as it is accelerated from rest to the aircraft speed, and the heating effect is independent of altitude.

An air temperature rise of 25 degrees C. occurs at 500 m.p.h., and as at 1,000 m.p.h. the air is heated to 100 degrees C., it will be necessary to cool it. Pressurisation of the air also occurs, due to forward speed, and is equivalent to a reduction in altitude. At 500 m.p.h. this equals an altitude reduction of 7,000 ft., i.e., at 50,000 ft. altitude, the pressure is equivalent to 43,000 ft.

A further consideration in cabin pressurisation is the humidity of the air. The temperature of the atmosphere at 50,000 ft. is −54 degrees C., and as no water vapour can exist at this temperature the air must be humidified, a 60-passenger machine requiring 25 lb. of water per hour to maintain 50 per cent. relative humidity. Separate auxiliary motors will be required to drive the cabin blower as it must be independent of engine speed to maintain equilibrium in cabin pressure irrespective of altitude.

As an example of what can be done, a Lancaster bomber fitted with Rolls-Royce Nene engines would have an all-up-weight of 60,000 lb., a cruising speed of 400 m.p.h. at all altitudes up to 35,000 ft. Without increasing tankage, it would have a range of 1,000 miles at 30,000 ft. and 500 miles at 10,000 ft. This, of course, could be improved by increasing fuel tankage. The four Nene engines fully installed would weigh approximately 8,000 lb. as compared with the weight of 12,000 lb. for four piston type engines, thus saving 4,000 lb. weight which is equivalent to 500 gallons of fuel. (In a later lecture he amended the unit weight figures to 7,000 lb. and 13,000 lb. respectively).

A range of between 500 and 1,000 miles is not good enough for all purposes and it will thus be necessary to build aircraft having a range of 3,000 to 4,000 miles. Enlarging upon this, he said that provided they could cruise at 50,000 ft. and at a speed of 460 m.p.h., machines of 100,000 lb. all-up-weight, with a structure weight of 25 per cent., will have a range of 3,800 miles. At 30 per cent. structure weight the range is reduced to 3,300 miles, while the payload of 15,000 lb. remains the same in both cases.

Passage Through the Sonic Barrier

Dr. Hooker stated that information on the velocity of sound is extremely scanty since it is impossible to test in wind tunnels at this velocity. By means of a curve he showed that the drag coefficient increased four times between a Mach No. of 0.6 and 1.0, whereas once the velocity of sound is exceeded, the coefficient falls and appears to become twice its own speed value. In considering the thrust required to reach the velocity of sound at 40,000 ft. and using the " Meteor " as an example he showed that the engines would have to develop about 17,500 lb. thrust. Engines having such an enormous thrust are possible today, and in fact it will be necessary to have engines with this enormous thrust to obtain the desired rate of climb.

Shortly after delivering the lecture abstracted above, Dr. Hooker spoke on the application of the gas turbine to aircraft propulsion before members of the Royal Aeronautical Society. He drew comparisons between the power-weight ratios and cruising performances of various aircraft, from which he adduced that, although improvements can undoubtedly be made in the streamlining of aircraft, it is clear that new advanced types will require a take-off power-weight ratio of the order of 4 : 1 if cruising speeds in the neighbourhood of 350 m.p.h. at the normal figure of 50 per cent. maximum power are to be achieved.

After outlining the principal advantages possessed by the gas turbine over the piston engine, the lecturer observed that an engine of the Merlin category develops about 1,000 b.h.p. for an air consumption of 120 lb./min. Hence each pound of air consumed per second yields 500 b.h.p. which, with an airscrew efficiency of 80 per cent., gives 400 thrust h.p. By contrast, the Derwent V jet engine on the world's record runs at 600 m.p.h. consumed $2\frac{1}{2}$ tons of air/min., or nearly 86 lb./sec. Under this condition the engine produced about 5,000 thrust h.p., i.e., about 60 thrust h.p. per pound of air consumed per second.

Compression Ratio

Our attack on fuel consumption for turbines must be made in increasing the maximum compression ratio of the cycle, and this can evidently be done by replacing the single-stage compressor by a two-stage, or a multi-stage axial compressor ; but at the same time, to get the full advantage we must maintain the overall compressor efficiency in conjunction with the increased compression ratio. As the compression ratio or temperature rise through the compressor is increased the efficiency falls, being 80 per cent. at 5 : 1 compression or 200 degrees C. temperature rise, and 75 per cent. at 7 : 1 compression or 290 degrees C. temperature rise. Further, it would appear that whatever the efficiency of the compressor the maximum power per pound of air will be obtained with the temperature rise of 250 degrees C. which corresponds to a compression ratio of 6 : 1, and thus it is clear that both maximum power and minimum fuel consumption will occur at these values.

Considering the effect of a two-stage compressor at 6 : 1 ratio upon the performance of a jet propulsion engine having a static take-off rating of 5,500 lb. thrust, it can be shown that at 400 m.p.h. at 20,000 ft. the two stage engine achieves an improvement of roughly 14 per cent. in fuel consumption.

Also, let us consider the effect of combining both a two-stage compressor and an airscrew upon the performance of a gas turbine engine. The comparison shows that at 400 m.p.h. at 20,000 ft. the jet engine produces 2,400 lb. thrust for a fuel consumption of 1.3 lb. fuel per lb. thrust per hour, whereas the compound engine produces 2,200 lb. thrust with a fuel consumption of 0.67 lb. fuel/lb. thrust/hour, that is, the fuel consumption has now been practically halved.

As a matter of interest let us examine the performance of the compound engine at 300 m.p.h., since we know that at this speed lb. thrust and equivalent b.h.p. are identical. At sea-level the engine produces 3,900 b.h.p. with a fuel consumption of 0.58 lb./b.h.p.   At 20,000 ft. the figures are 2,500 b.h.p. with a fuel consumption of 0.56 lb./b.h.p./hr., whilst at 40,000 ft. we have 1,300 b.h.p. and 0.55 specific fuel consumption figures, which are very good indeed judged by the best of piston engine performances, particularly when one takes into account that there is no main engine cooling required on gas turbine engines.

The examples given have all been worked out on the basis that the maximum combustion temperature at entry into the turbine is 1,100 degrees K (degrees Kelvin = abs. C.), and this temperature, said Dr. Hooker, is very close to the maximum which turbine blades of Nimonic 80 can withstand at the stresses of a modern gas turbine.   Better turbine blade materials are in hand and recourse can be had to such devices as water cooling or air cooling of the blades, and under these conditions high combustion temperatures can be allowed.

Importance of Flame Temperature

Flame temperature has a very important effect upon the gas h.p./lb. air/sec. available in the jet pipe, i.e., an increase in flame temperature from 1,000 degrees K to 1,300 degrees K more than doubles the power output of the engine for each pound of air consumed per second.   Again, the optimum power occurs at about 250 degrees C. temperature rise through the compressors. The effect upon fuel consumption is no less marked and the specific consumption falls from about 0.65 lb./hr./g.h.p. to about 0.53 lb./hr./g.h.p.

The incorporation of a heat exchanger can have a very great effect in reducing fuel consumption and, further, can allow the engine to be operated over a wide range of powers without appreciably affecting the specific fuel consumption, but since a heat exchanger must necessarily be rather heavy and bulky the additional engine weight will only be saved in terms of fuel if the range of the aircraft is sufficiently great.   Calculations indicate that somewhat more than five hours' flying must be done before a heat exchanger has paid for its own weight.   In addition, the problems to be faced in its development make it the radiator problem *in excelsis.*

On the score of performance with jet propulsion, Dr. Hooker illustrated some rather entrancing examples.   First, a Lancaster fitted with four Nene engines which gave the aircraft a cruising speed of about 400 m.p.h. at all altitudes up to 35,000 ft.   At 10,000 ft. each engine will consume 430 gal./hr., so that the air miles per gallon are 0.23.   At 20,000 ft. the corresponding figure is 0.31 a.m.p.g., and at 30,000 ft. 0.43 a.m.p.g.   Admittedly these are low figures, but it should be remembered that four units of this type when fully installed only weigh a total of about 7,000 lb., whereas the present four Merlins fully installed weigh 13,000 lb.

Further, jet fighter aircraft such as the Meteor, Vampire and Lockheed Shooting Star have drag figures very much lower than airscrew-driven machines of a similar category, e.g., the drag coefficient of the Meteor is only about two-thirds that of the Spitfire, and figures for the Vampire are even better. Consequently, at a conservative estimate the previous figures of a.m.p.g. can, in actual fact, probably be increased by about 25 per cent., and in addition jet engines with a fuel consumption some 14 per cent. less than that of the Nene can be designed and made.

So far as take-off is concerned the Lancaster with four Nenes will have a static take-off thrust of 20,000 lb., which is considerably greater than that from four Merlins.

To consider another case, namely, the celebrated D.C.3.   A cruising speed of 400 m.p.h. at 1,000 ft. and 5,000 lb. payload coupled with a range of 1,000 miles can be obtained at a take-off weight of 27,000 lb. using jet propulsion engines of about 6 : 1 compression ratio and a static thrust of 6,000 lb.

In consideration of the effect of altitude upon range the preceding figures for the Lancaster give an indication.   But to analyse the effect in more detail he instanced a machine of about Spitfire size having a drag of about 1,000 lb. at 300 m.p.h. at sea level.   For a sea level speed of 500 m.p.h. a thrust of 2,400 lb. will be required, and the air-miles/gallon of the machine will be reduced to about 1.0.   At 40,000 ft. the drag of the aircraft at the same speed of 500 m.p.h. will be reduced to about 800 lb., due both to the lower density of the air at this height, and also to the change in angle of incidence of the machine.   Consequently, at this altitude the air-miles/ gallon will be about 4.0.   In going from sea-level the thermal efficiency of the engine is improved from about 18 to 25 per cent., and this improvement is due to the lower air-intake temperature to the engine and the consequent high compression ratio of the cycle.   On the other hand, the propulsory efficiency of the jet has fallen from 64 to 58 per cent., due to the increased jet velocity at 40,000 ft. brought about by the increased thermal efficiency of the engine. Thus the balance is as follows :—

Improvement in thermal efficiency of engine from 18 to 25 per cent., i.e., 1.39.

Reduction in propulsion efficiency from 64 to 58 per cent., i.e., 0.90.

The overall improvement of the engine is, therefore, 25 per cent., but the range of the aircraft has actually been *quadrupled*.   Hence the improvement in range of a jet-propelled machine at altitude is not so much due to the engine, but in the main due to the aircraft.

In actual fact, at 40,000 ft. and 500 m.p.h. this machine does the same air-miles/gallon as a Spitfire, and consequently all the objections to jet propulsion can be overcome by flying high and fast.   It should be clearly understood that jet propulsion is efficient at any altitude provided the speed is greater than 500 m.p.h.   It should also be remembered that the higher the altitude the more efficient the aircraft.

Commercial Aircraft Considerations

At a special turbine session of the Royal Aeronautical Society Mr. R. M. Clarkson, chief designer of the de Havilland Aircraft Co., discussed the effects upon the speed and economy of commercial aviation of the two simplest and immediate variants of the gas turbine, the simple jet-producing turbine and the simple propeller-driving turbine.   The accompanying table

TYPE OF POWER UNIT	INSTALLED WEIGHT	*SPECIFIC CONSUMPTION	DRAG—LB. at 100 ft./sec.
1. Piston—air-cooled radial type.	2.0 lb./take-off b.h.p.	0.46 lb./cruising b.h.p./hr.	38 lb. per 3,000 take-off b.h.p.
2. Piston — liquid-cooled.	2.1 lb./take-off b.h.p.	0.53 lb./cruising b.h.p./hr.	22 lb. per 3,000 take-off b.h.p.
3. Propeller - driving centrifugal gas turbine.	1.2 lb./equivalent take-off b.h.p.	0.5 lb./equivalent cruising b.h.p./hr.	13 lb. per 3,000 equivalent take-off b.h.p.
4. Propeller - driving axial gas turbine—advanced type.	0.75 lb./equivalent take-off b.h.p.	0.45 lb./equivalent cruising b.h.p./hr.	9 lb. per 3,000 equivalent take-off b.h.p.
5. Simple jet—centrifugal.	0.5 lb./lb. static thrust.	†1.05 lb./lb. static thrust.	5 lb. per 5,000 lb. static thrust.
6. Simple jet—axial —advanced type.	0.35 lb./lb. static thrust.	‡0.90 lb./lb. static thrust.	0 lb. per 5,000 lb. static thrust.

* At 300 m.p.h. unless otherwise stated.   ‡ Gives 0.56 lb./equivalent b.h.p. at 500 m.p.h.
† Gives 0.65 lb./equivalent b.h.p. at 500 m.p.h.

compares several different types of engines and gives an indication of what may be expected from turbine engines compared with piston engines. Mr. Clarkson explained that engine No. 1 is in being, No. 3 nearly so, and Nos. 4 and 6 might be available to the operator within the period of five years to which he had limited his paper. The table gives general trends rather than precise engine capabilities and should be regarded as stages in a development programme.

Inherent Simplicity

On the subject of reliability, serviceability and maintenance he said, ultimately the gas turbine would be superior to the piston engine, owing to its simplicity, but the operator would want to know what was meant by "ultimately."

First cost was not one of the most important factors, but this should be relatively low, due to the inherent simplicity.

The noise of a gas turbine was rather irritating, but he did not think it would be unduly troublesome to passengers. With a simple jet engine, low-frequency vibration was non-existent, but there was a very high-frequency vibration which might possibly become troublesome. On the whole, the vibration characteristics could scarcely be worse and might be better than those of the piston engine.

On the subject of fuel, Mr. Clarkson said that besides providing greater

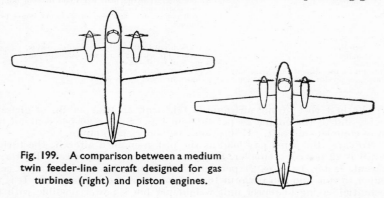

Fig. 199. A comparison between a medium twin feeder-line aircraft designed for gas turbines (right) and piston engines.

safety from fire hazard, paraffin ought to be cheaper than petrol. He took, for the purpose of the paper, petrol at 2s. per gallon and paraffin at 1s. 4d. per gallon.

The next step was to examine one or two representative types of aircraft when designed : (a) for piston engines and (b) for gas turbines. Taking first a medium-size twin-engined feeder-line type, Mr. Clarkson started with the following specification : Pay load with 500 miles still-air range at 5,000 ft. —3,000 lb. ; seating 12 passengers and a crew of two. Satisfactory compliance with A.R.B. safety requirements on a warm day.

The following engine characteristics were assumed :—

	PISTON ENGINE	TURBINE—AIRSCREW
Installed wt. per equivalent t.o. h.p. ...	2.4 lb./h.p.	1.5 lb./h.p.
Cruising specific fuel consumption ...	0.49 lb./b.h.p./hr.	0.52 lb./equivalent b.h.p./hr
Cruising condition	50 per cent. of take-off b.h.p.	90 per cent. of take-off r.p.m. (72 per cent. t.o. power)

On these assumptions the aircraft arrived at will have the following characteristics :—

	PISTON ENGINE	TURBINE-AIRSCREW
All-up weight	13,500 lb.	10,600 lb.
Installed power (take-off)	2 × 700 b.h.p.	2 × 550 equivalent b.v.p.
Gross wing area...	500 sq. ft.	390 sq. ft.
Overall span	69ft.	61ft.
Wing loading	27 lb./sq. ft.	27 lb./sq. ft.
Fuel for 500 miles	141 gallons	131 gallons
Cruising speed	185 m.p.h.	215 m.p.h.
Pay load...	3,000 lb.	3,000 lb.
Ton-miles of pay load per gallon of fuel	5.4	5.7
Ton-miles of pay load per hour ...	248	288
First cost of complete aircraft ...	£19,000	£15,500
Direct operating cost per ton-mile of pay load	13.9d.	9.4d.

Direct operating cost includes the following items :—

Fuel and oil	Petrol 2/- per gallon + 6 per cent. for oil. Paraffin 1/4 per gallon + 1 per cent. for oil.
Maintenance :	
Airframe	£1 10s. per aircraft flying hour per 10,000 lb. of air-frame weight.
Engine	£1 per aircraft flying hour per 1,000 take-off b.h.p. (for piston and turbine).
Crew	£1,600 per annum and 850 crew flying hours per annum.
Depreciation :	
Airframe	5 years' life with 25 per cent. residual value.
Engine	2½ years' life with 25 per cent. residual value.
Insurance	8 per cent. of the first cost.
Interest on investment	5 per cent. of the first cost.
Passenger service, overheads, etc., are not included in direct operating cost.	

The first cost of the airframe is taken at £2 10s. per lb. of airframe weight, and of the engine £4 per take-off h.p. Spares 20 per cent. of first cost of complete aircraft. Utilisation 2,000 hours per annum.

To carry the same pay load as the piston-engined aircraft, the turbine aircraft is 22 per cent. smaller, 18 per cent. cheaper, 22 per cent. lighter, 16 per cent. faster, requires 21 per cent. less installed power, is 32 per cent. cheaper to run, and can perform 16 per cent. more work in a year. It is the substantial saving in power unit weight per horse power possible with the turbine which is the chief cause of these improvements.

In the private-owner class of aircraft, with engines of some 150 h.p., he did not look for any significant improvement, but the practical advantages would be available to the private owner and would amply justify the introduction of the new prime mover. Ruggedness, low first cost and reliability would result in an engine of not very competitive economy and the huge gear reduction would tend to make the engine heavier and bulkier than might be expected.

Skipping several intermediate stages, Mr. Clarkson turned his attention to the long-range type of Empire airliners. He referred to non-stop stages of 2,200 miles (against a 50 m.p.h. headwind plus a 450 miles' allowance for reaching an alternative airfield), entailing a still-air range of 3,000 miles. For the purpose of investigation he stipulated the following design requirements : Cruising altitude not less than 25,000 ft. ; take-off under tropical conditions not more than 1,500 yards to clear 50 ft. ; maximum wing loading for take-off 70 lb./sq.ft. ; maximum wing loading for landing 55 lb./sq. ft. A range of cruising speeds from approximately 300 to 500 m.p.h. was covered.

Empire Airliners

For the 300 m.p.h. case he took an aircraft of 100,000 lb. all-up weight with 150 ft. span and 1,800 sq. ft. of wing area. In passing to the higher cruising speeds, more power was installed, and all-up weights allowed to rise. Structure weights were suitably adjusted, and fuselage dimensions and passenger accommodation suited to the resulting pay loads. At the high-speed end reduction in span was found to be desirable, the wing area remaining unchanged. All the aircraft are cruised at 15 per cent. above the speed for maximum L/D at 50 per cent. of take-off power for piston engines and 90

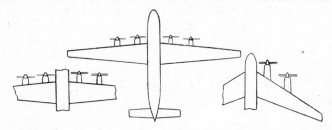

Fig. 200. Long-range Empire airliners. All-up weight 100,000 lb., 150 ft. span, 1,800 sq. ft. wing area. The full plan view shows, on the port wing, radial air-cooled piston engines totalling 4 x 2,250 = 9,000 h.p. Power-unit weight, 17.5 per cent. of a.u.w. Cruising speed, 280 m.p.h. On the starboard wing, axial gas turbines driving airscrews, totalling 4 x 2,550 = 10,200 h.p. Power unit weight, 7.5 per cent. of a.u.w. Cruising speed, 300 m.p.h. For the part-plan figures on the left are : Port wing, liquid-cooled piston engines totalling 16,000 h.p. Power unit weight, 25.5 per cent. of a.u.w. Cruising speed, 370 m.p.h. Starboard wing, axial gas turbines driving airscrews, total 25,600 h.p. Power unit weight, 15.5 per cent. of a.u.w. Cruising speed, 425 m.p.h. In the view on the right, sweepback has been used, and the power units are gas turbines driving airscrews. Total power, 4 x 11,400 = 45,600 h.p. Power unit weight, 26.5 per cent. of a.u.w. Cruising speed, 515 m.p.h.

per cent. maximum revolutions (45 per cent. of take-off power) for turbines. Fig. 200. gives a rough idea of the size and weight of some of the power units installed at different cruising speeds.

Of the commercial type of aircraft with simple jet engines Mr. Clarkson said that its high-speed possibilities made it most suitable for long-range work, but it was technically least suited to this duty on account of poor take-off thrust and high consumption. Assisted take-off would be required and a certain austerity in passenger accommodation. Some acute problems might be encountered owing to the high Mach number.

For operating from trans-ocean airports, wing loadings can be allowed to go up to 80 lb./sq. ft. and take-offs to about 2,000 yards to clear 50 ft.

Jet Propulsion and Military Aircraft

At the same meeting, Mr. W. G. Carter, chief designer of the Gloster Aircraft Co. Ltd., Cheltenham, expressed the view that the association of gas turbines with aircraft designed to make effective use of the special characteristics of jet propulsion has brought the trend of development into a state of transition and uneasy experiment. Already speeds equivalent to a low-level Mach number of 0.80 have been recorded under observed conditions. This has been done by a standard twin-jet fighter not specially designed to accomplish speeds exceeding a low-level Mach number of 0.66. The general handling qualities of the aircraft have been good, and although changes in the aerodynamic characteristics are just beginning to be noticeable these are regarded as moderate in effect and generally in line with predictions which had been made. It may, therefore, be possible to make more advanced explorations into the transonic region with similar twin-jet installations.

The percentage increase in drag over the low-speed value, as shown by Fig. 201 gives a clear indication that the prospects are there if successfully exploited. The curve is not necessarily an accurate representation, as the available thrust has yet to be calibrated in flight. Up to a Mach number of 0.825 it may, however, be regarded as reasonably accurate, and the extrapolation beyond this figure is the best guess that can be made at the present time.

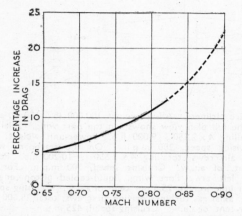

Fig. 201. Increase of drag with Mach number. The dotted portion is the best extrapolation that can be made at present.

This curve provides a clear indication that the twin-jet arrangement belies somewhat the first impression that, because of wing nacelles, it may not be so favourable for speed development as compared with its counterpart, the single-jet fighter. The low-speed drag value of the twin will obviously be higher, perhaps as much as 50 per cent. higher, than the single-jet machine designed to satisfy the same general operational requirements. But percentage increase in drag is the critical factor, and experience is beginning to show that wing nacelles do not greatly influence the rise in drag due to compressibility effects. Like the fuselage, they are three-dimensional bodies and, if precautions are observed to harmonise the associated airflow characteristics of wing and nacelle, there seems to be no reason to suppose that flight velocities exceeding sonic conditions could not be accomplished with engines on the wings.

The main concern with the twin-jet arrangement is to minimise the severity of buffeting effects due to turbulence.

With engines installed on the wings, it may be possible to accommodate more thrust in terms of all-up weight than could be done with the single-jet fighter ; or a three-engined arrangement could be considered to get even better results in improving the thrust/weight ratio. This over-abundance of thrust, so far as fighter types are concerned, is required for climbing performance rather than for speed. As an indication of the trend in this direction, the Gloster Meteor now has a combined thrust of 7,000 lb. At one time 4,000 lb. thrust was looked upon as a reasonable provision for aircraft of this type, and a corresponding figure of 3,000 lb. good enough for the single-jet machine. Now the outlook is that, however much thrust can be crammed in, it is unlikely to be more than can be used effectively, especially for climbing performance to great altitudes in the shortest possible time. This has become necessary in order to intercept bomber or reconnaissance types which, with jet engines, will be able to cruise at twice the speed and twice the height that has hitherto been possible. As climbing characteristics depend on the thrust/ weight value of the aircraft, the present trend of development will mostly be concerned with giving this the highest possible value.

Reduced Frontal Area the Aim

The outlook is that this can best be done by having two engines instead of one, but before this premise is firmly established it will be necessary to provide jet engines giving much more thrust per unit frontal area than is obtainable from those having centrifugal compressors. These are inevitably bulky in terms of diameter as compared with the axial, and there is no room for corpulence in the jet fighter whether it is propelled by one or more jets. The Rolls-Royce Nene engine, rated at 4,500 lb. thrust, is already outside the diameter limit for fighter-aircraft nacelles, so that the most significant comparison which can be made between various engines concerns their respective thrust value in terms of frontal area more than any other installational feature.

When the axial type is considered there seems to be no reason why the diameter should much exceed that of the air intake orifice. For the same thrust as the Nene, this diameter will be about 27in. Some further increase is to be expected over the combustion chambers and, making allowance for this and for structural considerations, the effective nacelle diameter should not exceed 33 in., indicating a thrust value of about 750 lb. per square foot as compared with 400 lb. for the centrifugal engine. This may be an optimistic estimate, but if it can be done, the twin-jet fighter may well have an overwhelming advantage.

These slim engines also provide the opportunity to consider their sideby-side installation in a fuselage widened sufficiently for this purpose, but the question of balancing the aircraft satisfactorily becomes difficult with so much weight aft of where the centre of gravity is best positioned. The available space to accommodate fuel is also severely restricted with this arrangement, while the problem involved in ducting the air supply to the engine is an embarrassing feature of the structural assembly.

Alternative Engine Positions

There is, of course, ample scope for considering other alternative arrangements, and it may be preferred to put the engines in nacelles forming part of the fuselage. This gets over the difficulty of balancing and provides room for plenty of fuel capacity between the engines. It introduces a difficult problem at the air intakes, and, if conditions here are not good, the breathing capacity of the engine is compromised, and thrust may be reduced under high-speed conditions. One of the outstanding advantages of the twin-jet arrangement is that ducting problems do not have to be taken into account.

Some curves given in Fig. 202. emphasise the outlook on climbing performance. Similar and comparable information concerning speed has not been included, as this aspect is more concerned with other features of design, such as aerodynamic refinement and special facilities to maintain precision control of the aircraft under all conditions. These matters relate to the uneasy experiments now rapidly coming into the aeronautical picture, but rates of climb may be very much further advanced before these formidable problems become too obtrusive.

The curve " A " represents a typical rate-of-climb performance for the Gloster Mark IV Meteor. This aircraft has a thrust/weight ratio of 0.5 and climbs to 30,000 ft. in five minutes. It represents about the best climbing

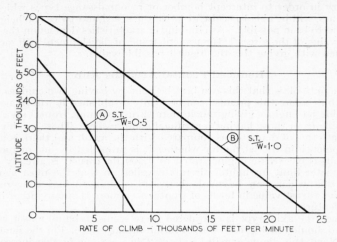

Fig. 202. Typical climb performance of twin-jet fighters with two different values of thrust loading.

performance for the present-day jet fighter. If a thrust/weight ratio of unity could be developed for a similar type of aircraft, rates of climb as shown by curve " B " would become possible. This can only be done by using axial-flow engines developed to provide a thrust of about 700 lb. per square foot of nacelle frontal area. The climbing performance of one of these engines in a single-jet fighter would not be nearly so good.

The alternative power installation for high-altitude interception would comprise rocket assistance. For this purpose, jet engines on the wings make it convenient to put the rocket combustion chamber at the rear end of the fuselage. As a type, the rocket-cum-jet interceptor combines the advantage of out-climbing the conventional jet-fighter, with the possibility of cruising facilities at the desired altitude. How far the trend of development may proceed in this direction depends largely on the extent it may be possible to improve gas turbine jet installations so that these can function satisfactorily without the need for rocket assistance.

Compounding Turbine and Piston Aero Engines

In March, 1946, Dr. H. R. Ricardo read a Paper " Turbine Compounding of the Piston Aero Engine " before the Royal Aeronautical Society and presented the case for combining a piston engine with a gas turbine. The gas turbine, he said, is inherently very greedy of fuel, but there are more complex forms of turbine at present in preparation which will be more economical in fuel, and it is with these more complex forms rather than with the simple types of the present day that the compound engine will have to compete.

Clearly the efficiency of any heat engine is a function of the range of temperature it can usefully employ. The turbine is handicapped by the fact that the upper limit of the temperature range through which it can work is in the region of 700 deg. C., while the flame temperature attained by the combustion of any hydro-carbon fuel in air lies between the limits of 2,200 and 2,500 deg. C. To bridge this wide gap between the maximum temperature available and that which we dare use, four or five times the amount of air required for combustion must be supplied as a temperature dilutant. The conventional piston engine, on the other hand, can utilise the upper ranges of temperature but can make little use of temperatures much below about 1,500 deg. C. Thus we have two forms of prime mover, the one eminently suitable for converting into power the heat available in the higher ranges, the other for conversion at the lower temperatures.

Additionally, the piston engine is eminently suitable to deal with relatively small volumes at high pressure and temperatures, and the turbine, by virtue of its high mechanical efficiency and large flow areas, to deal with large volumes at low pressures. Clearly then the logical development is to combine the two, in series, to form a compound unit. Instead of lowering the temperature by pumping large volumes of dilution air at a heavy cost in blower work, let us lower it rather by converting the high temperature heat into useful power ; in other words, let us interpose between the blower and the turbine a dynamic rather than a static combustion chamber.

In the combined plant we shall have available a considerable excess of air over and above that required for complete combustion, due to the gap between the minimum temperature of the piston engine cycle and that which the turbine can digest. The gap is such that we shall have to provide nearly $2\frac{1}{2}$ times the air required for complete combustion of the fuel, so we need not worry about thermal efficiency in terms of air consumed. Nor, so far as the piston engine is concerned, need we worry much about efficiency in terms of fuel, for what is lost in the cylinder by delayed or incomplete combustion will be recovered in the turbine. We must, therefore, revise entirely our ideas on piston engine design. Our objective is now to develop an engine which shall offer the freest possible passage of air through its cylinder, and which shall be capable of burning the maximum possible amount of fuel per unit of cylinder volume.

Two–stroke Engine Proposed

In the first place, thanks to the excess air, we can employ a two-stroke engine, and, therefore, a much smaller cylinder since a two-stroke engine can pass far more air than its cylinder volume defines. Again, we need not worry about scavenging efficiency and can use the simplest possible expression of two-stroke with piston controlled ports. Further, in view of the fact that we cannot, in any case, burn all the air available, we can with advantage employ compression ignition in preference to spark ignition—for in the former, as in the turbine, we are compelled to provide some surplus air. The use of C.I. confers additional advantages :—

1. We need not worry about maintaining specific relationship between fuel and air, hence control can be on fuel supply alone.

2. We are completely exempt from the menace of detonation as the hotter the air, within limits imposed by lubrication, the better the combustion and the smoother the running.

3. Fuels will be the same as those of the straight turbine.

4. We shall be free of electrical ignition with all it implies in weight, radio interference, and potential sources of failure.

The size of our piston engine will be determined almost solely by the amount of fuel we can burn under take-off conditions per litre of cylinder capacity per hour, and this in turn will depend largely upon the pressure at which we choose to operate our turbine.

It would seem that the best all-round compromise will be to work at a pressure of about six atmospheres absolute for the maximum power. Generally speaking, the higher the operating pressure the more will the burden of power production be thrown on the turbine, and the smaller the size and output of the piston engine.

Efficiency of 40 to 45%

With the component efficiencies which we realise to-day, and taking fully into account the losses due to direct heat flow to the cylinder walls and the pressure drop through the engine cylinders, the overall efficiency from the fuel to the airscrew shaft of such a compound plant should lie between 40 per cent. and 45 per cent. when cruising at 15,000 ft. at 50 per cent. take-off power—this corresponding to a consumption of diesel oil of 0.3 to 0.34 lb./shaft h.p./hr., rising to about 0.4 lb. under take-off conditions. Dr. Ricardo said these figures take no account of the additional jet thrust available, which would be there at all times as a bonus and, under some conditions, as a really substantial bonus.

He went on to say : We come now to this conclusion : the combined plant will consist of a blower, preferably of the axial flow type with, perhaps, a centrifugal for the last stage, a very small and simple piston engine in place of the usual combustion chamber, and a gas turbine. Of these three components the piston engine will deliver, and the blower will consume, about the same power, while the turbine will deliver about 50 per cent. more than either. With regard to the compound unit it is generally argued that the addition of a piston engine will involve a very great, if not a prohibitive, increase in both weight and bulk; but to consider this aspect more closely, the actual capacity of the engine is determined by the amount of fuel which can be burned per hour per litre of cylinder capacity. Preliminary experiments with a simple valveless two-stroke cylinder, working with an inlet pressure, so far, of only 4.4 atmospheres absolute at 2,800 r.p.m. show already that we can burn between 50 and 60 lb. of diesel oil per hour per litre with a maximum cylinder pressure not exceeding 1,400 lb./sq. in., and without running into any thermal troubles. When, as we intend, we go up to a pressure of six atmospheres and higher revolutions we shall be able to increase this figure to about 80 lb., but to be on the safe side let us assume that the weight of fuel burnt will be 64 lb./litre/hr. under take-off conditions. If, now, the overall specific consumption under take-off conditions is 0.4 lb./b.h.p./hr. then the net power output of the complete plant will be 160 h.p./litre of piston engine.

As to weight, the current weight of aero engines working at smaller maximum pressures, when stripped of their supercharger, ignition equipment, and such auxiliaries as will form part of the turbine plant in any case, is between 40 and 45 lb./litre. Valveless engines should be considerably lighter, but let us take the weight as 40 lb./litre. The weight then of the piston engine in the combined plant should work out at about 0.25 lb./shaft h.p. By no means all this weight is additional, for it must be remembered that the engine replaces the combustion chambers. Further, since the mass flow of air will be approximately halved, the blower, turbine, and all the ducting will be correspondingly lighter and smaller. Moreover, nowhere except inside the engine cylinder will the pressure exceed, say, six atmospheres absolute. As an illustration, an engine of the same cylinder capacity as the old Bristol Mercury should suffice for a net output of 4,000 shaft h.p.

Range and Fuel Economy.

A lecture by Air Commodore F. R. Banks, on the subject of Power Units for Future Aircraft, was delivered before l'Association Française des Ingénieurs et Techniciens de l'Aeronautique (AFITA), in April, 1946. Brief extracts are appended.

Aircraft of extreme range, say, 10,000 miles, or having a radius of action of 3,000–5,000 miles, are necessary for certain military purposes, but he could not see the gas turbine filling this need for some seven to ten years. Even the piston engine, for a range of 10,000 miles, must be developed to give considerably better fuel economy than it now does. He was thinking of the present cruising fuel consumption of 0.45 lb./b.h.p./hr. and, in some cases, 0.41 lb./b.h.p./hr. To obtain a reasonable payload, and to avoid oversize aircraft, built mainly to accommodate the fuel, a cruising fuel consumption of not greater than 0.35 lb./b.h.p./hr. should be the target.

To achieve a fuel economy of this order some form of " compounding " is necessary to give a higher expansion ratio to the working cycle of the engine. . . . There is a case for the two-stroke engine, but only if compounding is employed to make full use of the exhaust-gas energy. By this means, a high degree of economy can be achieved, and a cruising fuel consumption of, say, 0.37 lb./b.h.p./hr. is possible with a gasoline two-stroke/turbine combination and of about 0.32 lb./b.h.p./hr. for a similar combination arranged for compression-ignition heavy-oil operation. . . .

The specific weight of a simple turbine-jet engine is about 0.3 lb. per lb. of static thrust. Turbine-airscrews will have somewhat higher weight, between 0.75 lb. and 0.90 lb. per equivalent shaft horsepower.

Gas turbines work on the " constant pressure " thermodynamic cycle. And this can be demonstrated more clearly by a temperature/entropy diagram (Fig. 203). Referring to the diagram; the full line (0, 1′, 2′, 3′, 4′, 5′) represents the theoretical cycle, assuming no losses. Atmospheric air, in a condition represented by point o, is raised in temperature and pressure to conditions

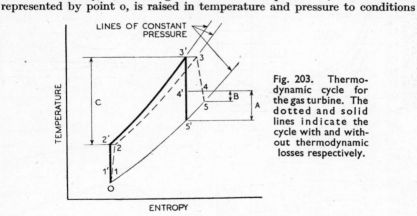

Fig. 203. Thermodynamic cycle for the gas turbine. The dotted and solid lines indicate the cycle with and without thermodynamic losses respectively.

corresponding to point 1′ by the effect of " ram." Point 2′ is reached after the air has passed through the compressor. From 2′ to 3′ heat is added at constant pressure, in an amount proportional to the temperature difference, C. The gas is then expanded from 3′ to 5′ where the pressure is, again, atmospheric.

The energy available in the expansion is proportional to the temperature drop from 3′ to 5′. A proportion of this energy 3′ to 4′, equal to 1′ to 2′ is required to drive the compressor. And the remaining energy, 4′ to 5′, proportional to A, may be used, in jet form, to propel the aircraft, or some may be converted into shaft power by means of a turbine.

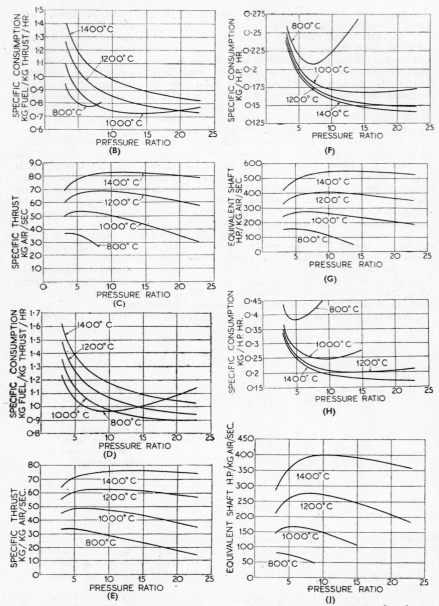

Fig. 204. Output per unit rate of air flow and specific fuel consumption for the simple jet (B) to (E), and the airscrew-turbine unit (F) to (J). (B), (H) and (J) refer to sea-level static conditions, and (C) to (G) are for 800 km./hr. (500 m.p.h.) (I.C.A.N.) at the tropopause (36,000ft.). Temperatures are in degrees C. absolute.

The actual cycle, with losses taken into account, is shown by the dotted line (0, 1, 2, 3, 4, 5). With the same input of work into the compressor, the resultant pressure at 2 is lower than 2', and, because of this lower pressure ratio, also, due to the losses during expansion, the available energy in expansion, 3 to 5, is much smaller. The work required to drive the compressor is, however, unaffected and, consequently, the useful net energy available, 4 to 5, proportional to B, is much reduced. The thermal input for both the cycles shown is proportional to C. Therefore, the thermodynamic efficiency of the cycle, with no losses, is $\dfrac{A}{C}$ and, with losses, is $\dfrac{B}{C}$.

The diagram shows the great importance of achieving low losses in the compressor, turbine and combustion chamber to obtain good efficiency in the gas turbine as a whole.

The temperature/entropy diagram may be used to illustrate the effect of increasing compression ratio and gas temperature at the inlet to the turbine. In Fig. 204. (B–J,) some results of calculations on these effects are shown. In the case of the turbine-airscrew, it will be seen that, as the turbine inlet temperature is increased, the specific consumption decreases, and the specific output rises. As the pressure ratio is increased, at a given turbine inlet temperature, the specific consumption passes through a minimum and the specific output through a maximum. But it will be noted that these two optimum points do not occur at the same pressure ratio. This is particularly marked in the curves for 800 and 1,000 deg. C. absolute, and is due to the increasing effect of losses in compression and expansion which offset any thermodynamic gain.

The effect of pressure ratio and temperature on the performance of simple jet engines, shown in Fig. 204 (B–E), is complicated by the additional factor of propulsive efficiency. The specific thrust varies in approximately the same way as the specific power output of propeller turbines. The specific consumption, however, generally rises as the temperature increases. This is the result of decreases in propulsive efficiency, which occur when the jet velocity is increased.

At any given temperature there is an optimum pressure ratio, which is shown most definitely on the curves for 800 deg. C. absolute. But, for temperatures now used, this occurs at a large value of the pressure ratio which is above that giving the maximum thrust.

The curves have been constructed for the following conditions :—

Compressor polytropic efficiency	= 87 per cent.
Compressor turbine overall efficiency	= 87 ,,
Jet pipe expansion efficiency...	= 95 ,,
Power turbine efficiency	= 88 ,,
Assumed propeller efficiency at sea level	= 75 ,,
at tropopause	= 74 ,,
Equivalent jet brake horsepower at sea-level static ...	= $\dfrac{\text{jet thrust}}{2.5}$
Combustion chamber pressure loss in lb./sq. in.	= 2 × relative atmospheric pressure.

Following these considerations, Fig. 205 shows characteristic curves of fuel consumption against thrust at different speeds from sea level to (approximately) the tropopause ; for (a) a simple jet engine of the " Whittle " type and (b) a turbine-airscrew having two compressors, in series.

To give some idea of the working conditions inside a simple jet engine at normal maximum speed, sections through one combustion chamber of the Rolls-Royce " Derwent " engine are included. Representing a typical " Whittle " type, they show particular conditions existing throughout its system when it is running. (Fig. 206.) . . .

In order to design compact and light turbine engines, it is necessary to obtain the largest output of work per stage of both the compressor and the turbine. It is also necessary to have the highest flow rates possible, in order to obtain an engine of minimum total cross-sectional area. To achieve this, high flow velocities through the components are required, extending well into the compressibility region. In addition, high blade speeds are desirable, but this obviously leads to high stresses. Consequently, the design, as in all mechanical engineering, must be a compromise ; which, in this case, is one

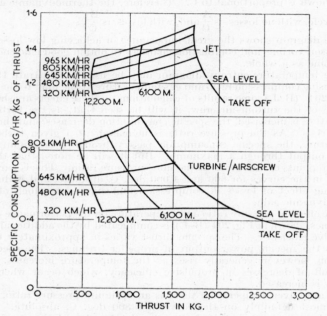

Fig. 205. Characteristic fuel consumption/thrust curves at speeds from 200 to 600 m.p.h. at sea level, 20,000 and 40,000ft. (I kg. = 2.20 lb.).

between the stressing of the turbine and its blading and the maximum flow velocities or Mach numbers which can be obtained without any appreciable loss in efficiency.

When referring to stresses, it is the British practice also to specify a value for the gyroscopic loading which must be allowed for in the design of the turbine, to meet the aircraft manœuvring conditions. This figure is 3.5 radians per second.

The gas turbine is a " full-throttle " engine and normally runs at or near maximum conditions. It has, therefore, the characteristics of such engines and the power falls off from sea level to altitude. The turbine is also critical to air-inlet temperature and it is very important to ensure that, when meeting a new aircraft requirement, allowance is made for the take-off and climb conditions in hot climates and also, under similar conditions, from high-altitude airfields.

There has been considerable difficulty in maintaining stable combustion conditions at altitudes around 35,000 to 40,000 ft., and the flame has extinguished itself at about these altitudes (rich mixture blow-out). There has

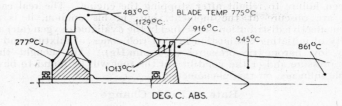

DEG. C. ABS.

Variation of temperature.

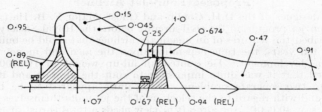

KG/SQ. CM.

Variation of pressure (1 kg./sq. cm. = 14.22 lb./sq. in.)

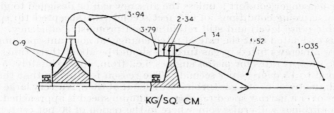

Variation of Mach number.

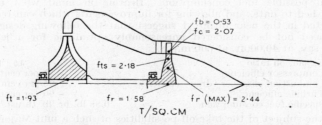

T/SQ.CM.

Principal stresses in the moving components. ft = tangential stress at the impeller bore (12.28 tons/sq. in.). fr = radial stress in the turbine disc (fr max = 15.49 tons/sq. in.). fts = the radial stress in the disc rim between blade root fittings. fb = the gas bending stress on the blades (3.39 tons/sq. in.). fc = the centrifugal stress on blades.

Fig. 206. Working conditions in a Whittle-type turbine-jet unit.

I

also been failure to relight after stopping the engine. The real cause, or causes, are obscure at the moment, but, in his opinion, it is mainly due to ineffective distribution of the fuel in the available oxygen (air) and the difficulty of initiating combustion in over-rich zones of mixture and at extremely low barometric pressures (200 mm.Hg). He thought that the vapour pressure and/or the volatility of the fuel will be found to have considerable influence on this phenomenon.

Rate of Pitch Change

The turbine-airscrew may present some difficulty in damping out the airscrew noise because, unlike the piston engine, the turbine will cruise near to its maximum revolutions and the airscrew tip speed may therefore be too high for passenger comfort ; unless the airscrew can be designed to give a tip speed, at cruising conditions, of 650 feet/second (the accepted tip speed for reasonable noise level) and still retain a good propulsive efficiency.

It is estimated that the rate of pitch change, at constant-speeding conditions, for airscrews fitted to gas turbines should be about three times greater than the present rates for piston engines, i.e., from, approximately, 5 degrees per second to 15 degrees per second. The reason for this is, that the speed/power characteristics of a gas turbine are such that there is a very large increase in power over a narrow speed range as maximum speed is approached. Since airscrew turbines will cruise somewhere in the region of 90 per cent. of maximum revolutions, close control is considered essential in order to cope with large power differences.

Proposed Four–Jet Airliner

The designer of the D.H. Goblin and Ghost, Major F. B. Halford, read a paper on jet propulsion for civil aircraft before the Royal Society of Arts and described the features of an imaginary airliner that could be built during the next ten years, the time depending upon the men and money devoted to such a development. He quoted an all-up weight of 190,000 lb. and maintained that it was quite impossible to split the aircraft and its power plant into two separate problems. Four units appeared to be the ideal number, and with regard to the selection of the jet units themselves he said :

"At, say, 40,000ft., the aircraft in view needs a total thrust of 10,200 lb. to propel it at its selected cruising speed. This means that each of the four units must be designed to give a thrust at 40,000ft. of 2,550 lb. for the minimum possible fuel consumption. Bearing in mind what has been accomplished to date, and allowing for improvements which can reasonably be expected in the near future, I suggest that the following design target figures need not be considered unreasonably optimistic for a jet engine cruising, say, at 40,000ft. at 600 m.p.h.

Expansion ratio	..	..	..	..	15 : 1
Compressor efficiency	..	..	..	..	85 per cent.
Combustion chamber 'drag' efficiency	..		..	..	95 per cent.
Turbine efficiency	..	..	..	..	90 per cent.
Specific fuel consumption	..	..		0.88 lb./hr./lb. thrust."	

On the subject of the take-off possibilities of such a unit Major Halford said : " Here we come up against a design ' critical.' It has become common knowledge that one of the main difficulties which faced Air Commodore Whittle and pioneers of the gas turbine was the lack of suitable material for the turbine blades, which have not only to operate in gas temperatures of over 600 deg. C., but which are, at the same time, subjected to centrifugal and bending stresses of high order."

" For take-off purposes we do not mind if the specific fuel consumption

increases ; all we want is the highest thrust in order to reduce the take-off
run to the minimum.   In a given turbine this would depend on what
temperature we dared to run the turbine blades, and for the turbine we have
in mind I think a maximum blade temperature of 850 deg. C.—corresponding
to a gas temperature of 1,000 deg. C. at entry to the turbine—should be
obtainable by 1950.

"The temperatures mentioned would ensure a maximum take-off
thrust from each of the four power units of 15,000 lb."

A schematic drawing of the imaginary jet unit is illustrated as Fig. 207.
The diameter is 5ft., length 17ft. and the weight 6,000 lb.   A nominal static
thrust of 12,000 lb. should be developed at 6,200 r.p.m. at 800 deg. C. before
the turbine, and at 1,000 deg. C. before the turbine the take-off thrust should
be 15,000 lb.   The 14-stage axial-flow compressor would be driven by a 3-stage
turbine developing a maximum of 28,500 h.p.

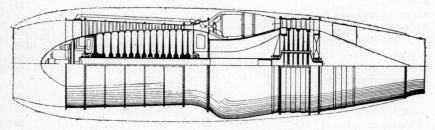

Fig. 207.   Major Halford's suggestion for an axial-flow jet propulsion unit with a
take-off thrust of 15,000 lb. at 1,000 deg. C before the turbine and a nominal static
thrust of 12,000 lb. at 800 deg. C before the turbine.   The weight would be
6,000 lb. diameter 5ft. and length 17ft.

INDEX

ROLLS-ROYCE

The foremost designers
and constructors of
Jet Propulsion Engines
in the World.

HEAD OFFICE:
Telephone: Derby 2424
Telegrams: Roycar, Derby

LONDON OFFICE:
Telephone: Mayfair 6201
Telegrams: Rolhead, Piccy, London

LODGE

PLUGS

always abreast
of engine design

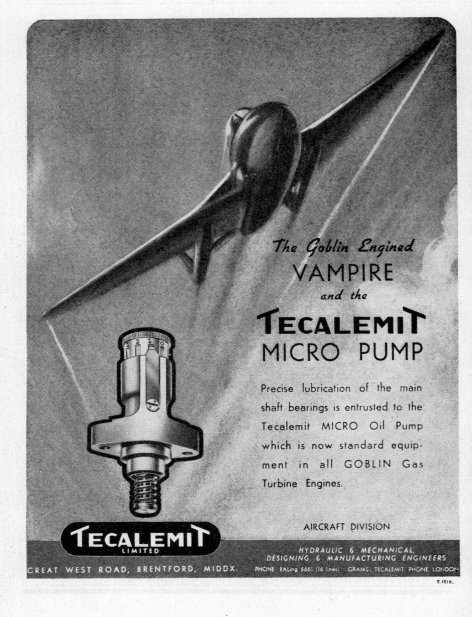

The Goblin Engined
VAMPIRE
and the
TECALEMIT
MICRO PUMP

Precise lubrication of the main shaft bearings is entrusted to the Tecalemit MICRO Oil Pump which is now standard equipment in all GOBLIN Gas Turbine Engines.

AIRCRAFT DIVISION

TECALEMIT
LIMITED

GREAT WEST ROAD, BRENTFORD, MIDDX.

HYDRAULIC & MECHANICAL DESIGNING & MANUFACTURING ENGINEERS
PHONE: EALing 6661 (16 lines)   GRAMS: TECALEMIT PHONE, LONDON

T.151C.

Bristol

Gas Turbines

Theseus The 2,000 B.H.P. "Bristol" Theseus is the first of a family of "Bristol" gas-turbine units for which the primary objective is the attainment of the highest possible thermal efficiency consistent with reasonable weight and bulk. The first unit satisfactorily to pass its tests, the Theseus, follows design principles whereby the greater proportion of the power output is used to drive a propeller and the residual thrust is utilised in the form of a jet. An unique feature of this engine is the provision of a heat exchanger by which means a fuel consumption comparable to that of a reciprocating engine is obtained.

The Proteus . . . this "Bristol" Gas Turbine, now in course of development, is the power unit which will be used for the second prototype of the "Bristol" Type 167 (often referred to as the Brabazon I). Details of other "Bristol" gas-turbine units now undergoing development and tests will be released shortly.

THE BRISTOL AEROPLANE COMPANY LIMITED · ENGLAND

252

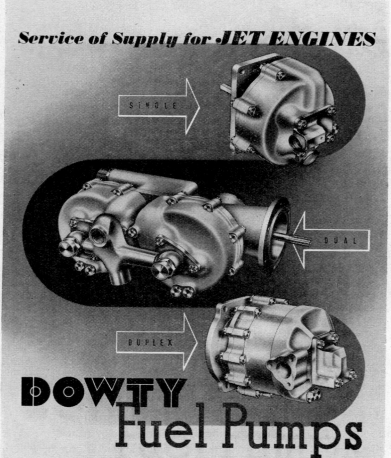

JESSOP
G.18 B. .
AUSTENITIC STEEL
for the highest
temperatures
and stresses

*Used in all the leading makes of
British Gas Turbine Engines*

WILLIAM JESSOP & SONS, LTD.
STEELMAKERS ~ ~ ~ SHEFFIELD

SAVED AGAIN

THE photograph shows an actual live ejection at 505 m.p.h. by B. I. Lynch, at Chalgrove Aerodrome. This seat has been standardised for the R.A.F. for all fighter and bomber aircraft.

via

THE MARTIN-BAKER PATENT EJECTOR SEAT

Designed and Manufactured by

MARTIN-BAKER AIRCRAFT
CO., LTD.
HIGHER DENHAM, NR. UXBRIDGE

Again pioneer development

Since the earliest days of the development of the Whittle Jet Propulsion Unit, R & M have been privileged to co-operate with the designers in supplying bearings that would meet the strenuous conditions demanded.

BALL & ROLLER
R&M
BEARINGS

RANSOME & MARLES BEARING CO. LTD.
NEWARK-ON-TRENT • ENGLAND

They rely on 'LION'
PACKING & JOINTING

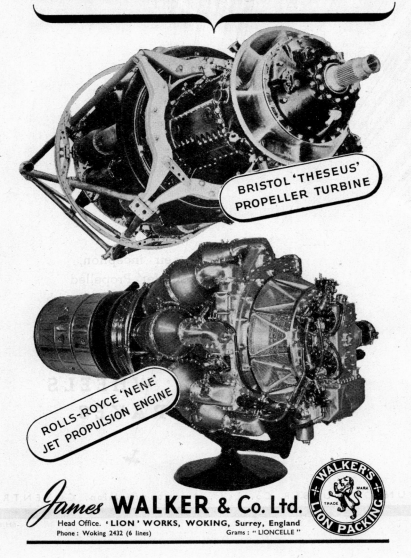

BRISTOL 'THESEUS' PROPELLER TURBINE

ROLLS-ROYCE 'NENE' JET PROPULSION ENGINE

James **WALKER & Co. Ltd.**

Head Office. 'LION' WORKS, WOKING, Surrey, England
Phone : Woking 2432 (6 lines)   Grams : " LIONCELLE "

WALKER'S LION PACKING — TRADE MARK

Since their inception,
all British Jet - Propelled
Aircraft have been fitted with

DUNLOP

TYRES · WHEELS
AND BRAKES

DUNLOP RUBBER Co. Ltd., *Aviation Division*, COVENTRY

6H/606

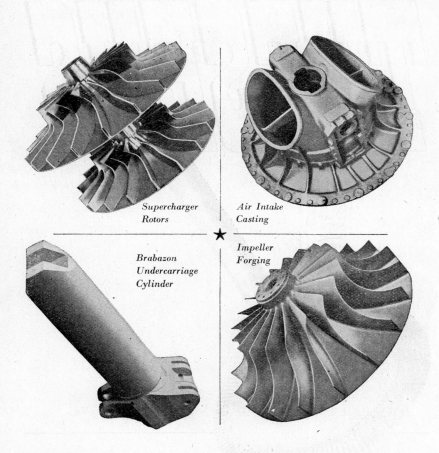

*Supercharger
Rotors*

*Air Intake
Casting*

★

*Brabazon
Undercarriage
Cylinder*

*Impeller
Forging*

These Aircraft forgings and castings in 'Hiduminium'
are typical examples of the ability of H.D.A. to keep
abreast of every new development in the industry.

HIGH
DUTY
ALLOYS

HIGH DUTY ALLOYS LTD., SLOUGH, BUCKS.
INGOTS, BILLETS, FORGINGS AND
CASTINGS IN 'HIDUMINIUM' (Regd. Trade Mark) ALUMINIUM ALLOYS

The world-famed
Rolls Royce "Nene" jet engine uses

FIRTH-VICKERS
STAINLESS
STEELS

FOR THE FOLLOWING VITAL DETAILS

Turbine Shroud Ring.
Turbine Labyrinth Seal.
Nozzle Guide Vane Support
  Rings.
Discharge Nozzle.
Discharge Nozzle Support
  Rings and Flanges.

Cooling Air Manifold.
Jet Pipe Casings.
The majority of the sheet
  metal work comprising the
  exhaust unit, e.g., inner
  and outer exhaust cones,
  fairings, etc.

FIRTH-VICKERS STAINLESS STEELS LTD., SHEFFIELD

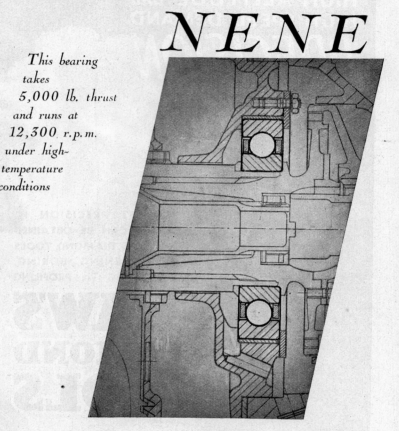

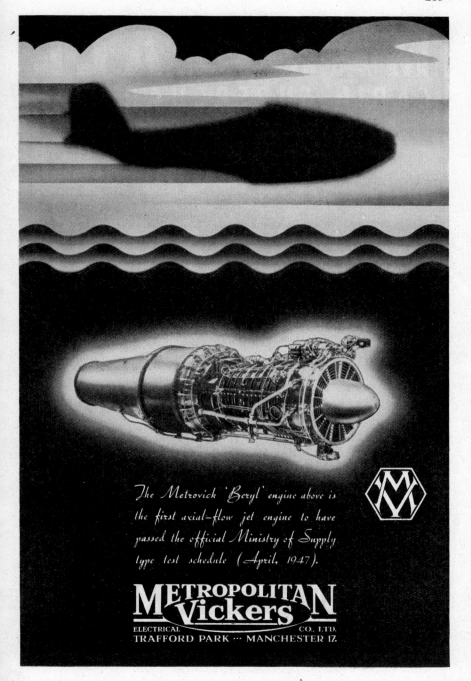

The Metrovick 'Beryl' engine above is the first axial-flow jet engine to have passed the official Ministry of Supply type test schedule (April, 1947).

METROPOLITAN Vickers
ELECTRICAL CO. LTD.
TRAFFORD PARK ··· MANCHESTER 17.

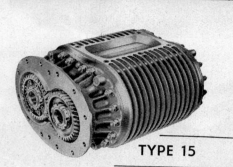
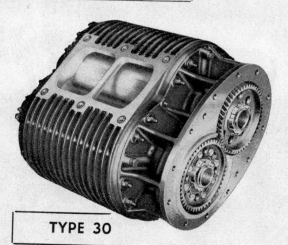

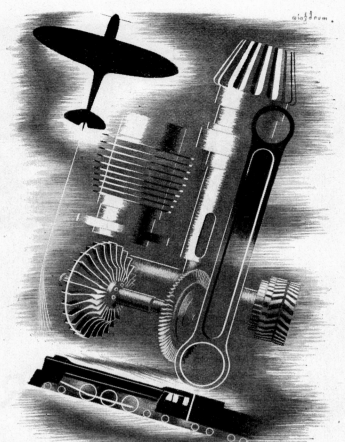

FOX ALLOY & SPECIAL STEELS

The Fox range of alloy and special steels serves the most modern demands of highly stressed mechanical devices in aircraft engineering.

Write for the FOX Alloy Steel Catalogue.

SAMUEL FOX & COMPANY, LTD.

Associated with The United Steel Companies, Limited,

STOCKSBRIDGE WORKS, Nr. SHEFFIELD, ENG.

VICKERS

SUPERMARINE

"ATTACKER"

VICKERS-ARMSTRONGS LTD.
AIRCRAFT SECTION
VICKERS HOUSE
BROADWAY
LONDON, S.W.1

Filtration — OF
VITAL IMPORTANCE IN
Gas Turbines —

The name VOKES had already become synonymous with Filtration on "conventionally-engined" aircraft. And now, from the very first jet propelled aircraft, VOKES have been in the forefront of filter development on gas-turbine engines. "Ghost", "Goblin", "Metro-Vick", "Naiad" ... these are some of the famous engines on which VOKES filters have already been fitted.

VOKES

Pioneers of scientific filtration

VOKES LTD · GUILDFORD · SURREY · also at Paris,
Brussels, New York, Sydney, Toronto, Johannesburg, Bombay

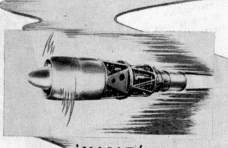

RoTol

Produced

THE WORLD'S FIRST TYPE-APPROVED TURBINE PROPELLER EVER TO FLY

Fitted to

THE FIRST PROPELLER TURBINE AIRCRAFT

THE FLIGHT WAS MADE IN
SEPTEMBER 1945

SINCE THAT DATE ROTOL HAS BEEN CONSTANTLY
ENGAGED UPON FURTHER PROJECTS AND ENTIRELY
NEW PROBLEMS IN THE LIGHT OF THE LATEST
REQUIREMENTS CREATED BY GAS TURBINE
ENGINES AND OTHER NEW RECIPROCATING
INSTALLATIONS.

ROTOL LIMITED · GLOUCESTER · ENGLAND

Nimonic 80

The name ' NIMONIC 80 ' is a Registered Trade Mark, and the alloy is the subject of patent application.

Nimonic 80 is the standard blading for all British jet propulsion engines. Nimonic 80 is chosen because of its exceptionally high creep-strength properties at red-heat temperatures.

Its background of extensive research and systematic high-temperature creep-testing gives an assurance of reliability in service.

Henry Wiggin & Company, Ltd

Wiggin Street, Birmingham, 16

W.S.23.g